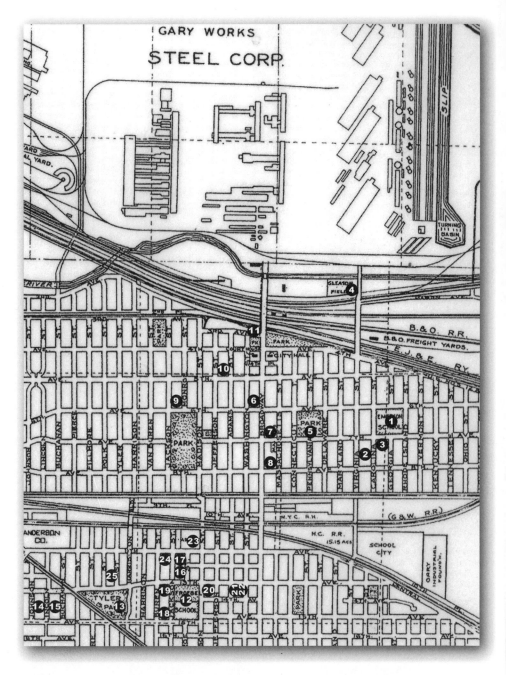

KEY:

1. Emerson School
2. Mrs. Matheus home
3. Rubin's confectionery
4. Gleason Field
5. Buffington Park
6. First Methodist Church
7. Gary Police Station
8. Palace Theater
9. Ambassador Apts. (Mrs. Wirt)
10. Gary Public Library
11. South Shore Station
12. Froebel School
13. Tyler/Norton Park
14. Boroskova home
15. St. Casimir's Lithuanian Church
16. Sts. Helen & Constantine
    Greek Orthodox Church
17. Corky's home
18. Gary-Alerding Settlement House
19. Hungarian Reformed Church
20. Miramar Ballroom
21. Balkan Bakery
22. Crimean Imports
23. Indiana National Guard Armory
24. Joe Plemich grocery
25. Sokolov home

An Ellen Anderson Mystery

THE GREAT EMERSON ART HEIST

A Novel Approach to

Vocabulary-Building

Kendall Svengalis

Kendall Svengalis

Best wishes and happy reading!

Duneland Press

Guilford, Connecticut, 2016

While this is a work of fiction, it draws upon people
living and dead, real and imagined, for its inspiration.
The story is a creative window into the world of
Gary, Indiana in the year 1942.

Published in the United States by Duneland Press,
Guilford, CT

www.dunelandpress.com

Library of Congress Cataloging-in-Publication Data

Svengalis, Kendall, 1947-
The Great Emerson Art Heist / Kendall Svengalis
p. cm.

Summary: Swedish-American girl detective, Ellen Anderson, travels to Gary,
Indiana where the art collection at Emerson High School is stolen. An SAT
vocabulary-building novel. Includes SAT word glossary.

ISBN: 978-0-9963524-4-4 (paperback)
ISBN: 978-0-9963524-5-1 (eBook)

Front cover design by Claudia Wolf
Interior and back cover design by Ellen Haffling Svengalis

Printed in the United States of America
First Edition

Preface

The concept of the Ellen Anderson Mystery Series originated more than twenty years ago, when my children, Hillary and Andrew, were students in the Barrington, Rhode Island public schools. As they grappled with vocabulary lessons, and later studied for the SAT exams, it struck me that a better approach to learning vocabulary would be to place these words in a narrative context that would better facilitate their mastery.

The Great Emerson Art Heist is the second in a series of novels that represent this unique approach to vocabulary building and SAT preparation. Each of the more than 2,100 SAT words appearing in this text is drawn from a variety of SAT word lists, representing the words most commonly used in the Critical Reading sections of the SAT tests. Each of these words is highlighted in boldface and is defined in a glossary at the back of the book. This list is supplemented by a list of names of leading political, historical and cultural figures, historical events, concepts, Emerson and Froebel High School faculty members, Gary personalities, and terms significant to the era and story line.

Mastering vocabulary is much more than an exercise in test preparation, however, but an essential path to a higher level of reading comprehension that can facilitate both academic achievement and professional advancement. The author is of the firm belief that "higher order thinking skills" can only be achieved through rigorous mastery of vocabulary and subject matter content, rather than through formal reading comprehension skills that devote insufficient attention to the broad vocabulary and world knowledge that children need to extract meaning from texts. To do otherwise is to put the cart before the horse.

As E.D. Hirsch elucidates in his estimable books *Cultural Literacy: What Every American Needs to Know* (1988) and *The Knowledge Deficit: Closing the Shocking Education Gap for American Children* (2007), educational success is highly dependent on the acquisition of world knowledge to advance effective reading comprehension. The Core Knowledge Sequence* developed by his Core Knowledge Foundation, is a coherent, cumulative, and content-specific course of study for grades Preschool-8 that is designed to help children establish strong foundations of knowledge, grade by grade. This knowledge deficit is one of the primary reasons why American students, particularly those from minority or underprivileged backgrounds, fail to achieve the level of educational success that is their birthright. This novel is intended to serve as a means of addressing this knowledge and vocabulary deficit. While designed primarily for high school students preparing for the SAT tests, high school English teachers, and SAT instructors, this book can be read by anyone desirous of increasing his or her vocabulary, and doing so in way that is both entertaining and educational.

The Great Emerson Art Heist is set primarily in Gary, Indiana, nine months after the attack on Pearl Harbor, and at a time when Gary was a center of the vital steel production that fueled the war effort. It is a nostalgic journey back to the city and neighborhoods of my youth, but set five years before my birth. While the story is fictitious, it draws upon real world people and places of the era to add an aura of historical verisimilitude to the narrative, many of whom I knew personally during my formative years in Gary, or interviewed for my research on the history of Emerson and Froebel high schools, including my brother, the late Cordell "Corky" Svengalis. It also utilizes a variety of 1942-era postcards, photographs, maps and other images to augment the historical milieu.

The author wishes to thank Claudia Wolf for her cover design and interior illustrations, the Library of Congress, Prints and Photographs Division, for the World War II posters and graphics, the Calumet Regional Archives at Indiana University NW, the Lilly Library at Indiana University, Bloomington, and my wife, Ellen Haffling Svengalis for serving as the inspiration for the book's heroine, for her photographs, and for her superb layout.

* Core Knowledge is not to be confused with the Common Core, a top-down attempt by federal and state officials to impose national academic standards on local communities.

Chapter 1

Candlewood Lake Idylls

Celebrity was not all Ellen Anderson had imagined it to be, particularly in July and August when she would have preferred a little **respite** from all the **kudos** and **adulation** that accompanied her around her hometown of Stratford, Connecticut. After all, catching Nazi spies in the act of stealing military secrets was not something that typically occupied the attention of seventeen-year-old girls not yet out of high school, even **precocious** ones like Ellen.

Her grandparents' vacation cottage on Candlewood Lake in New Milford was a **cherished sanctuary**, however, providing **sufficient** distance between her and the knowing glances of complete strangers who read about her **exploits** in the Stratford and Bridgeport newspapers. **Ironically**, Ellen had remained **stoic** and relatively **unaffected** by all the honors that were bestowed upon her in the wake of the events that had shaken Stratford's previous state of **complacency**. Perhaps it was the Swedish sense of **modesty** that she had inherited from her parents. Under the circumstances, it didn't take much **cajoling** on her part to convince her parents to **acquiesce** into allowing her the opportunity of using the cottage during much of the summer **hiatus**.

Since she was a little girl, Ellen had come to relish those **halcyon** summer days on the lake. As Connecticut's largest lake, Candlewood was an **aquatic** marvel, formed in the 1920s behind a **hydroelectric** dam situated south of the Rocky River's **confluence** with the **Housatonic River**. Straddling Fairfield and Litchfield counties in western Connecticut, the lake occupied land that was flooded after hundreds of local residents were **unceremoniously** relocated, their properties taken by the legal process of **eminent domain**. In former times, the region was home to scores of **ancient** and **dilapidated** farmhouses and barns dotting its thickly wooded hills and valleys, some dating back to the early years of Puritan settlement in the 17th century. Rumors among the local folk **recounted** tales of **sinister** and **macabre** events in these **environs**, the dark **remnants** of which were now **shrouded** in mystery and **submerged** by several **fathoms** of cool lake water. Now, its shores

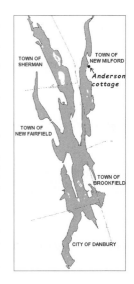

were populated by hundreds of **predominantly** summer homes owned by Connecticut and New York residents, or frequented by seasonal tourists fond of boating, fishing and other forms of **aquatic** recreation.

Ellen's grandparents were immigrants who came to the United States from the western Swedish province of **Värmland** and made their way to the Bridgeport area in 1899, after a brief **sojourn** in Dayton, Ohio. Her paternal grandfather, Eric Victor Anderson, hailed from the small town of **Ekshärad**;

her grandmother, Davida, from the neighboring town of **Hagfors**. With **toolmaking** skills he acquired in the old country, combined with a native business **acumen** and **dogged** determination to succeed, her grandfather established the E. V. Anderson Company in Bridgeport in 1923, recruiting many skilled **artisans** from his homeland.

Ellen knew her grandfather to be an **innovator** in his trade, willing to adopt new techniques for streamlining his company's operations. It was with the profits earned from this successful **tool and die** business that her grandfather acquired the little **rustic** cottage on Candlewood Lake, as well as a more **commodious** full-time residence in rural Easton, north of Fairfield. Ellen was also **cognizant** of the fact that her grandparents were consumed with a sense of **nostalgia** for their homeland across the sea, a **mindset** that was **manifest** in their continued use of the Swedish language in their home, a **penchant** for Swedish foods and decorative items, and their involvement in various Swedish-American **fraternal** organizations. They were also generous **benefactors** of the **North**

Star Singers in which their son, Eric, sang second tenor, as well as the Swedish Athletic Club of Fairfield and the Singing Society Norden of Bridgeport. Both were also strongly **susceptible** to the **evocative** power of Swedish folk melodies that Ellen's grandfather had taught himself to play on his Martin guitar. And when Ellen

was old enough, her grandfather taught her to play the guitar as well, beginning, not surprisingly, with *Hälsa dem därhemma* (Greet those back home), a song favored by Swedish-Americans who longed for their homeland across the sea.

And when Eric developed **asthma** as a boy, it was to friends in New Sweden, Maine that they sent him to escape the seasonal **allergies** of late summer.

Lying on the **weathered** dock and absorbing the warm rays of the late August sun was just the **sublime** relaxation Ellen needed before **contemplating** the start of her senior year at Stratford High School. Her **lithe** and tanned body was **reposed** across an oversized beach towel whose **frayed** edges **betrayed** years of summers past. A mystery novel by Agatha Christie – *The Mystery of the Blue Train* – lay face down on the smooth, cedar-boarded dock. It was a time of **blissful** freedom from the **quotidian** demands of the school schedule. And, best of all, it provided an uninterrupted opportunity for Ellen to **indulge** in her favorite passion – reading. Stacks of books on summer loan from the Stratford Public Library, the Dusty Corner Book Shop, Abby Wexler, and her own personal collection had quickly **proliferated,** and were neatly arranged on the small bookshelf or stacked on the end tables of the cottage's **rustic**, pine-paneled den.

Not surprisingly, Ellen's **proclivities** were inclined toward novels of mystery and suspense. She was particularly **enamored** of the works of the **prolific** novelist **Agatha Christie** and her assortment of sleuths, most notably Miss Marple and Hercule Poirot. The reading spark was **ignited** in 1940, when her parents gave her a copy of Christie's *The Man in the Brown Suit* for Christmas. That led in short order to *The Secret Adversary,* starring that plucky young couple, Tommy and Tuppence, two **quintessential** representatives of the Roaring Twenties who channel their thirst for adventure into a detective agency called 'The Young Adventurers.'

Ellen still enjoyed the adventures of that spunky girl detective, Nancy Drew, and had read every one in the series, beginning with the *Secret of the Old Clock*, and, most recently, *The Quest of the Missing Map*. But, primarily, her tastes had **gravitated** to more serious adult fare **befitting** her intelligence and growing **sophistication** with the **genre,** including the hard-boiled works of **Raymond Chandler**, **Dashiell Hammett**, Erle Stanley Gardner, and the whimsical Hildegarde Withers mysteries of **Stuart**

Palmer.

She also **revered** the novels of **James Hilton**: *Lost Horizon*, the story of Shangri-La, a land tucked away in the far-off **Himalayas** where the aging process was miraculously **arrested**; *Goodbye Mr. Chips*, the touching tale of an elderly schoolmaster at an English **public school**; and *Random Harvest*, the **romantic** story of a World War I **amnesiac** that was being adapted into a film starring her favorite actor, Ronald Colman, and the lovely British actress, Greer Garson.

But her **eclectic** reading tastes **encompassed** more than works of romance and adventure. She was also drawn to works of history and current affairs, notably those that addressed the current World War and the 20th century's **ideological** war of ideas that was being waged both in Europe and the United States. Between Ken, Miss Russell at the Stratford Public Library, Mr. Mueller at the Dusty Corner Bookshop, and her father, Ellen was amply supplied with books on history and political affairs.

Mr. Mueller's latest recommendation – *Why England Slept* – by a young

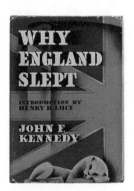

Harvard graduate named John F. Kennedy, provided her with an **insightful** examination of the failures of the British government in preventing World War II. Another book that influenced her philosophy of life was James Truslow Adams' 1931 bestseller, *The Epic of America*. It was Adams' view that the American dream provided opportunity for each according to ability or achievement. It was not merely a dream of motorcars and high wages, but one of a social order in which each man and each woman exercises the ability to **attain** the fullest **stature** of which they are **innately** capable, regardless of the **fortuitous** circumstances of birth or position. Ellen once had the opportunity to meet Mr. Adams, who lived in nearby Southport, Connecticut, after he gave a lecture at the Stratford Public Library.

Ellen's **voracious** reading habits had helped her formulate a **coherent** political **philosophy** that **abhorred** the **statist** ideologies of the age to which so many Europeans and a not **inconsiderable** number of Americans, mostly in the intellectual and **chattering classes**, had **succumbed**. It was not merely the twin **totalitarian** impulses of **communism** and **fascism** on the left that were **anathema** to her. She also **abhorred** the **social democratic** tendencies of Franklin Roosevelt's **New Deal** that placed **excessive** power in the hands of a **centralized** government and threatened individual liberty, **federalism,** the **separation of powers,** and free market **capitalism**. To her mind, it was a far cry from the intentions of the **Founding Fathers** whose fear of centralized power drove them to limit the size and scope of government to those powers **enumerated** in Article 1, Sec. 8 of the **United States Constitution**, a document she considered **sacrosanct**. As an **individualist**, she knew **instinctively** that, without those limits, government would expand **inexorably** toward a **socialist welfare state**, which would threaten individual liberty and **stifle** individual **initiative**, particularly when it was **propelled** by **unscrupulous,** vote-buying politicians eager to **sacrifice** freedom for political gain.

Ellen was also **cognizant** of the fact that the central values of civilization were under **assault** across the globe from **philosophical** views that denied **absolute** moral standards, and **jettisoned** the **rule of law, private property**, and **free markets** in favor of a **totalitarian** world view of command and control. Nazism and Soviet Communism had replaced God with an all-embracing **totalitarian** state, **ravaged** Europe, and killed millions of innocents in the process. And, even in the United States, an expanding regulatory and welfare state was subverting the principles of America's founding and undermining the free market economy.

Ellen credited the **sagacity** and **keen** understanding of Miss Satterfield, her high school history teacher, as well as her parents, with helping her comprehend these **ominous** developments, and **formulate** her political **philosophy**. It seemed **axiomatic** to Ellen that the more government did for people, the less they would do for themselves, eventually lapsing into a state of **indolence** and **dependency**. Ultimately, despite the **purported** good intentions of the government class, and its **ideological** allies, civil society would **disintegrate** as individual **initiative**, enterprise, and private charity **atrophied**.

As Ellen saw it, this was the **inherent flaw** in the political philosophy now **ironically** known as 'liberalism,' but bearing a closer relationship to European-style **democratic socialism,** or **fascism**. And while she observed such ideas being promoted by politicians and **arrogant elitists** in the **intelligentsia**, she also realized that, ultimately, the problem was less with **pandering** politicians than it was with **myopic** voters willing to **sacrifice** their sacred **birthright** for promises of government **largesse**. It was difficult for her to remain **sanguine** in the face of these threats.

Ellen and her friend, Betsy Dalrymple, who not only shared Ellen's passion for reading, but her political philosophy as well, had the Candlewood Lake cottage all to themselves during these **idyllic** August days. Her parents used the cottage infrequently now that the war was on, her grandparents even less so, largely for the same reason. This gave Ellen and her friends free **reign**, particularly during the **languorous** weeks of July and August when their free time **vacillated** between the **sustained** periods of **strenuous** physical activity that consumed their daytime hours and the more **sedentary** pursuits that occupied their evenings.

Ellen had an **unfailing** devotion to her parents. Her father, Eric, a tool designer by trade, was much consumed with war-related contracts at her grandfather's **tool and die** establishment in Bridgeport. Ellen admired the **industrious** and **conscientious** dedication he applied to his trade. Her mother, Edna, stayed home to cook his meals, darn his socks, and engage in a variety of social activities, including bowling, golf, and a sewing club consisting of close friends in the Swedish-American community who were possessed of **dexterous** hands and **nimble** fingers. She was also a member of the **Good Templars**, a fraternal organization whose members **abstained** from the use of alcoholic beverages. After graduating from high school, her mother had worked in the bookkeeping department of Howland's, a leading Bridgeport department store, but was forced by company policy to give up employment after she and Eric were married. Ellen's other close friend, Linnea Matthews, was working full-time at a Stratford dress shop for the summer and had difficulty getting up to the lake, even on weekends.

Ken was also an occasional visitor to the Candlewood Lake cottage between his working hours at the Dusty Corner Book Shop, where he had become an **indispensable** aide to store owner, Klaus Mueller, as well as another local celebrity. Sadly, his visits to Candlewood Lake were becoming infrequent after the government in Washington imposed the **strictures** of gasoline **rationing** on the nation. Those visits were entirely dependent on his opportunities to **scrounge** enough **rationed** gasoline from friends to make the sixty-five mile round trip to New Milford. And, once at the cottage, joy riding was simply out of the question. He had to be content to join the girls in swimming, canoeing,

sunbathing, reading, and listening to the radio, not that he would have turned up his nose at any of those pursuits.

Once a week, usually on the day the new picture came to town, the girls rode their bicycles five miles to the Bank Street Theatre in the **quaint** little village of New Milford, which also boasted a small grocery store and a pharmacy with soda fountain that served the most delicious chocolate malts. The prior week's offering was *Woman of the Year*, with Spencer Tracy and Connecticut's own **Katherine Hepburn**. Ellen adored Katherine Hepburn and had seen most of her films, including The *Philadelphia Story, Holiday, Bringing Up Baby, Sylvia Scarlet, Stage Door,* and *Little Women*. She fondly remembered the opportunity she had of meeting Miss Hepburn at the **USO** dance in Bridgeport when **Ozzie Nelson** and his orchestra entertained the troops.

Evenings at the cottage were typically spent reading and listening to the radio. Between bulletins of the war on the Eastern Front, and in the Pacific, the girls listened to their favorite mystery, comedy, and musical programs on Ellen's Crosley Model 517 Bakelite radio, which she had brought with her from Stratford. **Fortuitously**, she also brought along the August issue of *Radio and Television Mirror*, which provided monthly listings of the radio programs on the CBS, NBC-Red, NBC-Blue, and Mutual Broadcasting networks. That radio was their lifeline to the outside world, and a source of endless enjoyment.

The girls had a special **affinity** for such crime and mystery programs as *Gangbusters, Bulldog Drummond, Inner Sanctum Mysteries,* The Shadow, and *I Love a Mystery,* a line-up that mirrored much of Ellen's read-  ing fare. But, they also enjoyed a **profuse litany** of comedy and musical programs, especially *Jack Benny, Baby Snooks, Burns and Allen, Edgar Bergen and Charlie McCarthy, The Aldrich Family, Fibber McGee and Molly,* and the big band **remotes**. She loved it when the fast-talking Fibber opened the door to the front closet, and waited in joyous anticipation for its contents to come crashing down on his head.

Judging by the **serenity** which characterized this peaceful lakeside **enclave**, one would be hard pressed to **compre- hend** that the United States armed forces were engaged in a life and death struggle on two military fronts. Two months earlier, on June 4, a **pivotal** air and sea battle **commenced** when the Japanese naval fleet inflicted **grievous** damage on the Pacific **atoll** of Midway, 1300 miles northwest of Pearl Harbor. By June 7, however, the American Air Force had **retaliated**, inflicting massive damage on **Admiral Isoroku Yamamoto's** Pacific **armada**, and sending three aircraft carriers and two destroyers to the ocean bottom. It was a **decisive** victory for the American Navy, which not only **avenged** the surprise attack on Pearl Harbor, but also **arrested** Japan's previously **inexorable** advance across the Pacific.

On the European front, the German **Wehrmacht** was in the process of closing in on the city of **Stalingrad** for what was shaping up to be an **epic** land battle, this after the **Red Army** had abandoned the **Crimean Peninsula** and destroyed its own **strategic** oil **refineries** to prevent them from falling into German hands. The **collateral** damage was **horrendous**, involving the death of thousands of innocent **civilians** who stood in the path of the conflict.

Having just barely survived the **Battle of Britain**, the British, **buttressed** by an **infusion** of men and war material from the United States and Canada, were **hunkered** down on their island nation trying to keep the Atlantic supply lanes open in the face of **persistent** attacks by **wolfpacks** of German **U-Boats**. And in North Africa, the assault of **Erwin Rommel's Afrika Korps** on the **Egyptian** town of **El Alamein** was halted by a **stalwart** British Eighth Army under the command of General Claude Auchinleck. The **stalemate stymied** the **Axis** in its **ultimate** goal of taking Egypt and the oil rich fields of the **Middle East** for the **Third Reich**.

On the home front, cartoonists in American newspapers were having a field day drawing **demeaning caricatures** of Hitler; and Spike Jones was **eliciting** uproarious **guffaws** from **jubilant** crowds whenever his band performed *Der Fuehrer's Face*. But, for the present, these **momentous** events seemed so far away in the peaceful isolation of this small lakeside community. And Ellen had to be satisfied with the **vicarious** pleasures of reading mysteries rather than solving them herself.

Dressed in the stylish new powder blue bathing suit she had purchased at Howland's, Ellen was in the process of returning to her reading when she detected the distinctive sound of Ken's Ford roadster coming up Juniper Lane and turning into the driveway. A few seconds later, she heard the car door slam and observed Ken emerge from the side of the cottage.

"Hey, **Esther Williams**, have I got a surprise for you!" Ken shouted, standing on the deck overlooking the lake. Running up from the dock, her book and towel in hand, Ellen spied a package wrapped in brown butcher's paper and quickly **surmised** that it must be something for the charcoal grill.

"Let me guess. Porterhouse steak?"

"How did you know? Can't I ever put one over on you, Miss Anderson?"

"What's this Miss Anderson stuff?" she replied, planting a soft kiss on his cheek.

Hearing the commotion from inside the cottage, Betsy, who was curled up with an **abridged** edition of Dickens' *David Copperfield*, emerged from the cottage's screened-in porch and joined the two on the deck.

"We'll if it isn't our trusty **chaperone**, Miss Dalrymple," Ken exclaimed.

"At your service, Mr. Swenson. And don't get fresh, because I take my job seriously." Being the soul of **propriety**, Ken just smiled innocently.

"Look what Ken brought us, Betsy – a porterhouse steak. And, on a bookstore clerk's salary. Did Mr. Mueller give you a raise?"

"Are you kidding? He pays me the **minimum wage** – 43 cents an hour and all the used books I can read, and return. There's not much to spend it on, though, particularly when you're up here all summer. I did take my neighbor, Marge Blake, to the movies once, but, then, she's like a sister to me. I paid 25 cents for her ticket and twice that for the popcorn, soda and candy she consumed. I'm just glad it wasn't a double feature because she's got a **voracious** appetite. I'll also have you know that I've been trying to elevate Marge's reading habits from those **saccharine** romance novels she reads to more **sublime** forms of literature. I'm trying to convince her that there's a big difference between the kind of **maudlin sentimentality** that **infuses** most **pulp fiction** and the genuine **romantic sentiments** that are a characteristic of great literature. I left her with my personal copy of *Pride and Prejudice* in the hopes that it will help her **distinguish** the silver from the **dross**."

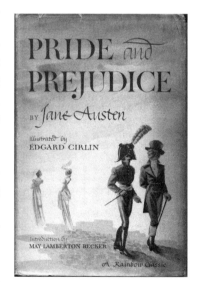

"Good for you, Ken, my **literary evangelist**." Ellen knew Ken could be **pedantic** at times, what with all that knowledge rolling around in his head, but he displayed it with **circumspection,** befitting the Swedish sense of **modesty** he shared with Ellen.

She also knew Ken as a **phlegmatic** sort, one not easily upset, excited, or angered, except by the consequences of idiotic government policies, or brutal dictatorial **regimes**.

"So, what did you see at the movies, may I ask?"

"*Yankee Doodle Dandy*, with James Cagney. I had no idea that he was such a great dancer. I thought he just played gangster roles. They say he may be up for an **Academy Award** for Best Actor."

"Yes, that's what I heard, too. Say, how would you like to start up the grill? The charcoal and lighter fluid are in the garage," Ellen suggested.

"Sure thing!"

While Ken took charge of the grill, Ellen took the steak into the kitchen, cut it into thirds, applied seasonings, and put them on a platter. A few minutes later, she brought them out on the deck, where Ken was firing up the charcoal.

"Here you go, Ken. I'll take mine medium rare. Betsy likes hers well done, just like you do."

As Ken monitored the progress of the steaks sizzling on the grill, Ellen and Betsy prepared carrots and mashed potatoes in the kitchen. Ellen set the picnic table with dishes, silverware, and napkins, and brought out a pitcher of cold lemonade. Twenty minutes later, the steaks were done to their liking, and the three friends were enjoying their dinner on the deck. Their light-hearted **banter** was accompanied by the comfort of the crisp late afternoon breezes blowing off the lake. Ellen found herself staring at Ken and reflecting back to the night of the Stratford High School Prom at Quilty's Ballroom in Bridgeport. They had already been through so much, and their relationship had blossomed in the process. She could not imagine sharing her life with anyone else. Then, she was quickly restored to reality as the conversation turned to the upcoming school year, war developments, and the latest letter from Ken's brother.

"Carl's just completed his training exercises on **Oahu** and is about ready to be **deployed** to some unknown destination, probably in the South Pacific. He says that the unpredictable winds on the island have prepared him for anything. In fact, one member of his squadron – **Harry Warnke**, from **Gary,**

Harry Warnke

Indiana – was killed when his plane crashed in the **treacherous** mountains dividing **Honolulu** from the **leeward** side of the island. The **fuselage** was spotted on the mountainside, but they were unable to retrieve it because the site was just too **inaccessible.** He's just sick over it. Carl can't tell us where's he's going to be stationed, however. That's top secret."

No sooner had their hunger been **satiated**, than the trio heard another motorcar pulling into the driveway. Ellen ran to the corner of the cottage and spied her parents coming down the walk.

"Well, what brings you two here tonight? I thought you weren't coming until tomorrow morning?"

"That's what we thought, too," replied Ellen's father, as he and Edna kissed their daughter on the cheek, and collapsed in two of the deck's Adirondack chairs.

"Can we offer you some lemonade, Mr. and Mrs. Anderson?"

"Thank you, Betsy. That would be great," Eric replied.

"I was hoping to get in a day or two of fishing while we were up here, but our plans have been **altered** dramatically. There've been some important developments at the shop and we decided to drive up here and share them with you this evening. Your grandfather's sending me out-of-town on business, and I want to know if you'd be **amenable** to taking a little vacation?"

Chapter 2

An Unexpected Vacation

"Vacation?" Ellen replied. "What did you have in mind?"

"How would you like to take a trip to Indiana?"

"Indiana? Where in Indiana?"

"Gary, Indiana, to be exact. Your grandfather's sending me there to do some on-site work at the Gary Armor Plate plant, one of the defense contractors for whom we're doing tool design. Most of it has to do with tank components. As you may know, Gary has the world's largest steel mill and produces the steel that goes into many of our armaments, including **artillery** pieces, tanks, aircraft, and such."

"Are you in **earnest**? **Ironically**, we were just talking about Gary, Indiana. You wouldn't be pulling my leg?"

"Of course not."

"But, what about school? I'm sure you realize that it starts in a couple of weeks."

"I've already thought of that. I don't expect we'll be in Gary for more than two months – six weeks if all goes well. You may miss a few weeks of school in Stratford, but you can attend classes in Gary, which, I've been told, has an excellent school system. You won't be there much longer than when my parents sent me up to **New Sweden, Maine** in August and September for my **asthma**, and to escape the ragweed that **aggravated** it."

"Is Mother going?"

"No, I'm afraid she'll have to stay home to care for your Grandmother Eliason who's still **recuperating** from an attack of the **gout**. So, I'll need you to cook my meals and help with the housework, that is, when we're not dining out. I've already taken care of our accommodations. Gus Bloomquist, the superintendent of the Gary Armor Plate, has found us a nice two-bedroom apartment on the East Side of Gary, just a half block from the high school. It's owned by a Swedish lady by the name of Eleanor Matheus. In fact, I just spoke with her on the phone yesterday. She told me she has a son serving in the **Seabees**. The apartment's completely furnished, down to linens and kitchen **accoutrements**. I'm sure she'll make us very comfortable. Besides, she's from Värmland, just like your grandparents."

"Mathews? Any relation to Linnea?"

"No, it's spelled with a 'u,' instead of a 'w.' Besides, it's her married name.

She was originally a Larson, and you know how many Larsons there are."

"Well, as long as it's for no more than two months, I think I can **tolerate** the absence from school. But, I wouldn't want to be away any longer than that during my senior year, as I'm sure you can appreciate. I'm hoping to land a part in the spring musical, after all. Say, perhaps, I can rustle up a mystery or two while I'm there."

"Now, hold on just a minute, young lady. I'd rather you keep your **propensity** for getting **embroiled** in mysteries under control. Your last adventure gave me a major case of **agita,** as it was. And your mother lost a lot of sleep as well."

"Agita? What's agita?"

"Agita is Italian for anxiety. Think of your dear old parents, sick with **indigestion,** living on **Pepto-Bismol.**"

"Oh, Dad, you're hardly old. You were only forty-two on your last birthday. I put the candles on your cake. Remember? And, besides, we're Swedish. What's the Swedish **equivalent** for agita?"

"Halsbränna, I suppose – for **heartburn.**"

"I didn't mean to give you heartburn, Dad. It certainly wasn't my intention."

"I know, dear. I don't mean to **proscribe** your every move, but I would appreciate it if you could **eschew** your taste for adventure for a few weeks while I tend to important business matters."

"I'll try, Dad, but I can't very well ignore a mystery if it falls in my lap."

"Well, I'm hoping your school work will keep you busy enough that nothing out of the ordinary falls into your lap – if you catch my drift."

"Funny you should mention Gary, Indiana. Ken was just telling us that his brother, Carl, lost a friend from Gary, Indiana. His plane crashed on Oahu during a training flight."

"I'm sorry to hear that. And so young..."

"So, when are we actually leaving? I'll have some packing to do. And I'll need some new clothes, too."

"I anticipated that. We leave on Monday. I've already purchased our tickets to New York City, and reserved sleeper compartments on the **Twentieth Century Limited** for the **excursion** to Chicago. They're a bit **exorbitant** – far more than coach seats – but your grandfather's footing the bill."

"The **Twentieth Century Limited**! That's fantastic!! Isn't that an **exclusive** train?"

"You bet – complete with red carpet service, Pullman porters, private sleeping compartments, and dinner in the diner."

"Nothing could be finer, than to have your ham and eggs in Carolina..." Ellen sang, in her clear soprano voice.

"Well, not exactly. That's the *Chattanooga Choo Choo.* But, you get the idea."

"Just teasing, Dad. The diner part made me think of Glenn Miller."

"Anyway, from Chicago, we'll take the South Shore interurban back to Gary."

"Excuse me, but why don't we just get off in Gary, if it's east of Chicago?"

"Because the Twentieth Century only makes four **intermediate** stops along its route. It's an **express** train – averaging about 60 miles an hour – and adding station stops would just slow it down. People who aren't in a hurry can always take a local train that stops more frequently. Anyway, we'll be leaving **Grand Central Terminal** at five in the afternoon on Monday and arriving in Chicago at nine o'clock the following morning, sixteen hours later. Here, I brought a timetable for you to **peruse**."

"How exciting! My first trip on the most famous train in the world, and my first time in a sleeper compartment!"

"I'm afraid we're going to have to cut your weekend a bit short, however – that is, if you want to go."

"If I want to go? Are you kidding? I wouldn't miss it."

"Then, your Mother and I will drive you and Betsy back to Stratford tomorrow morning so you can go shopping and start packing."

"Did you say shopping? Now, you're talking my language. Say, I almost forgot. Have you two eaten? I'm afraid the three of us have already polished off the steak Ken brought, but we still have some carrots and mashed potatoes left over and there are cold-cuts in the **Frigidaire**."

"Thanks, but we've already eaten. We stopped at that swell little diner on Main Street in Newtown, the one with the famous hamburgers and chilidogs. If I'm going to get indigestion, I'd rather it be from their chilidogs." Ellen knew that chilidogs had a way of **compromising** her father's normally **abstemious** dietary **regimen**.

After dinner, and as the sun drifted behind the western hills, Ellen and her **jovial** companions retired to the cottage's recently **refurbished** pine-paneled den. It was a warm and inviting **sanctuary**, featuring a stone fireplace, a soft **davenport**, three cloth-covered wing chairs, and a pine mantle over which a black metal figure of a Viking ship was mounted. A wind-up **gramophone** from **His Master's Voice** and an album of Swedish 78s rested **conspicuously** on a small corner table. On the wall, opposite the fireplace, hung a **walleyed pike** Ellen's grandfather caught in the lake when she was a little girl, and had mounted by a local **taxidermist**. Settling into one of the wing chairs, Ellen turned on the radio, while her parents relaxed in the Adirondack chairs on the screened porch. As she adjusted the dial to the

Mutual Broadcasting Network, they heard the now familiar introduction from across the airwaves to the strains of Rossini's *William Tell Overture*:

A fiery horse with the speed of light, a cloud of dust and a hearty Hi-Yo Silver! The Lone Ranger! ... With his faithful Indian companion, Tonto, the daring and resourceful masked rider of the plains led the fight for law and order in the early West! Return with us now to those thrilling days of yesteryear! From out of the past come the thundering hoofbeats of the great horse, Silver! The Lone Ranger rides again!

In no time at all, the girls were completely engrossed in another gripping adventure story from the early West. Ken made an effort to listen, too, but was mostly preoccupied with a new book he had gotten from Mr. Mueller. When the program ended, and went to a commercial for General Mills' Kix cereal, Ellen leaned over and put her hand on his shoulder.

"Good book?"

"You bet! It's called *In Stalin's Secret Service,* by **Walter Krivitsky**. I can't put it down. Mr. Mueller said it would explain the political **undercurrents** of the present **conflagration** in Europe better than most books currently on the market."

"Walter Krivitsky? I seem to have heard that name before."

"You probably have. In 1938, **Walter Krivitsky** was the first high-level Soviet intelligence officer to **defect** to the West. He tried to warn the United States and its allies that the Soviet Union and Nazi Germany were about to enter into a **non-aggression pact**. Up to that time, the Soviet Union had been employing its **propaganda apparatus** to promote the **Popular Front** – in other words, the idea that the Soviet Union was **virulently** opposed to **Fascism**. But, it was all a **ruse**, designed to recruit **useful idiots** and **fellow travelers** to the communist cause. From 1933 on, when Hitler took power in Germany, Stalin initiated secret negotiations with him in an effort to come to an understanding with the Nazi **regime**. The **Popular Front** became the public face of Soviet **foreign policy**, designed to

galvanize public sentiment in support of the Soviet Union and Communism under the **guise** of **anti-Fascism**. Through it, the Soviet Union influenced a wide range of opinion leaders in the West, including **liberal** and left-leaning intellectuals, labor leaders, artistic types, academics, writers, journalists, and some Hollywood actors, writers and directors, to name just a few. Their tool of choice is the **front organization**, a group that, on its surface, proclaims some **noble** or **laudatory** purpose. The **American League for Peace and Democracy** is just one example of many such groups. In reality, these front groups were used to secretly advance communist goals among the broader population and recruit new members to the **Communist Party USA**. Politically **naive** types, chiefly in the **Liberal** or **Progressive** camps, were its **unwitting prey**. People in Hollywood were among the most **gullible**, signing on to the phony fronts in **droves**."

"I've read about that group. But, didn't it lose much of its support after the **Hitler-Stalin Pact** was signed in 1939?"

"That's right. Many of the non-communist members withdrew once they realized that Stalin was in **collusion** with Hitler and was simply using them as **dupes**. Although the Nazi-Soviet Pact was officially one of non-aggression between the two powers, it also **allegedly** included a secret **protocol** that divided territories of Romania, Poland, Lithuania, Latvia, Estonia and Finland into Nazi and Soviet **spheres of influence**. A week later, on September first, the Nazis invaded Poland, starting the Second World War. Then, the Soviets invaded and **annexed** eastern Poland on September 17th. Although Britain and France declared war against Germany after the invasion of Poland, the Soviet Union was equally **culpable**, having swallowed up eastern Poland. And less than a year later, they occupied the Baltic countries as well, presumably under the same secret **protocol.** The **Communist Party USA** quickly shifted gears and began supporting peace with Nazi Germany as soon as the Pact was signed. After that, only the hard-line Stalinists held firm and followed the Soviet line. This included people like the playwrights, **Lillian Hellman** and **Arthur Miller**, and the detective novelist, **Dashiell Hammett,** among others.

"This was a defining moment that separated the hard-line Stalinists from the previously **deluded** leftists. After the **American League for Peace and Democracy** was dissolved, the remaining communist elements **coalesced** under the banner of the **American Peace Mobilization**. It was Krivitsky who exposed the communists' deep-rooted **cynicism** about the democratic political process and the contempt they have for the vast majority of people in the western democracies. He explained how skillfully they employ **euphemistic** names to disguise their **nefarious** aims, and how **adept** they are at luring sympathetic, but **naïve**, intellectuals and artistic types to their cause."

"Wasn't it Lenin who called them '**useful idiots**?'" Ellen added.

"That's correct. He applied that term to communist sympathizers in the West who could be **exploited** as tools for spreading communist **propaganda**. While he was willing to use such people for his own ends, ultimately, he held them in **contempt**."

"But what I don't understand is why Stalin would want to **appease** Hitler in the first place. Didn't he view him as an **existential** threat?"

"True, but Stalin respected Hitler's power and hoped that by **appeasing** him, and solidifying the Soviet Union's western border, he would induce Hitler to focus his attentions on the western democracies, particularly France and England. Stalin anticipated that Hitler wanted to avoid a two-front war by coming to a **rapprochement** with the Soviet Union. Their **collusion** took the form of the **Molotov-Ribbentrop Pact** that was signed in August 1939. Stalin reasoned that, after the Nazis and Allies were done destroying, or weakening, each other, the Soviets would be in a much stronger **strategic** position, and be able to move in and pick up the pieces. That's why he was willing to **placate** Hitler. The trick is never to take Stalin's actions at face value, however, but to consider his long-term **strategic** objectives.

"Of course, it didn't take long for Hitler to **abrogate** his **accord** with Stalin, when he invaded the Soviet Union in June 1941. By that time, the **Wehrmacht** had already consumed most of Western Europe, including France, Denmark and Norway, and now turned its attentions to the East. The war between these two **belligerents** is shaping up into the largest land war in world history, with the action now centered on **Stalingrad**."

"So what happened to Walter Krivitsky after he spilled the beans?"

"He was assassinated!"

"Assassinated? Where?"

"In Washington, DC! And get this... it was just a few blocks from the U.S. Capitol."

"But how could something like that happen in the nation's capital? Where was the F.B.I. while all this was going on? Why didn't they protect him?"

"Good question. **Ironically**, Krivitsky had trouble convincing Western intelligence officials that Hitler and Stalin were about to sign a **non-aggression pact**. So, before his book was published, he came out with a series of articles in the *Saturday Evening Post* that **chronicled** the activities of communist agents in the West. The forces on the left – you know, the communists, socialists, Progressives, including the **useful idiots** in the media – tried their best to destroy his **credibility**, because they feared his secrets would expose Soviet intelligence operations. Using their network of **fellow travelers** in the media, government and academia, the communists tried their best to **marginalize** him. He was sort of a voice crying in the wilderness – a modern day **Jeremiah**, if you will. But, this made him a marked man. After a short time in the United States, he took a trip to England to **confer** with **British Military Intelligence** and share what information he had with them. When he returned to the United States by way of Canada, however, he was tracked by Soviet agents to the **Bellevue Hotel** in Washington, DC. That's where he was killed. They made it look like **suicide**, but most authorities are convinced he was killed by Soviet **operatives**. And if it was suicide, it was a forced suicide. It is common practice for the Soviets to force suicides by threatening harm to family members. That's how ruthless they are."

"When did all this happen?"

"February 1941."

"It looks to me like no one is safe from such a **malevolent** communist **apparatus**, even in this country."

"That's right, particularly if you're a **turncoat**, and possess secrets about the Soviet **regime** and its **clandestine** operations. The **tentacles** of their secret police reach across the oceans and their spy networks into the deepest **recesses** of the American government. Just look at what happened to **Leon Trotsky**, who was one of the leaders of the **Russian Revolution** in 1917 and one of the **contenders** for leadership of the Soviet Union after the death of Lenin. Eventually, after Stalin had **usurped** all power, the men developed an **inimical** relationship and Trotsky became **persona non grata** within the Soviet Union. They were both communists, of course, but differed as to **methodology**. Stalin's primary goal was building socialism in one country first, while Trotsky was firmly committed to world revolution. This put him at odds with Stalin and the Community Party leadership. He was **deported** from the Soviet Union in 1929, and later took up residence in a guarded compound outside of Mexico City, where he continued to write books and articles **denouncing** Stalin's regime. But, that didn't stop Stalin from plotting his assassination. A few years later, an undercover **NKVD** agent named **Ramón Mercader** had the **effrontery** to infiltrate the guarded compound where Trotsky resided and **deftly** drove an ice ax into his brain."

"Eew! Those communists really mean business. I thought my **migraines** were painful. And to think that we're now allied with Stalin in the war against Nazi Germany. It's like that old **adage**, coined in the 19th century by **Charles Dudley Warren**: 'Politics makes strange bedfellows.'"

"No kidding. And don't think that because we're temporarily fighting on the same side that they've suspended their **espionage** campaign against the United States. They'll steal as many of our military secrets as they can and then use them against us when the war's over. As it is, we've given them so much war material under **Lend Lease**, that it will make it that much easier for them to exert their control over Eastern Europe and Germany as the war comes to an end. So, keep that in mind in case you should ever get yourself mixed up with communists in the Midwest."

"I'll remember that. By the way, Ken, what's this **NKVD** you referred to?"

"The **NKVD** is the People's Commissariat of Internal Affairs. It's the law enforcement arm of the Soviet Union that executes the **mandates** of the All Union Communist Party. It's also closely tied to the Soviet secret police, an equally **malevolent** organization."

"May I interrupt you two political analysts for a moment?" Betsy interjected. "I thought you might like to know that it's time for *Information Please.*"

"O.K., Betsy, we're listening."

At that moment, Eric and Edna entered the cottage through the screen door that connected it with the enclosed porch.

"Mind if we join you?"

"Not at all. We're just getting ready to listen to *Information Please.*"

"Great! Your father enjoys matching wits with the guests on that program. His co-workers call him 'The Professor' and accuse him of having an **encyclopedic** knowledge of the most **arcane** facts."

"Oh, Edna, please, let's not exaggerate. I'm no match for those literary types that **Clifton Fadiman** has on his show. Those are college professors, and such."

"I've never been very impressed with **eggheads.** They seem to have their feet planted firmly in the air. Give me a practical man any day," Edna replied, reflecting her **wry** sense of humor.

The evening passed quietly as the small **coterie** listened to several programs, then **succumbed** to **drowsiness** and departed for one of the cottage's three bedrooms. Ellen's father was snoring in one of the Queen Anne wing chairs when her mother finally shook him on the arm and dragged him off to bed.

"Eric, you'll wake the dead." He opened his eyes.

"You're pulling my leg, Edna. It couldn't have been that bad."

"Well, almost. Come to bed, now."

Ellen was the last to **yield** to the **nocturnal** urges, having listened to *Gang Busters, First Nighter, Wings of Destiny,* and *News of the World.* Ken had already retired to the bedroom in the cabin's lower level, and Betsy was sound asleep in one of the two upstairs bedrooms. As Ellen climbed quietly into the other twin bed, she remained **preoccupied** with the tales of Soviet espionage that Ken had recounted from Walter Krivitsky's gripping **expose**, as well as the chilling realization of the author's **ultimate** fate. She was determined to get her hands on the book that had brought death to its author.

Chapter 3

Vacation Preparations

"First call for breakfast," Ellen's mother shouted down the hallway leading to the cottage's two upstairs bedrooms.

"Are you awake, Betsy?" Ellen whispered to her high school chum who occupied the room's other twin bed.

"Yes, I'm awake. I was just waiting for you to make the first move."

"Do you smell that? Mom's making breakfast this morning, and I'll bet Swedish pancakes are on the menu. That should be sufficient **inducement** for you to hop out of bed and get yourself dressed."

"I was hoping to sleep a bit longer, but who could resist Swedish pancakes," Betsy replied, as she sat up in bed and stretched her pajama-clad arms to the ceiling.

Without further hesitation, the girls quickly removed their pajamas and prepared to take turns in the bathroom. Scooping up her toilet articles, Ellen donned her yellow cotton bathrobe and was the first to head off down the narrow hallway. Standing at the sink in her **bandeau** and matching peach rayon **step-ins**, she washed her face and hands and combed out her shoulder length blond hair. Then, putting on her robe for the trek back down the hall, she returned to her bedroom and completed dressing.

Ellen was a few months shy of her eighteenth birthday – on October 4, 1942. A senior at Stratford High School, she had blossomed into an exceptionally attractive, yet **sagacious**, young woman. Her bright face was accentuated by high cheekbones, sparkling eyes, a narrow, pointed nose, and a delicate mouth and chin. She stood five foot, five inches tall in her bare feet. Possessed of a **vivacious** personality, she maintained a **lithe** figure thanks to her various high school athletic activities, and despite being **enamored** of chocolate in a multitude of forms. Like many girls her age, she had a **reputation** as a stylish dresser, with an **impeccable** eye for the latest **fashion** trends. Her physical appearance had undergone a genuine **metamorphosis** since her awkward early teenage years. She was an excellent student and exhibited **uncanny** powers of judgment and observation far beyond her **chronological** age. Ellen had many friends at Stratford High, but Betsy Dalrymple and Linnea Matthews were the kind of friends with whom she could share her innermost secrets.

Not that Ken was much of a secret around Stratford High School for that matter. After nabbing a ring of Nazi spies, an adventure that **culminated** in their dramatic capture on the Hudson River docks in New York City, the whole world seemed to know they were an item. But, war was still raging in Europe and the Pacific, and Ken anticipated enlisting in the Navy following graduation at the end of the upcoming school year. Whatever plans they might have had on the **matrimonial** front would have to be **deferred** for the foreseeable future. It was a **forbidding** time to come of age, particularly for draft-eligible young men.

Ellen's father, Eric, was a graduate of Stratford High School and had studied tool design at the **Bridgeport Engineering Institute**. After that, he went to work in his father's **tool and die** establishment. The success of the company was due, in no small part, to Eric's technical **aptitude** and **fastidious** design work that had been employed in a variety of **intricate** and exacting projects, from automobile and aviation engine parts, to model railroad castings and other toys. Unlike some of its **impecunious** competitors, the E. V. Anderson Company was so successful that Ellen's grandfather was able to invest in real estate, purchasing not only a home in rural Easton, but the cottage on Candlewood Lake, north of Danbury. While he was not excessively **parsimonious**, Ellen's grandfather was **frugal** and not given to **extravagant** tastes or **profligate** spending habits.

Both Eric and Edna were active members of the local Swedish-American community, centered in Bridgeport. Eric sang second tenor with the North Star Singers, a Swedish-American chorus that was **affiliated** with the **American Union of Swedish Singers (AUSS)**, a national singing **federation** of Swedish male choruses. The North Star Singers had established themselves as a leading cultural institution in southern Connecticut. In addition to the concerts given for local clubs and organizations, the chorus participated in regional and national singing **conventions** sponsored by the A.U.S.S. Like most chorus wives, Edna was a member of the North Star Auxiliary, which supported the singers by preparing after-concert refreshments, holding fund raisers, and selling tickets. Eric and Edna were also members of a Swedish folk dance group that performed for local Swedish organizations and at the North Star Farm in Monroe, a rural retreat owned by the North Star Lodge of the **Good Templars**, a Swedish **temperance** society that encouraged **sobriety** and **abstained** from the use of alcohol.

Edna was an avid golfer, as was

Eric, and belonged to two bowling leagues. She was also an excellent cook and seamstress, and was a member of a sewing club that included many of her Swedish-American friends, including Florence Edgar, Evelyn Adolfson, and Karin Hanson. In recent months, however, she was spending more of her time **regaling** her friends and acquaintances with the story of how her now famous detective daughter caught Nazi spies in her spare time.

Anticipating the drive back to Stratford, Ellen retrieved her suitcases from the shelf of her bedroom closet and began packing, while Betsy completed her morning **ablutions.** By the time the girls entered the kitchen, the smell of Swedish pancakes and crisp bacon had **wafted** through and **enveloped** the small cabin. Ellen's father and Ken were already spreading **lingonberries** on their pancakes.

"It's about time you two joined us," Ken remarked, as the girls took their seats at the kitchen table. "One thing I'll say for hanging around your house, Ellen, is that I am certainly well-fed. Your mother's a fantastic cook."

"Oh, Ken, flattery will get you another Swedish pancake," Edna replied, as she slid another of the **delicacies** onto his plate.

"So, Dad, what can you tell me about Gary, Indiana? If I'm going to spend two months there, I suppose I should know something about the place."

"Well, I can tell you that it has the largest steel mill in the world and is the largest American city founded in the 20th century. It has a population of over 110,000, making it a little smaller than Bridgeport. It also has a sizable immigrant population, like Bridgeport. Not so many Swedes, but a lot of folks from Southern and Eastern Europe. The city is also famous for its schools, and the **Work-Study-Play** system of education that was introduced by its school superintendent, **William A. Wirt**, shortly after the city's founding in 1906. In addition to regular academic classes, the schools offer industrial arts, music, hands-on science classes, physical education, and auditorium class. Gus Bloomquist, my contact at the Gary Armor Plate plant, is a graduate of Emerson High School, the school you'll be attending. He sent me a copy of the **WPA's** *Calumet Region Historical Guide* that should get you up to speed on the city and its **amenities.** It's much like the Guide the **WPA** produced for Connecticut, only this one is limited to Northwest Indiana. Here's what it says about Emerson School:

> *Emerson School, the first unit built, served as a model for the twenty succeeding school plants, and includes three buildings, containing 29 classrooms, 12 studies, 4 laboratories, 6 gymnasia, 2 libraries, 6 shops, 2 kindergarten rooms, and a sight-saving room. Surrounding the buildings are ample playgrounds, baseball diamonds, tennis courts, a*

zoo, and gardens which the children tend as part of their school work. The zoo is tended by students and contains sixty pens of fowls and animals. The gardens and zoo are self-supporting and in some years have netted as much as $300."

"That's novel – a school with its own zoo! I've never heard of such a thing, and certainly not in Connecticut. This should be quite an interesting experience, even if it is for just a couple months," Ellen observed.

"I understand that Emerson School also has its own art collection, too, including both original oils and copies of the great masters, to promote an appreciation of the fine arts," Eric added.

"Interesting. But, what about movie theaters? I hope Gary has movie theaters. Movies are an art form, too, are they not?"

"Of course. I had a feeling you'd be asking about movie theaters, you being such an **inveterate** fan of the cinema. Gus told me that there are at least a half dozen movie theaters in downtown Gary, just a short walk from our apartment, and that one of them is an **opulent aesthetic** showplace. And, if that's not enough, there are plenty more in Chicago, which is less than an hour away on the **South Shore Railroad**."

"You've convinced me. Where do I sign up?"

"You don't have to do a thing. As I said, I've already purchased your tickets. All you have to do is sit back and enjoy the ride."

Following their breakfast of Swedish pancakes, with **lingonberries**, bacon, and orange juice, Ellen and Betsy retired to their bedroom to finish packing. Ellen stuffed all her summer clothes into two suitcases and loaded them in the trunk of the family's Hudson convertible. Betsy, likewise, stowed her overnight case in the trunk, alongside Ellen's parents' bag. Ellen's collection of books alone filled three cardboard boxes.

"Don't forget your radio, Ellen," Ellen's mother shouted from the kitchen.

"Gee whiz, Mom, there's not a chance of my forgetting that. How would I ever listen to *Little Orphan Annie* or *Inner Sanctum*?"

Ellen knew she was going to miss Ken terribly, but hoped that he would at least be there to see her off at the Stratford train station upon her departure for Indiana. She found him in the lower level of the cottage, packing his **rucksack**. Outside the gaze of her parents, she gave him a warm hug and a kiss on the cheek.

"You take good care of yourself while I'm gone. I'm sorry we had to cut your visit so short. I'm going to miss you. You be sure to write?"

"Of course, I'll write. But, don't forget to give me your address before you leave."

"I'll get it from Dad. If I happen to forget, I'll write to you first."

"That reminds me. Here's Walter Krivitsky's book. Mr. Mueller said there was no hurry returning it. It's a secondhand copy. I finished it last night after you all went to bed. I simply couldn't put it down. I know you'll find it as **engrossing** as I did."

"Oh, thank you so much. Reading it on the train will be such fun. But, I won't be able to forget that he was murdered for writing it."

The ride back to Stratford was an **exhilarating** one, particularly with the convertible top down, and the wind blowing in their faces. Ellen's father followed Route 7 out of New Milford, connecting to Route 25 in Brookfield Center that took them all the way to Bridgeport. The winding road passed through a succession of **picturesque** towns and scenic villages, including Newtown, Monroe, Stepney, and Trumbull, and past dozens of **venerable** New England homes, barns, and stonewalls, many dating back to the **Revolutionary era**. A little over an hour later, they pulled into the driveway of Ellen's Freeman Avenue colonial style home of more recent **vintage**.

Ellen was always very **meticulous** about packing, **methodically** making a list and checking off each item as she placed it in her luggage. She had to have enough dresses, skirts, blouses, shoes for both school and more formal occasions, not to mention underthings, stockings, socks, slacks, play clothes, bathing suit, a hat, gloves, and an overcoat in the case the weather turned **unseasonably** cold. She also made a point of packing her Crosley Bakelite radio, a few mystery novels, some spiral-bound notebooks, pencils, and her favorite fountain pen. Last, but not least, she packed her Kodak box camera which she loaded with a brand new roll of film from Hamilton's Pharmacy.

Ellen also took advantage of her father's offer to buy her some new clothes for the fall season. That afternoon, she and her mother drove to Howland's department store in Bridgeport, which had two floors devoted to the latest misses and women's apparel. She picked out two new dresses suitable for school, and one more **appropriate** for church or a trip to downtown Chicago. She also selected a pair of gray woolen slacks, a cream-colored blouse, a pair of black-and-white saddle shoes, and a pair of dark blue dress shoes, a new Revlon lipstick, rouge, and finger nail polish. She spent the remainder of the day, and most of Sunday, packing her railway trunk and two suit-cases. By the time her head hit the pillow on Saturday evening, she was a bundle of anticipation for the journey ahead – her first trip on the **Twentieth Century Limited**.

TRACK 34
PULLMAN
CAR
NUMBERS
CLUB-LOUNGE
259
258
257
256
255
DINER
254
253
252
251
2517
2501
250
OBS
20TH CENTURY
LIMITED
5-30 P.M.
CHICAGO
LOS ANGELES

Chapter 4

On the Twentieth Century Limited

"Ellen, are you all packed? Our train leaves at two o'clock and your mother's driving us to the station in ten minutes."

"Dad, I've been ready since early this morning. I've been sitting here waiting for you," she replied, with a chuckle.

Ellen was dressed in a Carolina blue pleated skirt and matching jacket over an elegant white blouse, with cut out work on the collar. In **lieu** of silk or nylon hose, she wore Liquid Stockings, a form of leg cosmetics necessitated by wartime shortages of nylon that **simulated** the real thing. Her father was dressed in a light gray business suit and red and white-striped tie.

Eric loaded three suitcases and a railway trunk into the Hudson convertible, then checked his inside jacket pocket for their train tickets. Slinging her purse over her right shoulder, Ellen climbed into the back seat, while her mother took the wheel and backed the car out of the driveway. Proceeding down Freeman Avenue, she turned right onto Main Street and drove south to the Stratford train station, passing the new Town Hall and Stratford High School on the way.

Several of Ellen's friends were already standing on the platform when their car pulled into the station parking lot, including Linnea Matthews, Betsy Dalrymple and Christine Applegate. Ellen looked in vain for Ken, but he was nowhere in sight. Ellen's father lugged Ellen's trunk and their three suitcases up the platform steps.

Ellen kissed her Mother 'Goodbye,' then turned to her friends.

"Hi, Ellen! We brought you some movie magazines to read on the train, and a bag of candy to satisfy your sweet tooth," Betsy exclaimed.

"Gee, thanks! What have we here: Milk Duds, Raisinets, Mounds, Bonomo Turkish Taffy, a Milky Way, and Malted Milk Balls. What more could a girl ask for?"

"A toothbrush, perhaps?" Linnea **retorted**.

"It's swell of you to see us off. But, where's Ken? He promised to be here."

"Isn't he working at the book store?" suggested Christine.

"Yes, that's what he said, but ..."

At that moment, Ellen could hear the sound of the westbound train approaching, but Ken was still nowhere to be seen. Then, as the train started easing into Stratford station, its wheels squealing against the rails, she spotted him at street level, a bouquet of flowers clutched in his hand. When he saw the train, he broke into a sprint and raced up the concrete steps to the platform.

"Oh, thank goodness. I was afraid you weren't coming."

"Sorry I'm late. I wouldn't have been able to forgive myself if I'd missed your train. I was covering the store for Mr. Mueller and almost lost track of time. He's out **appraising** a collection of **antiquarian** books for an estate auction. When he didn't return, I just locked the front door and took off for the station. I bought you these flowers this morning, on my way to work."

"That was very thoughtful of you."

Stepping a few yards away from the others, Ellen and Ken exchanged glances and smiled affectionately at each other.

"I'm going to miss you. Here, I've written out my new address: 750 Carolina Street, Gary, Indiana. You be sure to write, now."

"Don't worry. I'll write every chance I get."

Ken took Ellen by the shoulders, pulled her close, kissed her softly on the lips and gave her a prolonged embrace. She kissed him back, just as the New York, New Haven & Hartford train came to a stop at the platform.

"Goodbye, everyone. I'll see you in a couple of months, God willing. Be sure to write. I promise to answer all your letters."

While Ellen finished saying goodbye to her friends, her father made arrangements with the porter to check their luggage through to Chicago. Once that was accomplished, they boarded the Yankee Clipper for Grand Central Terminal in New York City.

"All aboard," shouted the conductor, as he checked the platform for any stragglers, then closed the door to the coach. Ellen quickly slid into a window seat in the middle of the car, after placing her jacket and small overnight bag in the overhead luggage rack. Her father soon joined her. Ellen waved 'goodbye' to her Mother and her friends as the train eased out of Stratford Station on its way West. But, the image that remained with her was the **mournful** expression on Ken's face as he passed from view.

For the next thirty minutes, her eyes remained **mesmerized** by the unfolding landscape of Connecticut coastal towns: Bridgeport, Fairfield, Westport, and Norwalk. It was as their train approached Stamford that she finally opened Walter Krivitsky's expose of life inside Stalin's secret service and began reading. After that, her eyes rarely looked up, except to **ponder** some **astounding revelation**, or reach for another malted milk ball. Before she knew it, more than an hour had passed and their train was stopping at 125th Street in Harlem, where massive apartment houses and **brownstones** were a **ubiquitous** feature of the landscape. Before long, however, their train was enveloped by the darkness of the tunnel system that would take them to Grand

Central Terminal at 42ⁿᵈ Street and Park Avenue in Midtown Manhattan.

Constructed between 1907 and 1913, **Grand Central Terminal** was named for the **New York Central Railroad**, the line that served most of the Northeastern United States. The massive station, designed and built in the grand **Beaux-Arts style**, was the world's largest, with 44 platforms and 67 tracks on two levels. Its 42ⁿᵈ Street **façade** was dominated by an **opulent** clock containing the world's largest example of **Tiffany glass**, surrounded by sculptures of Minerva, Hercules, and Mercury, a creation of the noted French sculptor **Jules Felix Coutan**. Spilling onto its expansive marble Main Concourse were passengers from all over the Northeast and greater New York metropolitan area.

The Yankee Clipper, out of New Haven, was just one of dozens of trains that arrived and departed the station daily. As Ellen and her father stepped out of their car and onto the platform, they were swiftly engulfed by a sea of passengers that propelled them up the ramp to the exit. Passing through one of the elegant marble archways and into the **cavernous** space ahead, they were immediately **buffeted** by hundreds of commuters crisscrossing the floor of the Main Concourse, or stopping to buy tickets at one of the **myriad** ticket windows.

"Dad, I'm hungry. What do you say we catch a bite to eat on the lower level."

"Hungry? After all that candy? I was watching you pop those malted milk balls in your mouth. Fine, but we don't want to spoil our appetites. We'll be having dinner on the train about seven thirty and it's already four o'clock."

"Then, how about some of that delicious New York cheesecake, and coffee? That should be enough to tide us over until dinner."

"Sounds good to me."

The two travelers made their way to the Gotham Delicatessen and approached a counter where an enticing array of desserts drew their attention. A handsome young man in a white apron and soda fountain cap approached.

"And what can I get for you folks?"

"Two cheesecakes and two coffees," Ellen replied, looking at her father for confirmation. She knew instinctively, however, that her father **relished** cheesecake.

"That'll be ninety cents, please."

After paying the clerk, they found an open table against the wall and sat down. Eric took a sip of coffee, while perusing a copy of the *New York Herald Tribune* someone had left on an adjacent chair. Ellen remained fixated on her book.

"What's that you're reading, sweetie?"

"A book Ken lent me: *In Stalin's Secret Service*, by Walter Krivitsky. He was the first high-ranking Soviet spy to defect to the West. The book is an inside look at the Soviet spy apparatus and its **subversive** activities. His revelations about Stalin are chilling."

"How so?"

"Mostly his **paranoia**. He's obsessed with consolidating his power and willing to **arbitrarily** exterminate anyone who might pose a threat to his rule. Krivitsky estimates that, about four years ago, during the **Great Purge**, Stalin arrested over four hundred thousand people and had many shot without trial. Others were made to confess during show trials at which they were accused of being traitors. Most were loyal **Marxist-Leninists**, and **sycophants** of Stalin, but their loyalty was for **naught.** He also had most of the Red Army senior staff executed without trial. Why, he even has spies to spy on his spies."

"You know, I seem to have read something by him in the *Saturday Evening Post*."

"Yes, that's right. After his defection, he first went to Washington to inform the FBI and members of Congress that Stalin was about to enter into a non-aggression pact with Hitler. But, they didn't believe him, thinking the idea too **preposterous**. So, he wrote a series of articles for the *Saturday Evening Post*, exposing their plans. That made him a **pariah** in the Soviet Union and among its **disciples** in the West. The Russians had him killed in his Washington hotel, but not before he had his book published."

"When was that?"

"In 1939, soon after the **Molotov-Ribbentrop Pact** was signed."

"So, what drove him to defect?"

"He seems to have experienced some kind of **epiphany** after seeing so many of his friends being **liquidated**, most of them loyal members of the Communist Party, and true believers in the communist **utopia**."

"He liquidated them, eh?"

"Yes, I was thinking about the *Wizard of Oz*, too, and the way Dorothy liquidated the Wicked Witch of the West. But, Stalin used real bullets, not water. Krivitsky calls the environment inside the Soviet Union a 'madhouse' because there was neither rhyme nor reason to why people were arrested and **exterminated**. Those who confessed during the Moscow show trials likely did so in an effort to protect their innocent family members, but it didn't do any good because, in most cases, they were killed, too. The country had really degenerated into a **personality cult** of Stalin."

"Scary stuff. It's hard to imagine being subject to the **arbitrary** rule of a madman like Stalin."

"No kidding. I'm just glad we live in a free country with Constitutional protections against such behavior."

"What does Krivitsky say about the communist **infiltration** in the United States?"

"Well, I'm not that far along, yet, but it's obvious that the Soviet secret police have a network of spies, not only in this country, but in other western democracies. Many of them are in sensitive government positions, the media, and academia – anywhere their influence can be most effectively **deployed** to advance the Soviet goal of world domination."

Now boarding, on track 34, the Twentieth Century Limited, for Chicago.

All Aboard!

"Say, that's our train. I'm anxious to find our compartment and get settled in," Ellen's father suggested. Ellen nodded enthusiastically.

Having polished off their cheesecake, and taken the last few sips of coffee, Ellen and her father picked up their carry-on items and headed upstairs to locate the track.

"There it is – track 34," Ellen shouted, her voice overcome with emotion, as she and her father walked briskly in the direction of the numbered archway toward the platform.

Standing on the track was the world's most famous train, pulled initially by an electric locomotive as far as Harmon-Croton where it was replaced by a classic **Art Deco**-inspired Hudson locomotive. The Twentieth Century

Limited contained twelve cars: a postal car, a baggage-club car, two dining cars, seven sleepers, and a combination sleeper-buffet-lounge and observation car. The sleeping cars consisted exclusively of compartments, replacing the open sections with upper and lower berths, with curtains, from an earlier era. Ellen and her father were escorted to their car on the elegant red carpet created specifically for the Twentieth Century Limited, a feature that added an **aura** of glamour to the first-class service the train **exuded**. Leading the way was one of the smartly dressed Pullman porters in white jacket and black trousers, one of an exclusively Negro staff originally consisting of ex-slaves recruited by **George Pullman** after the Civil War. Theirs was a proud fraternity – the **Brotherhood of Sleeping Car Porters** – and they took their responsibilities with considerable pride.

"Here's your car, Mr. Anderson – the *City of Albany*. It's a seventeen room-ette sleeping car. And here's your compartment – 16B. I hope you and your daughter will find it to your liking. My name is George. If there is anything I can do to make your trip more enjoyable, please call upon me. My station is at the end of the car. Dinner will be served beginning at seven o'clock in the dining car. I can take your reservation now, if you'd like."

"Yes, thank you, George. We'd like to eat at seven thirty."

"Seven thirty it is. Just present yourselves to the steward at the head of the dining car upon entering."

"I trust our bags have made it safely to the baggage car?"

"Yes sir! I took care of them personally."

Ellen was **ecstatic** about traveling in her very own private room on the Twentieth Century Limited, and thought it the **pinnacle** of luxury. She marveled at the **punctilious** red carpet treatment and personal service for which it was famous. The train was noted for its **exclusivity** and **sophistication**, and its passengers were treated like royalty. Their room was small, but comfortable. The compartment could be easily converted by the Pullman porter from a sitting room by day to a sleeping room at night. With fifteen minutes to departure, Ellen made herself comfortable with her book and a pillow. At six o'clock, she felt the train begin to move, almost **imperceptibly** at first, then gradually **accelerating** as it made its way through the **subterranean** tunnel system, before approaching the Hudson River at the north end of Manhattan Island. The train passed through a **succession** of river towns on its way to Albany – Yonkers, Irvington, Harmon-Croton, Poughkeepsie, Peekskill, and Rhinecliff. Ellen remained curled up with her book, while her father read the *New York Herald Tribune*, with the latest news of the war in Europe and the Pacific.

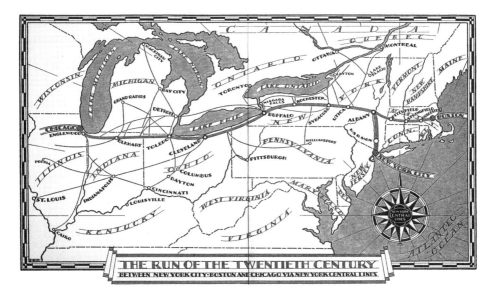

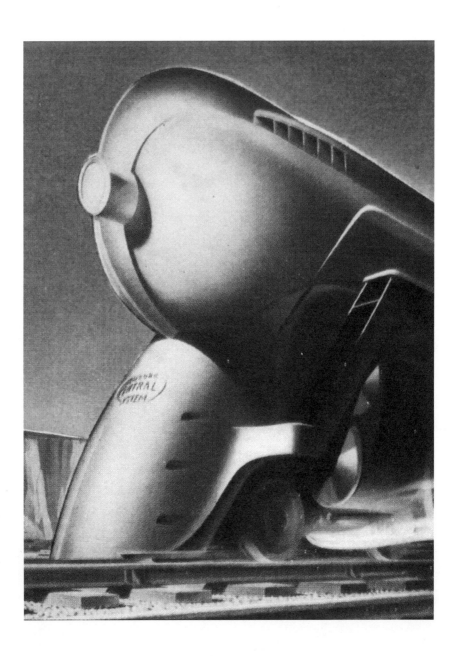

Chapter 5

Dinner in the Diner

As seven thirty approached, Ellen and her father made their way through the corridors of several Pullman cars to the first of two elegant dining cars that served the train's more than 800 passengers. Greeted by the uniformed Negro steward, they were promptly escorted to a table already occupied by two older passengers. Ellen observed the elegant table linens, silverware,

and fresh flowers that graced the tables and the courteous service of the waiters who stood at attention while chefs busily prepared dinners in the kitchen. The passengers were all well dressed, the men in business attire, the women in smart dresses or suits. The train had the **lavish aura** befitting a country or private club, not that Ellen had much experience with either. Ellen and her father smiled at their table companions as their waiter handed them menus. Scanning the offerings as their train sped along the eastern shore of the Hudson River, Ellen surveyed a variety of mouth-watering entrees, including pork chops, lobster, and filet mignon. She looked up at her father for direction.

"You order whatever you'd like, Ellen. This is a special occasion and, besides, your grandfather's footing the bill."

"Great! Then, I'm ordering the Fresh Devilled Lobster Twentieth Century, New Peas with Mint, and Allumette Potatoes."

"I think I'll have the Prime Filet Mignon, Shallots Butter, Grilled Tomato, New Brussels Sprouts Polonaise, and Au Gratin Potatoes."

Ellen's father signaled the waiter, who approached their table and took their orders. Their tablemates had already ordered.

"Would you like a cocktail while you wait, sir?"

"Yes, please, bring me a very dry martini. And a Shirley Temple for my daughter."

"Coming right up, Mr. Anderson."

"A Shirley Temple? Dad! You must think I'm a juvenile! I was going to order ginger ale on the rocks!"

"Sorry, dear, for being so **presumptuous**. You'll have to forgive your dear ol' Dad. It'll take a few years before I stop thinking of you as my little girl."

Ellen smiled at him affectionately. And, although she had brought her book along with the intention of reading while they waited for dinner, she quickly found herself engrossed in conversation with the people at their table, a **gregarious** retired couple from New Jersey on their way to visit children and grandchildren in Milwaukee. Her book sat unopened on the table, its cover plainly visible.

"New Jersey, you say. Where in New Jersey?" Ellen's father inquired.

"**Perth Amboy**, not far from Raritan Bay. It's an easy commute on the ferry to Manhattan from our home. Marge and I love the city, but are far enough away to avoid the congestion, the noise, and the politics – not that Perth Amboy's some kind of political **nirvana**. We also have a special **affinity** for the opera, and have season tickets to the Met. When the kids were still at home, we also took advantage of all the cultural attractions in the city. New York has so much to offer: the Metropolitan Museum of Art, the American Museum of Natural History, the Museum of Modern Art, the Cloisters, the Bronx Zoo, the Brooklyn Botanic Garden. There's something for every taste. How about you?"

"We live in Stratford, Connecticut, near Bridgeport. Ellen and I are on our way to Gary, Indiana on business. My wife had to stay home to care for her mother who has been suffering from the **gout**. We go to the city on occasion, when work allows. Right now, our shop has been so **inundated** with war-related contracts, that I don't get much time away. You mentioned the opera. My wife and I are also opera lovers. I assume you've heard that fabulous Swedish tenor, **Jussi Björling**? We were **enthralled** with his performance in Verdi's *Il Trovatore* last year."

"Funny you should mention him. Marge and I adore Björling. We were at his Met debut in 1938 in *La Boheme*, and have heard him in *Il Trovatore*, *Un Ballo in Maschera*, and *Rigoletto*. We've also heard him in recital at Town Hall and in Verdi's *Requiem* at Carnegie Hall, with **Toscanini** conducting. His *Ingemisco* sent chills down my spine. In my younger days, I had the opportunity to hear both Caruso and Gigli, but **Björling** is in a class all by himself. By the way, I have to apologize for not introducing myself. My name is Bertelsen – Edvard Bertelsen. And this is my wife, Gerda."

"Pleased to meet you. I had a feeling that you might be fellow Scandinavians. My name's Eric Anderson, and this is my daughter, Ellen. Our **ancestry** is Swedish. My parents emigrated from the province of Värmland, along the Swedish-Norwegian border. Perhaps, you've heard of it?"

"Yes, of course. We know the area quite well. I grew up just east of Oslo and, when I was a youngster, we took the train to Stockholm on occasion. My father was in the lumber business and had dealings with timber merchants and paper-mills in Värmland, which, as you probably know, is famous for its timber, pulp and paper industries. Gerda and I came here in 1928, just before the Depression hit. I was in paper sales before my retirement. What kind of work do you do?"

"I'm a tool designer by training and work for my father's tool and die business in Bridgeport. I've worked on a variety of projects over the years, but, lately, my work has been exclusively devoted to war production – armaments, **precision** airplane parts, and so forth. That's what's taking us to Gary."

"Speaking of the war, Eric, my family back in Norway has been suffering terribly from the Nazi occupation. My brother and sister are toughing it out in Oslo, but they sent their children across the border to friends in **Årjäng**, Sweden, to wait it out. They haven't seen them for more than two years. We just hope that the Nazis don't violate Swedish **neutrality**."

"The Swedes are walking a real political tightrope right now," Eric added. "I understand the Swedish government has **acceded** to Nazi demands to transport soldiers, prisoners and equipment to and from Norway. Much of that traffic is passing through Värmland."

"It's probably why the Germans have allowed the Swedes to maintain their **neutrality**. Had they not cooperated, they might have been occupied as well. And you know as well as I what would have happened to all the Jews and other refugees who have sought **asylum** in Sweden."

As her father continued conversing with Mr. Bertelsen, Ellen observed a young, dark-haired woman sitting across the **aisle** who gazed **persistently** in her direction. She was a **winsome** girl who **exuded** an **inexplicable** air of **exoticism**. She had a smooth, honey-colored complexion, dark eyes, and slightly **aristocratic** features. Her striking dark green belted silk dress was accented with a gold scarf secured with elegant gold pin. She wore bright red lipstick, but, otherwise, was not overly made-up like most American girls her age. Ellen **surmised** that she might be European. Not wanting to stare back, however, Ellen rejoined the conversation with the Bertelsens. A few moments later, however, she, again, found herself the object of the young woman's repeated glances, which appeared to take notice of the book Ellen had resting on the edge of her table. A **nondescript** middle-aged man with a **dour** expression sat **impassively** across the table from the young woman, but, from what Ellen could **discern**, they were not together. When she had finished her dessert and coffee, the woman took a pencil from her purse and scribbled something on a piece of paper. Then, on her way out of the dining car, she placed it next to Ellen's book.

Neither Ellen's father nor their two table companions were **cognizant** of the woman's movements. Ellen **nonchalantly** picked up the paper and turned it over. It read: *Please meet me in the observation car at 9:00.* She put the paper in her purse and rejoined the conversation. Ellen had no idea what this was all about, but her natural curiosity had been **piqued** and she was determined to meet the woman at the appointed hour. *Was it her book that attracted the woman's attention, or had she been eavesdropping on their conversation?*

The next hour was spent **savoring** the **succulent** lobster she had ordered and engaging in more **scintillating** conversation with the Bertelsens, who questioned her about her school activities and interests, including her love of Scandinavian music. Dinner was topped off with a delicious piece of apple pie and vanilla ice cream. Her father ordered the pecan pie, also with vanilla ice cream. With their hunger **satiated**, Ellen and her father **sauntered** back to their compartment, but not before extending warm wishes to their tablemates for an enjoyable visit with their family in Milwaukee.

By the time they had finished dinner, their train had crossed the Hudson River at Albany, made its scheduled station stop, and began climbing its only mainline grade before rolling on through the Mohawk Valley on its westward journey across New York State. By the time they returned to their compartment, George had prepared their beds. Ellen glanced at her watch. It was already eight forty-five, and she was determined to meet the unknown young woman at nine o'clock.

"Dad, if you don't mind, I'd like to take a walk back to the observation car and do a little reading before turning in?"

"Sure, honey. You go right ahead. I'm ready to settle in for the evening and read my newspapers. Don't stay up too late, now."

"No, I promise to be back by eleven o'clock."

With that, Ellen grabbed her book and began walking in the direction of the observation car, trying to steady herself against the train's irregular movements. As she passed through the two dining cars, Ellen observed that most of the tables were now empty, with the last of the diners finishing their meals. The observation car was the last carriage on the train, its **panoramic** windows affording maximum viewing enjoyment, at least with what remained of daylight. The car's curved, streamlined design was a variation on the observation platforms of an earlier era, providing passengers with the ability to enjoy drinks and conversation while either taking in the unfolding landscape or **hypnotically** observing the tracks **recede** into the distance.

Ellen counted eight passengers sitting on the couches or individual lounge chairs, but the dark-haired woman she had seen in the dining car was not among them. But, it was still early. She chose an unoccupied lounge chair at the end of the car where she could best observe the tracks as they faded into the darkness. She opened her book and turned to chapter eight: "Why Stalin Shot His Generals." She read:

> *There are **conspiracies** plotted by men lusting for power or vengeance, and there are **conspiracies** plotted by the course of events. Sometimes the paths of two such **conspiracies** cross and interlace. Then the historian finds himself confronted by tangled **skeins** which challenge his utmost powers. To this category belongs the mystery of the **annihilation** by Stalin of the flower of the Red Army as spies in the service of the German government. It is a mystery which continues to **baffle** the mind of the world ...*

"Hard to believe, isn't it?"

Chapter 6

Astounding Revelations

Startled, Ellen looked up to find the young, dark-haired women hovering over her, and staring down at her book. *Could she read upside down, or was she just guessing?*

"I'm so pleased you accepted my invitation to meet here," said the woman, pulling a chair up next to Ellen's, and some distance from the next closest passenger, so as to afford a **modicum** of privacy.

"What drew you to this book, may I ask? I saw you had it with you in the dining car."

"Actually, my boyfriend gave it to me. He knows I have a taste for mystery and **intrigue**, particularly of a political nature. And he knew I'd like it because we share the same **abhorrence** for **totalitarianism**."

"I can't tell you how gratifying it is to hear you say that. I knew that I might have been taking a chance by asking a complete stranger to meet me here, but now I know I made the correct decision. One can never be certain, of course. But, my **intuition** told me that you are a person most likely to be sympathetic to my **plight**."

Ellen stretched out her hand to the woman and shook it warmly.

"My name's Ellen Anderson. And yours?"

"Natalia Boroskova. It's Russian, in case you hadn't guessed. I suppose you're wondering why I wrote you that note and asked you to meet me here?"

"Well, I'm assuming it had something to do with this book?"

"That's correct. I gathered that you wish to understand the nature of Soviet espionage."

"You're very **perceptive**. I do have a deep interest in comprehending the nature of the **totalitarian** threats our country faces. We may be allied with the Soviet Union to defeat the Nazis, but, in my view, it's a pact with the devil, a devil we will confront once the war is over. And, after all, Stalin and Hitler were virtual allies until June of last year, when the Germans invaded your country. We mustn't lose sight of that."

"You are very **prescient**, Miss Anderson. The Soviet Union is the devil and Joseph Stalin is its un-questioned master. I should know. Both my parents were killed in the **Great Purge** and I was only able to escape the **horrendous** conditions in my country at great personal risk."

Ellen immediately felt a **profound** sense of **empathy** for the young woman.

"I am so sorry, Natalia. Do you feel uncomfortable telling me why your parents were killed?"

"Not at all. In fact, it may be **therapeutic** for me to get it off my chest. My father, Vladimir Boroskova, was a high-ranking official in the Soviet secret service, just as Walter Krivitsky was. He had been a loyal member of the Communist Party since the **Bolshevik Revolution** in 1917. While his **ascent** was not **meteoric**, he gradually managed to work his way up in the party **hierarchy**, eventually landing an appointment as deputy **consul** at the Soviet embassy in London – certainly a plum assignment for any diplomat. Of course, what most westerners don't realize is that most Soviet diplomatic officials are, in reality, members of the secret service whose primary responsibility is spying on their host countries. The Soviet diplomatic service is mostly just a **façade** for activities far more **pernicious** than the mere outward trappings of diplomacy. I spent seven years attending **public schools** in London while he was assigned to that post – what you would call private schools."

"So that explains your **fluency** in English."

"Yes. I received high marks in English and fell in love with the English novelists: Jane Austen, Thomas Hardy, Charles Dickens, George Eliot, D.H. Lawrence. But, that all came to an end in 1937, the year my father was recalled to Moscow. Like all faithful party members, he obeyed orders, and my mother and I were **obliged** to accompany him. Shortly after our return, he was called to an appointment in the **Kremlin** and disappeared, never to be seen again.

My mother was **overwrought** and hunted frantically for him, only to learn that he had been arrested and imprisoned in the **Lubyanka**. They told us that he died of a **cerebral hemorrhage**, but we knew better than that, particularly after they refused to return his body to us for a proper burial. When my mother

protested to the Soviet authorities, she, too, was arrested. This was not an **aberration** because, by that time, Stalin had made a habit of arresting the wives of accused traitors, believing them to be **irreparably tainted** by their **familial** relationship. When my mother failed to return to our apartment, I learned from friends that the same fate had probably befallen her. I, too, tried to confront Soviet authorities, but was met with **curt** and **peremptory** responses. I became almost **inconsolable** and cried for days afterwards. It left an **indelible** scar on my **psyche**. Indeed, I was to learn that only my youth had saved me."

"What was your father accused of?" Ellen inquired.

"I can't say for sure why my father was arrested, but, after reading Walter Krivitsky's book during my **sojourn** in Sweden, I imagine that he was reported by a Stalinist **sycophant** trying to **curry** favor with the regime. You have to understand that there were no rational **criteria** for arresting people. Stalin's **paranoia** infected the whole country. Soviet citizens were actively encouraged to spy on their fellow citizens and report them for **suspicious** activity. Political **dissent** was simply not tolerated. And since no one wanted to risk incurring Stalin's **wrath**, many **canny** citizens felt that their best hope of saving themselves and their family members was to **denounce** other citizens or party members, or to cast doubt on them by **innuendo**, even those they knew to be innocent.

"Once some **canard** was sewn in the minds of the authorities, often for petty or **venal** reasons, the government could be **merciless**, and there was no way to **expunge** the blot on your reputation with the Communist Party. The **credulity** of Party officials was astounding. Not surprisingly, my parents did not receive a public trial. I can only assume that they were shot in the basement of the Lubyanka, like so many others. Guilt or innocence meant nothing to Stalin and his **ilk**, nor did evidence. Once they suspected you, they simply employed **chicanery** to manufacture the evidence and lined up **adverse** witnesses to **denounce** you, whether privately, or in open court."

"Then, how did you escape from the Soviet Union? They certainly wouldn't have let you leave **voluntarily**."

"That's correct. In fact, as the child of so-called 'enemies of the State,' I was told that I was fortunate to have been spared **internment** in a prison camp, or other **punitive** measures – as if that was any **consolation**. After my passport was **confiscated**, I would have been **precluded** from legally crossing the border. The Soviet Union became, in effect, my prison. For nearly four years, my life was **circumscribed** by a poverty-ridden and **austere** environment. I lived a **draconian** existence with my mother's cousin, in a **squalid** little village outside of Moscow. We suffered **abject privation**, **exacerbated** by **acute** shortages of food, **rancid** meat, and **putrid** vegetables. Our clothes were increasingly ragged and **threadbare**. And rationing was so **stringent** that I don't know how we survived on the **dearth** of food we were **allocated**. And, yet, we were better off than many others who were positively **emaciated** as a result of the food shortages, particularly those in **Leningrad**, where several hundred thousand died during the German **siege.** What's more, my education was **replete** with **substantial** doses of Marxist **dogma** of the most **puerile** sort.

"Things got even worse in 1941. During the **rancor fomented** by the **protracted** Battle of Moscow, my cousin and I were **conscripted** to dig tank trenches to halt the German advance. In November, after **prolonged** exposure to sub-zero temperatures, I suffered **frostbite** and almost lost the toes on my left foot. It was a strange sensation, almost as if they were under the effects of **anesthesia.** That was in December 1941. Under the circumstances, I could have continued to **wallow** in self-pity, but, after **ruminating** during my long hours of **convalescence,** I **resolved** to make my way to the West. The major **impetus** behind my desire to escape was to expose the **genocidal** nature of the Stalinist regime. Yet, I was **cognizant** at the time that I had only an **infinitesimal** chance to **elude** both the Soviet authorities and the **Wehrmacht.**

"As the weather warmed in April 1942, however, my thoughts began to **crystallize,** and I entertained the **quixotic** hope of joining my uncle Stanislaus in America. One day, I dressed extra warmly, said 'farewell' to my cousin, and set off on foot across the **desolate** landscape, eventually making my way to **Lithuania,** where I was able to join a **score** of Lithuanian Jews fleeing to Sweden. It was an **arduous** and **harrowing** journey **fraught** with **peril** at every **juncture,** but I was determined to **extricate** myself from that **oppressive** police state."

"Jewish refugees? Do you mean to say that not all had been arrested by the Gestapo?"

"Yes, there were some who managed to escape **detection** by passing themselves off as ethnic **Lithuanians,** or **Poles** – in other words, as **Gentiles.** And some had been concealed by sympathetic Lithuanians. In **Kaunas,** a group of Lithuanian patriots provided me with **forged** identity papers to aid my escape. One of them was the former head of the Lithuanian Information Service, a woman by the name of **Madeleine Avietenaite.** Another was a

remarkable Roman Catholic priest, **Father Stasys Yla,** who has **consecrated** his life to Jesus Christ and the salvation of his people. After the Nazis occupied Lithuania, these two **resilient** Lithuanian patriots published **samizdat** newspapers on the top floor of a building in Kaunas that was used primarily as a medical **dispensary**. Luckily, the Nazis never ventured beyond the second floor where the dispensary was located. They were able to provide me with a forged passport and other forms of **documentation**, which made my already d**aunting** adventure somewhat less **precarious**."

"But weren't all the transportation depots heavily guarded?"

"Of course. German soldiers guarded all the train stations and ports. So, I not only had to navigate the **demarcation** line between the Russian and German armies, but also had to avoid the German soldiers occupying Lithuania. When I got to the Baltic port of **Klaipeda**, I used my feminine **wiles** to **beguile** an **amicable** young German soldier into helping me cross the **cordon** thrown up around the harbor. Luckily for me, he was not sympathetic with the Nazi cause and was willing to assist me in making contact with Jewish refugees who had already contracted with a Lithuanian sea captain to transport them across the Baltic. Thanks to the captain's expert navigational skills, the small fishing trawler in which we were concealed was able to **elude** the German patrol boats under the cover of fog. Had they spotted our vessel, they could easily have **dispatched** us with a few quick blasts from their machine guns.

After a day in the **Baltic Sea**, we made our way to the island of **Gotland** and, from there, to **Stockholm**. Several months later, despite **maritime** restrictions, I was able to book passage on a steamship from

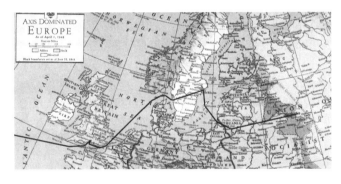

Gothenburg to **Southampton**, and then to New York."

"Where did you get the money to come to America? Did the Swedes pay your way?"

"No. I had several thousand dollars in British pound notes sewn into the lining of my overcoat. It was money that my mother had left in my safekeeping after my father disappeared, and before she left to search for him. I used it **sparingly**. But, more importantly – and here I must **entreat** you to maintain the utmost secrecy – I carried with me secret documents hidden in a book that my father had left in the care of our London housekeeper."

"In a book? How did he manage that?"

"As a member of the intelligence service, my father had become rather **adroit** at dealing with various forms of microfilm. Over several months, he succeeded in converting a number of documents to **microdots** that he inserted into a copy of **Alexander Pushkin**'s novel in verse, ***Eugene Onegin***, a classic of Russian literature. Perhaps you've read it?"

"No, I haven't."

"Oh, you must read it. In fact, Tchaikovsky composed a beautiful opera based on the text. It's a deeply emotional work, richly melodic in the Russian musical tradition. It's performed often at the **Bolshoi**. Well, in the next to the last chapter of my father's copy of the novel, the periods are not periods at all, but **microdots** containing the photographic images of secret documents from the Russian embassy in London. I think my father had a **premonition** about what the future might hold. He **explicitly** told me that, if I was to escape from the Soviet Union, I was to visit the home of our former housekeeper in London who would give me this book. It was to her apartment on Mermaid Court in Southwark that I went after landing in **Southampton**. Once I had the book in my possession, I was instructed to deliver it to my uncle – my father's brother – in the United States. I was determined to carry out his wishes, particularly after he and my mother were killed by Stalin's **henchmen**."

"I assume your father was a communist?"

"Naturally. Achieving such a high-ranking position in the Soviet government would have been **foreclosed** to anyone not a member of the Communist Party. Promotions were made only after **exhaustive scrutiny** of a candidate's **credentials**, personal history, and associations. If you harbored any doubts about communism, or the government, you were **obliged** to keep those thoughts to yourself. Being assigned to an embassy in one of the major European capitals, or the United States, was a privilege awarded only to those **deemed** most trustworthy. However, as the **Purge** progressed in Moscow, my father became **disheartened** and began to confess **misgivings** about what had become of the once great Soviet experiment to my mother and me. He began as a true believer, one whose goal was world-wide communist domination – a **workers' paradise**, if you accept the **misnomer**. But, as he observed Stalin's ruthless attempts to consolidate power, and the death and misery he **inflicted** on millions of Soviet citizens, my father became increasingly **ambivalent** about communism, an outlook that was swiftly transformed into **revulsion**.

"My father began to see the **Marxist-Leninist ideology** as just a **smokescreen** for Stalin's ruthless **dictatorship** and **paranoid** lust for power. As my father became **disillusioned** with the government, he came to understand that those in the Soviet leadership **feigned** an interest in the workingman, while maintaining **extravagant** and **lavish** personal lifestyles that heightened the **disparity** between government officials and the poor. Finally, he **abjured** the communist ideology altogether and **disparaged** everything the government was doing. Those sentiments were **solidified** as my father saw many of his **erstwhile** and loyal communist friends – innocents all – disappear into the Lubyanka."

"What are your plans now?"

"I'm on my way to Gary, Indiana, where my father's brother, Stanislaus, lives. I hope I can start a new life there. But, I'm afraid I'm being followed."

"Followed? How could that be? How would anyone have known about your movements after you left the Soviet Union?"

"I can't be sure, but I believe that I may have been overheard by a Soviet operative when I made the crossing from Stockholm to Southampton. I remember my father telling me that the Soviet secret service has spies on many vessels, including those from neutral Sweden, who are the eyes and ears of Soviet intelligence. I now believe that I may have been followed to London and, on the Queen Mary, from Southampton to New York City. And I'm certain they've followed me onto this train."

"What makes you think so?"

"I recall conversing with a Swedish gentleman who worked for an import-export firm in New York City. **Inadvertently**, I told him about my parents and their fate at the hands of the communists, but failed to notice that one of the ship's stewards was eavesdropping on our conversation. He hurried away when I observed him. I'm now convinced he was a Soviet agent. Naturally, he would have had access to the ship's **manifest** with my name on it. And, having my name, he would have had no difficulty in tracing my identity by contacting Soviet authorities in Moscow. It's most **disconcerting**."

"That certainly sounds **plausible**. If they realized who you were, or discovered as much from their contacts, they would have reason to suspect that you might go to the authorities with what you know, even if they are unaware of the secret documents you carry with you," Ellen suggested.

"I should have done a better job of remaining **inconspicuous**. Now, I've put myself in danger, even though I'm thousands of miles from the Soviet Union."

"By a strange **quirk** of fate, we're also going to Gary, Indiana. My father will be there for several weeks doing war-related production work and I'm going along to keep house for him. I'm sure we can assist you after we arrive. Where does this uncle of yours live?"

"I have his address," she said, while digging to the bottom of her purse for a slip of paper.

"Here it is: 1334 Lincoln Street – just like your President. Uncle Stanislaus responded to the letter I sent him while I was in Stockholm. He wrote that he works for the United States Steel Company as a **scarfer** – whatever that is – in the **Sheet and Tin Mill**, and that he and his wife, Veronika, live across the street from the Lithuanian church in Gary. I know little more about him. As a child, I knew him only from his infrequent letters which, under the circumstances, were rather **bland** and **innocuous,** given Soviet **censorship**. He did say in his recent letter that I was most welcome to live with him and his wife, Veronika. My father told me he was a **White Russian** who had fought against the Red Army during the **Russian Civil War** and was forced to emigrate, or risk death or imprisonment. As a communist, my father did not have much **forbearance** for White Russians. In fact, that was the cause of their **estrangement**. It's my understanding that my uncle hired on as a **stevedore** at the port of **Odessa** and eventually made his way to Baltimore, where he jumped ship. From there, he moved to Gary and found a job in the steel mills. My father and he exchanged letters infrequently for some years, but their correspondence, naturally, came to an **abrupt** end with my father's death."

"Where is your compartment? If you're still being followed, you could be in serious danger. It wouldn't be difficult for a clever spy to force his way into your compartment."

"I'm in compartment 22A."

"I believe that's in the car next to ours. I assume your luggage is in your room?"

"Yes. I have only one suitcase, a brown leather one with two straps around it. I left the Soviet Union **unencumbered** by luggage and with just the clothes on my back. Everything I have now, including my overcoat, was purchased either in Stockholm or New York City."

"What about the book you mentioned? I hope it's in a safe place?"

"Yes. I keep it with me always. When I was in Stockholm, I sewed pockets inside several of my skirts and dresses to hide valuables. The book is in just such a pocket, in the lining of this dress."

"Allow me to make a suggestion. I'm going to take you back to our compartment and then I'll retrieve your suitcase from yours. We can share my bunk. Then, in the morning, you can accompany us to Gary. Does that sound like a reasonable plan? I should tell you that I have some experience in these matters. I recently solved an espionage case in my hometown **implicating** Nazi spies. Of course, nobody knows about me in Gary, which is to our benefit. And, I rather prefer the **anonymity**."

"But you are so young to be involved in espionage activities."

"Yes, I suppose you're right. It happened all by accident, but became much more serious than even I might have imagined. I'll have to tell you about it sometime."

Ellen led Natalia to her compartment and unlocked the door. As they entered, Ellen's father, now in his pajamas, sat up and reached for his robe.

"Ellen, you didn't tell me we were having company."

"Sorry, Dad, but this is an emergency. This is Natalia Boroskova and she's in danger."

"Danger? What kind of danger?"

"She's being trailed by Soviet agents, and is afraid to go back to her own compartment."

"Soviet spies, on the Twentieth Century Limited? You can't be serious?"

"No, Mr. Anderson, Ellen is telling you the absolute truth."

"That's right. And we have to help her."

"What can we do, Natalia?"

"Would you allow me spend the night in your compartment? Ellen says she will share her bunk with me."

"Of course. If you're in danger, we're not about to throw you to Soviet wolves, not if I have anything to say about it."

"Thanks, Dad. I knew you'd understand. But, first, I'm going to Natalia's compartment and retrieve her suitcase."

"O.K., but watch yourself. If there are Soviet spies on board, there's no telling what they might be capable of."

Ellen stepped into the Pullman car's narrow corridor and looked **apprehensively** in both directions. **Undaunted,** she walked toward the dining cars, scanning the doors for Room 22A. Natalia's compartment was the

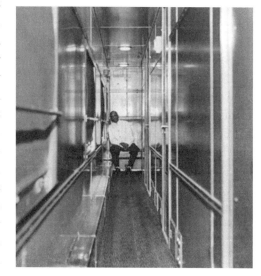

last one in the adjacent car, just before the dining car. Nervously, she opened the sliding door and entered the compartment. Her bed had already been prepared by her porter. Quickly, she located Natalia's suitcase and pulled it from the overhead luggage rack. As she emerged from the compartment she looked both ways, again, before proceeding. It was at that moment that she saw a pair of eyes glowing in the darkness, **furtively** observing her from the **vestibule** connecting the Pullman to the connecting dining car. Hurriedly, Ellen ran down the corridor in the direction of her car, pounding on the door when she reached her room. She quickly slipped inside before her pursuer made it around the corner at the far end of the car, and locked the door.

"Shush! I'm being followed."

Unnerved, Ellen put her ear to the door and listened for sounds in the corridor. Rapid footsteps crossed in front of the door and continued on down the hallway. The voices she heard at the far end of the corridor suggested that her pursuer was **interrogating** George, whose station was located at the far end of the car, if anyone had passed through the coach. But, since Ellen had seen George napping, it was not at all clear that her pursuer obtained the information he sought. In any event, the corridor went silent as, presumably, the man, continued on through the train in **vain** pursuit.

"We need to call the authorities," Ellen suggested, her voice **suffused** with emotion.

"No, please!" Natalia urged. "It is **imperative** that I remain **anonymous** for the present. Any **rash** attempt to alert the authorities before I have had an opportunity to consult with my uncle will only draw attention to me and make my position more **precarious**."

Ellen's father, who was following the conversation with **heightened** interest, offered his counsel:

"I think we should **accede** to Natalia's wishes. I'm confident that, once we reach Chicago, we can **allay** her concerns and **spirit** her away with us to the Illinois Central Station. I'll make arrangements with George to check all our bags through to Gary. Then, we can take some **elusive maneuvers** to lose whoever may be following us. Leave it to me."

Ellen was gratified that her father had adopted a **solicitous** concern for Natalia's **plight**, and had a **calculated** plan to escape their **predicament**. This despite the fact that he had cautioned Ellen about keeping out of trouble on the trip.

"Well, I suppose you girls would like to change for bed? I was about ready to turn in myself."

With that, Ellen's father got back into bed and pulled the covers up over his head to afford the girls some privacy in changing into their pajamas. Ellen, who was still charged with emotion, removed her jacket, pleated skirt, and fancy blouse, and hung them in the compartment's compact closet. She pulled her slip up over her head, and placed it in her overnight case. Modestly, she donned pink cotton pajamas over her pale-blue rayon satin **bandeau** and matching lace-edged **step-ins**. After emerging from the bathroom, Natalia removed her green silk dress and slip and hung them in the closet. She dropped a knee-length white cotton nightgown over her bra and simple white rayon bloomers. After brushing her teeth, Ellen climbed into bed next to Natalia.

The events of the past few hours made it difficult for Ellen to fall asleep. Reading was the only cure for her **insomnia**. After all, the realization that the events described in Walter Krivitsky's book were being acted out on American soil was a bit **unnerving**. *Who was this man shadowing Natalia? Was he acting alone or, as Krivitsky described it, possibly one of a global clandestine apparatus? What would happen on Tuesday morning when their train arrived in Chicago?*

"Are you asleep, Ellen?"

"No. I can't fall sleep. I'm terribly worried about you. You've already been through so much, and now your nightmare has followed you here to America."

"You're right. I have been through a lot. There were times when I wasn't sure if I would live or die. Losing both my parents at the age of fifteen was bad enough. And after living in London for seven years, the cold of Moscow was simply unbearable. Then, when I left Moscow, I had to escape both the Soviet authorities, and the German soldiers. I was scared to death that I would be **accosted** by the authorities or shot by either Russian or German soldiers along the front who would mistake me for an enemy soldier, or a spy. Our small boat to Sweden was barely seaworthy, and overcrowded with refugees. At any moment, we feared being detected by German patrol boats. I still have nightmares about those searchlights scanning the sea through the fog, and fearing they would see us, or hear the sounds of our engine. Although I was raised without any religious faith because Communism is an **atheistic ideology,** I still remembered the prayers I had learned as a small girl from my **sainted** grandmother, Tatiana, who was a **devout Russian Orthodox**. It is to her that I owe my faith today. I prayed to God for my deliverance and He answered my prayers."

"Your experience makes me realize how much we take for granted in this country. We tend to think that people everywhere enjoy the blessings of political and religious freedom. We forget that millions of people around the world are not so fortunate."

"I'm so **gratified** that I took the chance of speaking with you, Ellen. You are a **godsend**."

"We'll get you through this," Ellen responded. "If they are following you, it's because they've had the advantage over you. Now, that we know you're being followed, we can take appropriate countermeasures to **elude** them."

"I hope you're right, Ellen."

A few minutes later, after closing their eyes, the two girls were sound asleep.

Chapter 7

Arrival in the Windy City

Ellen awoke to the clattering of wheels on the steel rails and a sliver of light on the floor that peaked out from the bottom edge of their compartment's drawn window shade. Both Natalia and Ellen's father were still in a state of **somnolent repose**. She looked at her watch. It was barely six thirty. **Stealthily** lowering herself out of the top bunk, she stepped to the window and peaked out the side of the shade. Based on the hour, the 20th Century Limited was speeding its way across northern Indiana. The landscape was dominated by mile after mile of **lush** farmland, mostly corn and soybeans, and the occasional small **municipality**. Ellen estimated that they would pass through Gary about nine o'clock Eastern time. After climbing back into her bunk, her mind reflected on the events of the night before, and waited for her father and Natalia to awaken. About seven o'clock, their porter passed down the corridor making the first call for breakfast.

"Breakfast now being served in the dining car. First call for breakfast!"

Ellen's father and Natalia began to stir in their bunks, while Ellen entered the bathroom to begin her morning **ablutions**. By the time she was finished, both were sitting up in their bunks.

"I suppose you heard George's breakfast call? I'm wondering if we should sit together or act as if we're not acquainted?"

"There's no question that you were observed removing Natalia's suitcase from her compartment, Ellen," her father observed. "Your pursuer may not have gotten a good look at your face, but I think the cat's out of the bag by now. I suggest we just sit together and take our chances. It's after we **disembark** that we'll have to employ some clever **legerdemain** to elude Natalia's pursuers."

After dressing, the three travelers proceeded in the direction of the dining car, where they were greeted by an overly **officious** and **obsequious** dining car steward. About fifteen passengers were already seated. Escorted to their table, they found menus waiting. Ellen's father ordered bacon and fried eggs, with orange juice and coffee; the girls each ordered French toast, bacon, orange juice and hot chocolate. Eating on the train in such elegant surroundings was an experience Ellen would not soon forget. She **lamented** that it was soon coming to an end.

The view of the countryside through the large picture windows was rather **mundane** and uneventful at this stage of their journey. The **monotony** of

farms, barns, **defunct** gas stations, small houses and commercial establishments was periodically broken up by medium-sized towns, like Elkhart, or
Mishawaka. Ellen observed signs for South Bend and the University of Notre
Dame, and soon spied the school's golden dome in the distance. She also observed a rather **sullen** looking middle-aged man enter the dining room and
take a seat several tables away from theirs. He eyed them **nonchalantly**,
but without exhibiting any outward **manifestation** of friendliness.

"Don't look now, but there's a man two tables down from us who looks suspicious to me. He may be the man who was watching your compartment last
night, Natalia. I could be wrong, but he bears **scrutiny**. I'd advise that we
keep our conversation **innocuous** for the time being," Ellen suggested.

"I understand. So, where do you go to school, Ellen?"

"I'll be a senior at Stratford High School, in Connecticut. Stratford's about
sixty miles east of New York City, and about an hour and a half by train.
That's where I was born and raised. But, I'll be attending another school for
the next month or so while my father has business in Gary."

"Well, my word, here's our breakfast, and so quickly," exclaimed Ellen's
father.

"Waiter, may I have some cinnamon for my French toast; perhaps you'd like
it, too, Natalia."

"No, thank you, I would like to try the maple syrup. It comes from Vermont,
does it not?"

"That's right, but it's also made in other New England states, including
Connecticut."

As the girls consumed their French toast, the **arable** landscape outside their
window was transformed from farmland to the sand dunes and scrub vegetation that characterized the Lake Michigan shoreline. A sign designating the
entrance to Indiana Dunes State Park passed before their dining car window,
the road marked by flashing lights and lowered crossing gates.

116—La Salle Street Station, Chicago

"We should be about sixty miles
from Chicago at this point," Ellen's
father explained. "If our train is
on schedule, we'll be pulling in
to LaSalle Street Station at nine
o'clock Central Time. In fact, it's
time we turned our watches back
an hour."

The train sped through Michigan
City, Baileytown, Beverly Shores,
Ogden Dunes, and Miller, over a

terrain comprised of sand, oak and poplar trees, and scrub vegetation. As they approached Gary, the landscape, though still of a sand base, became progressively more bleak and industrial. Ellen spied a large harbor slip where a **behemoth** freighter was being unloaded of iron ore with the aid of giant **gantry cranes**. Nearby, towering piles of coke awaited being fed into the blast furnaces of the United States Steel Corporation. Continuing on past Gary's Union Station and Railway Express office at Broadway, the train crossed the Grand Calumet River, where they observed a succession of massive gray industrial buildings, including those of the Sheet & Tin Mill, and the American Bridge Company. These were accompanied by the vast railroad yards of the Elgin, Joliet and Eastern Railroad. From Gary, the train continued on into East Chicago, Whiting, and Hammond with their **conglomerations** of factories, oil refineries, and **unsightly,** or abandoned, industrial wasteland. Ellen had to admit to her father that it was a far cry from the quaint New England scenery to which she had become accustomed.

"This is America's industrial heartland," Eric explained. "It became an industrial magnet because of its proximity to Lake Michigan, the inter-continental railroad lines, and the ability to ship iron ore from the Mesabi Range in Minnesota directly to the steel mills at the southern shore of Lake Michigan. While many might turn their noses up at a region like this, it's obvious that the concentration of industrial production in Northwest Indiana spares us having it in our own backyard. Why, the space for these steel mills alone would swallow up most of Stratford. More trains pass through Chicago and Northwest Indiana than any area in the country, making Chicago the most important railroad hub in North America. And Gary produces more steel than any place in the world."

Natalia sat **mesmerized** by the **magnitude** of the industrial might **encompassed** by this relatively small corner of the state. But, she also could not avoid scrutinizing the movements of the man who appeared to be eavesdropping on their conversation.

"Where did you learn all this, Dad?" Ellen inquired. "Have you been here before?"

"Yes, a few times. My latest visit was last year – I think you were at summer camp. Don't you remember? I sent you a postcard from Chicago. It was my first meeting with Gus Bloomquist. He put me up in his home, gave me a tour of the plant, and drove me around the area. We spent most of a Saturday at the **Museum of Science and Industry**, after which we had dinner at the **Stockyard Inn**. The rest I read about in the *Calumet Region Historical Guide* he sent me."

"Thanks for the geography lesson, Dad. But, hadn't we be getting back to our compartment?"

"Say, you're right. Thanks for reminding me. Our train will be arriving in about fifteen minutes, and I need to speak to George about transferring our luggage."

As they left the dining car, the man that Ellen suspected of being a Soviet agent was nowhere to be seen. Indeed, there were few passengers still left in the dining car as they made their way back to their compartment.

A few minutes later, an announcement could be heard over the loudspeakers: "LaSalle Street Station, Chicago! LaSalle Street! Last stop!"

While Ellen's father spoke briefly with the porter, Ellen and Natalia assembled their carry-on bags in preparation for **disembarking**. He returned a few minutes later.

"All right, girls. George gave me this postcard of downtown Chicago. Here's the plan: Stay close to me. We're going to hail a cab as soon as we leave

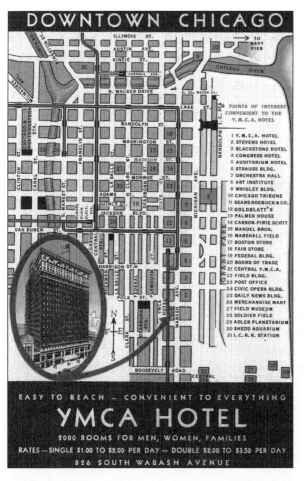

the station. I'll ask the driver to circle around the loop for a few minutes. Then, I'll have him drop us off on the State Street side of Marshall Field's, the big department store. We'll enter the store and take the escalator to the fourth floor. From there, we'll cross to the Wabash Street side of the store and take an elevator back down to the first floor. Upon leaving the store, we'll walk two blocks east to the Illinois Central Station where we'll catch the South Shore to Gary. If any Soviet agents can keep up with us after all that, I'll turn in my honorary Dick Tracy badge."

"That's a good one, Dad – your Dick Tracy badge. That should go well with my Radio Orphan Annie Secret Society decoder ring."

Ellen's father opened their compartment door and stuck his head into the corridor. The coast appeared to be clear. Stepping out of their compartment, they walked down the corridor with their carry-on luggage. George was standing on the platform to assist them as they **disembarked** from the train. Eric patted him on the shoulder and handed him a five-dollar tip.

"Thank you, Mr. Anderson. I'll see that your bags are sent on to your destination. Yes sir!"

"Thank you, George, and please make sure no one examines them to determine their **ultimate** destination."

"Yes, sir. Leave it to George. I won't let anyone get close to those bags."

"O.K. girls. Stay close."

"Dad, there's that man, again, leaning on the post up ahead, smoking a cigarette."

Ellen was sure that the man in front of them was the same one she had observed the previous night. Above average in height, his slick black hair was combed straight back, his **visage** framed by gold, wire-rimmed spectacles. He wore a dark gray suit and a **nondescript** blue print tie. He turned his face away and reached for his cigarette as they approached.

"Pay no attention to him. Just stay close to me," Ellen's father urged.

The three travelers walked briskly down the long cement platform, into the station proper, across the brightly lit station concourse, and out to West Van Buren Street. Without hesitation, Ellen's father hailed the first in a procession of Checker Cabs that lined the curb. The air around them was **suffused** by the **din** of honking horns, squealing tires, and jackhammers.

"Get in, quickly," Ellen's father urged.

"Driver – there's a party that might try to follow us and it's **imperative** that we lose them. I think it would be **expedient** if you drove us around the Loop for a few minutes. Make as many **elusive maneuvers** as you can. When you're sure that no one's following us, I want you to drop us off at the State Street side of **Marshall Field's**. Have you got that? There's a nice tip in it for you."

"Sure thing, mister! Ya know, I've had people tell me to follow a car before, but this is the first time I've been asked to lose a car."

Ellen turned around to see their mystery man hail the next cab in the succession. Two other men, one of them exceedingly **corpulent**, joined him in the back seat. A chill coursed across her shoulders and radiated down her spine.

"Dad, that's him, and two men got into the cab with him."

"Don't worry. I can lose him. That's Sammy. He's a new driver and doesn't know the streets like I do."

Driving east on Van Buren, the driver made a left onto Franklin Street, then a right onto Jackson Boulevard. From there, he drove east for three blocks and turned south on Clark Street, going as far as Harrison, then east, again, to Michigan Avenue. He turned north on Michigan and, at the Art Institute, turned west on Adams until he reached State Street, turned right, then drove four blocks north on State Street. Detecting no cab in his rearview mirror, their driver pulled to the curb in the middle of the block and discharged his passengers. Eric handed him a $5.00 bill as the three jumped out with their carry-ons.

The cab driver left them standing in the shadow of the massive Marshall

Field's department store. Field's was Chicago's **premier** shopping **emporium**, founded in 1881 by a Massachusetts businessman who moved to Chicago before the Civil War in search of new commercial opportunities in the **burgeoning** West. The first section of the elegant flagship store on State Street opened in 1902. From its inception, Field, with the able assistance of Harry Selfridge, offered customers a plush shopping experience driven by enlightened retailing practices reflected in its mottos: "Give the lady what she wants," and "the customer is always right." For Ellen's father, the **labyrinthine** complexity of Marshall Field's provided the perfect environment for losing their pursuers.

Scurrying into the store through the revolving door, the girls were promptly **dazzled** by the **grandeur** of the retail space. There was nothing **pedestrian** about this department store. High ceilings, stately **Corinthian columns**, and elegant wood and glass counters displayed jewelry, leather goods, **millinery**, and other wares, both **luxurious** and **utilitarian.** Not pausing for more than a **cursory** glance, they quickly made their way to the escalator at the north end of the store. Riding the moving stairs, they had nearly reached the second floor when they observed their pursuers run past the escalator on the ground floor.

"There they are. Darn it! And after that **convoluted** route we took, I thought sure we had **eluded** them. I just hope they didn't see us on the escalator. I want you girls to keep going to the fourth floor and wait for me in the book department. I'm going to stay right here on the mezzanine and see if they take this escalator. Then, I'll join you."

Apparently, Sammy was no **novice** to driving a taxi, just to Checker Cab. He knew Chicago like a book and had little trouble keeping Ellen and her father's cab in sight. After jumping out of their cab, the trio of pursuers, led by Hyman Petrov, hurried through the same revolving door.

"All right. Now what? This is like a maze. I don't think they came here to shop. But, where in the blazes would they go? Upstairs? Randolph Street? Wabash Avenue?"

"I'm sure they're just passing through here on their way to someplace else," replied one of his associates. "We have to assume that they're behaving as if they're being followed."

"But we can't take that chance. Here's the floor directory. There are nine floors open to the public. Alex, you scout around on floors one to four. Serge, you take floors five to nine. I'll take this floor and the basement. We'll meet up at the corner of Randolph and Wabash in fifteen minutes. Now, get moving. We can't afford to let that girl **elude** us."

"O.K. boss," they nodded.

Ellen and Natalia followed Eric's instructions**, simultaneously** riding and walking up the escalator treads until they reached the fourth floor. The book department was unusually swamped that morning. More than a hundred customers were already awaiting the eleven o'clock appearance of **Beryl**

Markham who was scheduled to sign copies of *West with the Night*, her best-selling memoir of her career as a bush pilot in Kenya. **Wending** their way though the crowd, they passed through the rare book department and current fiction, to the far corner of the room. There, huddling nervously behind a wooden bookrack, they waited for sight of Ellen's father.

"Well, would you look at that! We're in the **Nancy Drew** section," Ellen exclaimed.

"Nancy Drew? Who's Nancy Drew?" Natalia inquired.

"Nancy Drew is a girl detective. Her mystery stories are all the rage with

American girls. I've read them all myself."

"Interesting. I read **Agatha Christie** when I was living in London, but don't know this Nancy Drew."

"Nancy Drew's attraction is that she is only slightly older than her readers. Agatha Christie's Miss Marple could be their grandmother," Ellen explained.

A few minutes later, Ellen spied her father across the broad expanse of the book department as he stepped off the escalator. She **beckoned** him by waving her arms **animatedly** until she captured his attention. A few seconds later, they were reunited.

"I saw two of them get on the escalator," he said, breathlessly. "They're probably going to make a sweep of the upper floors. We've got to move quickly. Follow me."

Eric led them through the history and religion sections, through the shoe department, ladies' wear, and the children's departments, until they located the elevators in the northeast corner of the store.

"Dad, you act like you've been here before."

"I have. Your mother and I spent a few hours in the store back in '39. I spent most of my time in the book department, while your mother, not surprisingly, looked at clothes and craft supplies. We also ate in the Walnut Room on the seventh floor. I guess I formed a mental picture of the store's layout."

"Going down?"

An attractive young woman in light brown uniform beckoned them to her elevator. They stepped in. Ellen looked at her father. A **steely resolve** was written across his face. A few moments later, the elevator operator deposited them back on the first floor, not far from the store's Wabash Avenue entrance.

"This way, girls."

Eric directed them through the revolving door and onto the Wabash Avenue sidewalk. Standing in the shadow of the iron **superstructure** that supported the elevated trains around the **Chicago Loop**, he and the girls hurriedly crossed Wabash Avenue and followed Randolph Street two short blocks east to Michigan Avenue, where they entered the terminal that served both the **Illinois Central** and the **Chicago, South Bend & South Shore Railroad**. Eric hurriedly grabbed a copy of the *Chicago Daily*

News at the corner newsstand before escorting the girls down a flight of stairs and through a short tunnel to the underground station that served the two railroads. The Randolph Street Station was rather **spare** and **nondescript**, particularly in contrast with the **grandeur** of Grand Central or the smaller and somewhat less **grandiose** LaSalle Street Station. The trio made their way past several lunch counters, a newsstand, florist shop, and a juice bar to the South Shore ticket window.

"Three one-way fares to Gary, please. And can you please tell me when the next train leaves?"

"The next train leaves in fifteen minutes, but it's boarding now on Track number 2," replied the ticket agent. "Here, don't forget your change."

Walking through the swinging doors and down the wooden platform, the travelers found the orange cars of the Chicago, South Shore & South Bend Railroad waiting at trackside. It was ten fifteen local time, and they appeared to have successfully **eluded** their pursuers.

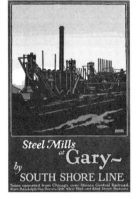

Steel Mills at **Gary~**
by
SOUTH SHORE LINE
Trains operated from Chicago over Illinois Central Railroad, from Randolph-Van Buren-12th-43rd-53rd-and 63rd Street Stations

By the time the pursuers had completed their sweep of the store and met up on Wabash Avenue, they were filled with **consternation** and a sense of **chagrin**.

"O.K. Now what? I'm totally **flummoxed**. We might as well be looking for a **Kulak** in the Gulag," Alex mused.

"Very funny, comrade. But, if they're no longer in the store, where would they go? They might have gotten on the **L**, or taken the North Shore to Kenosha or Milwaukee," Serge suggested.

"What about the Illinois Central, or the South Shore?" Alex added.

"Why don't you see if they're on the platform upstairs, Alex. Serge and I will head for the Illinois Central Station. We'll meet you at the newsstand at Michigan and Randolph, just outside the entrance to the station in five minutes." It was ten minutes after ten.

Eric and the girls walked to the third car, and took the two seats that faced each other at the end of the car, placing their carry-ons in the overhead rack. They each breathed a sigh of relief as they sank back into the soft leather seats and waited for the train's departure, confident that their **ruse** had succeeded. Ellen, however, couldn't help wondering whether their adventure was over, or just beginning.

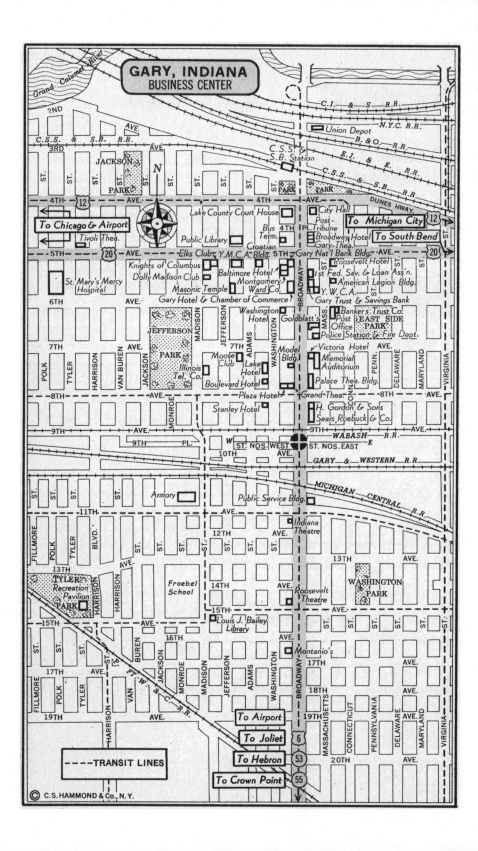

GARY, INDIANA
BUSINESS CENTER

Grand Calumet River

2ND AVE.

C.S.S. & S.B. R.R.

3RD AVE.

JACKSON PARK

N

C.I. & S. R.R.

N.Y.C. R.R.

B. & O. R.R.

E.J. & E. R.R.

Union Depot

C.S.S. & S.B. Station

PARK

PARK

4TH AVE. 12

To Chicago & Airport

Tivoli Thea.

DUNES HWY.

Lake County Court House

City Hall
Post-Tribune

To Michigan City 12

Bus 4TH PL.
Term.

Broadway Hotel
Gary-Thea.

To South Bend

Public Library

Croatian

5TH AVE. 20

Elks Club Y.M.C.A. Bldg. 5TH

Gary Nat'l Bank Bldg.

20

Knights of Columbus

Dolly Madison Club

St. Mary's Mercy Hospital

Baltimore Hotel

Masonic Temple

Montgomery Ward Co.

Gary Hotel & Chamber of Commerce

Roosevelt Hotel
1st Fed. Sav. & Loan Ass'n.
American Legion Bldg.
Y.W.C.A.
Gary Trust & Savings Bank

6TH AVE.

JEFFERSON PARK

MADISON

JEFFERSON

ADAMS

WASHINGTON

Washington Hotel

Goldblatt's

Bankers Trust Co.
Post EAST SIDE
Office PARK
Police Station & Fire Dept.

7TH AVE.

Illinois Tel. Co.

Moose Club

Lake Hotel

Model Bldg.

Victoria Hotel
Memorial Auditorium
Palace Thea. Bldg.

Boulevard Hotel

8TH AVE.

Plaza Hotel

Grand-Thea.

H. Gordon & Sons
Sears, Roebuck & Co.

Stanley Hotel

9TH AVE.

WABASH R.R.

9TH PL.

W ST. NOS. WEST

E ST. NOS. EAST

10TH AVE.

GARY & WESTERN R.R.

Armory

MICHIGAN CENTRAL R.R.

Public Service Bldg.

11TH AVE.

Indiana Theatre

12TH AVE.

FILLMORE

POLK

TYLER

BLVD.

HARRISON

13TH

TYLER
Recreation
Pavilion
PARK

Froebel School

14TH AVE.

Roosevelt Theatre

13TH AVE.

WASHINGTON PARK

15TH AVE.

Louis J. Bailey Library

16TH

Montanio's

17TH AVE.

18TH

To Airport

19TH AVE.

To Joliet 6

MASSACHUSETTS

CONNECTICUT

PENNSYLVANIA

DELAWARE

MARYLAND

VIRGINIA

To Hebron 53

20TH AVE.

To Crown Point 55

— — — TRANSIT LINES

Chapter 8

Gary – City of the Century

Promptly at ten thirty, and with most of their luggage safely stored in the baggage car, the South Shore eased out of Randolph Street Station on its way to South Bend, traveling on tracks it shared, for a time, with the Illinois Central Railroad. Running below grade for nearly a mile, the train passed Grant Park on the left and the cluster of world-class museums that drew millions of visitors to Chicago yearly, including the **Field Museum of Natural History**, the **Shedd Aquarium**, and the **Adler Planetarium**. Just south of the **Field Museum** loomed the massive **Soldier Field** which opened in 1924,

the venue for many classic **gridiron** events, including the 1926 Army-Navy football game for the na-

tional championship. As their train clattered along, Ellen observed the morning sun glimmering on nearby Lake Michigan.

"That's where they held the World's Fair in 1933 and '34. It was called the **Century of Progress**, celebrating Chicago's centennial," Eric explained.

When their train approached 59th Street, they could make out the impressive **gothic architecture** of the **University of Chicago** and the stately **spire** of Rockefeller Chapel west of the tracks.

"See that building over there, near the lake? That's the **Museum of Science and Industry**, the only building that remains from the **Columbian Exposition** of 1893," Ellen's father explained. "Of the 200 buildings at the fair, all but two were designed to be temporary. One of these – the Palace of Fine Arts – became the **Museum of Science and Industry** in 1933. When the fair closed, an amusement park called 'White City' began operating on this site. You can see the Ferris wheel over there. My uncle, Bill Johanson, lived for a time on the South Side of Chicago. He's the one who told me about it. Also, the

American Union of Swedish Singers held its first singing festival at the Columbian Exposition."

"Natalia, you're probably wondering what Dad is talking about? He sings in a Swedish male chorus, called the North Star Singers, in Bridgeport, Connecticut. The chorus is part of a national **federation** of Swedish male choruses called the American Union of Swedish Singers made up of men of Swedish birth or ancestry who love singing the songs of their homeland. Every four years, they have a national convention. The first one was held here, in Chicago, at the Columbian Exposition."

"I understand. We have male choruses in the Soviet Union as well, but now they're mostly singing **paeans** to Stalin and the Revolution, not to the beauty of nature, or the **Volga.** I also have a great love of music. I have played the violin since I was six years old. And my mother sang Russian folk **ballads** to me when I was child. I have come to love the great Russian composers – Tchaikovsky, Rachmaninoff, Rimsky-Korsakov, Ippolitov-Ivanov, Borodin, and Prokofiev. My favorite opera is Borodin's *Prince Igor,* which I saw once in Leningrad with the **Bolshoi Opera Company**. It was a beautiful production, **replete** with gorgeous sets and **exotic** costumes, and impressive in its historical **verisimilitude**. Music is a great way of instilling the **nationalistic** spirit and love of homeland. It pains me to think that that spirit has been so corrupted by Joseph Stalin, under whom the country has become one giant **asylum**, just as Walter Krivitsky has described it. Sadly, in Stalin's Soviet Union, all art is in service to the state."

As their train neared the Kensington Street Station at 115th Street, Ellen's father pointed out the village of **Pullman,** on the east side of the tracks.

"This is where the Pullman cars are manufactured," Eric explained. "George Pullman designed his community with company housing, company stores, a library, hotel, fire department, churches, and other **amenities**. In many ways, it was a model community. Unfortunately, the **paternalistic** model also became the cause of labor **strife** because workers in his plant failed to earn enough to feed their families, after paying Pullman's rents. In the 1890s, the American Railway Union staged a nationwide **wildcat strike,** forcing **President Cleveland** to send in federal troops to **quell** the disturbance. It was one of the most significant episodes of labor unrest in the late 19th century.

There, you can see the company administration building, and the Pullman car factory."

"Do they still make Pullman cars here?" Ellen inquired.

"They sure do, but what was once the town of Pullman has now been **incorporated** into the City of Chicago."

The South Shore rattled on through the gritty working-class neighborhoods and factories of Chicago's South Side, making its last Illinois stop in the village of Hegewisch, before crossing the border into Indiana. The landscape was much like what they had already observed as the Twentieth Century Limited approached Chicago. After stopping in Hammond, the train took a street level route through the City of East Chicago and discharged more passengers at its small brick station. Nearly an hour after leaving Dearborn Station, and after a brief stop at Clark Road, they heard their conductor shouting from the other end of their car:

"Gary! Gary next!"

As their train neared Gary Station, the vista to the north was dominated by those same massive industrial buildings they had observed earlier that morning. The city of Gary proper extended to the south, its streets lined with brick, frame, and **stucco** dwellings of modest proportions. A few moments later, the train came to a stop on the wooden platform that adjoined a small stucco and wood station.

"Watch your step," shouted the conductor, as they stepped onto the station platform. Eric suggested that Ellen hail a cab while he secured their large items from the porter.

Ellen and Natalia walked to the curbside on Broadway and waved for a Safeway Taxi, which approached them from under a nearby railroad **viaduct**. The South Shore station sat at the north end of Broadway, a few short blocks from the gateway to the **immense** steel plant. The air was **acrid** with the smoke that belched from the towering smokestacks and open-hearth furnaces, blackening the sky overhead. Indeed, the entire city appeared to be bathed in a layer of soot whose **noisome** odors **permeated** the nostrils of all who walked its streets. But, it also signified full employment for a population that had recently suffered through the **deprivations** of the Depression and was, doubtless, glad to be working again. A moment later, the cab pulled up and the driver began loading their luggage into the trunk.

"Natalia, shall we take you to your uncle's house first?" Eric suggested.

"Oh, yes, would you please? I know he will be thrilled to see me. I sent him a postcard from New York, but I couldn't wait for his reply."

"What did you say his address was?" Ellen inquired.

"1334 Lincoln Street."

Eric climbed into the front seat, with the driver, while Ellen and Natalia sat in the back.

"Driver, would you please take us to 1334 Lincoln Street, first. We would like to drop off this young lady."

"Sure thing, mister."

"Oh, and, if you don't mind, would you be good enough to point out some of the landmarks of the city as we drive. This is the girls' first time in Gary and we'd like to know what we're looking at. We plan to be here for a while."

"My pleasure. It's not often I get a chance to be a tour guide. Mostly, everybody's in a hurry and not much interested in sightseeing. After all, Gary's a working class town and not much of a tourist **mecca**."

As the cab approached Broadway and 4th Avenue, the driver pointed out the City Hall on the left and the County Building on the right.

"That's where Mayor Schaible has his office. The **incumbent** mayor is a Republican, if you can believe it, but this town's mostly Democrat and has been since **President Roosevelt** was first elected. There's an **inextricable** alliance between the Democrats and the labor unions that **mirrors** the course of na-

tional politics. President Roosevelt and the Democrat Congress give the labor unions what they want, and the unions return the favor with their campaign donations and votes. It's your typical political **quid pro quo**, masked by the **veneer** of worker **solidarity**.

"There on the left, next to City Hall, is the *Gary Post-Tribune* building. I used to peddle the *Post-Tribune* at the mill gates when I was a just a kid and before I got a permanent paper route in my neighborhood. That's the Gary Theater on your left, which shows re-runs, and used to have **vaudeville** acts. Now, we're at 5th and Broadway, Gary's main intersection."

Ellen noted a tall office building as they stopped for the traffic light. "What's this big building on our right?' she asked.

"That's the Gary National Bank, the tallest building in the city. My **op-**

tometrist has his office in there – Dr. Max Gold. He takes great pains to make sure my glasses fit just right. Lots of doctors and lawyers and business people have their offices there. This is our downtown business district. The best shopping is here on Broadway between 5th Avenue and 9th Avenue. We just passed Lytton's department store there on the right. That's one of our classier clothing stores. The other big stores on Broadway are J. C. Penney, Goldblatt's, Gordon's, and Sears and Roebuck. We also have lots of smaller specialty stores, and your typical five and dime stores, like J. J. Newberry, F. W.

Woolworth, Kresge's, and W. T. Grant. Take it from me, Kresge's has a great little lunch counter near the front of the store that serves the best wieners in town. My wife likes Goldblatt's the best 'cuz of the low prices. You can find all kinds of stuff in there, including a delicatessen you can smell all over the store. Frankly, I don't like my clothes smelling like **salami**."

"Where are your other movie theaters?" Ellen inquired.

"We've got five theaters downtown. The Gary Theatre, which we just passed on the left, the Family there, also on the left. The Grand and the Palace are at 8th and Broadway. Then there's the State Theater on West 7th Avenue, right off Broadway. The State and the Palace show mostly the latest first-run pictures. The others show mostly re-runs. The Gary Theatre was the last theater to have vaudeville acts. I saw the Marx Brothers there a few years back. There are other theaters further south on Broadway, like the Indiana at 11th Avenue and the Roosevelt near 14th Avenue that also show re-runs. And out in Glen Park, there's the Roxy, near Ridge Road, and the Ridge, which is right around the corner. And, I almost forgot, we got two theaters on 5th Avenue: the Tivoli, near Tyler Street, and the Fifth Avenue, near Buchanan Street; and the Tolleston at 11th and Taft, on the west side of town. At one time or another, my wife and I have been in all of them. We love the movies. A night out for us means dinner and a movie, with popcorn and a pop – sort of a working man's night out."

"Do you have a favorite theater?"

"Oh, that would have to be the Palace. There it is on the left, at 8th Avenue. That place really is **palatial**. It's like you were in a Spanish castle, or somethin', with stars in the ceiling and statues in wall **niches**. They even have balcony seating, but sometimes them kids throw stuff down on ya. I wanna strangle 'em. We saw *Invisible Agent* there last week, with Jon Hall, Ilona Massey, and Peter Lorre. It was about an invisible man fighting the Nazis – that was really something. They also had the usual newsreels, a cartoon, and an episode of *Don Winslow of the Navy* – ya know, one of them serials. The Grand theater is right across the street. They show a lot of western pictures. If ya want something to eat before the show, you can either go to Princess Confectioners – that's my favorite – or Walgreen's lunch counter. Both have great food.

"This store on your right is H. Gordon's & Sons. That's probably Gary's swankiest department store – too rich for my wallet. And next to it is Sears Roebuck – that's for us workin' stiffs. I got my Philco floor model radio and record player there last Christmas. That's where my wife shops for clothes for herself and my daughter, although she also shops at Goldblatt's and Penney's.

"Now, we're crossing the Wabash Railroad tracks and entering what we call the Central District. It's mostly immigrants and their children who live here and, further down, the colored folks. When my father moved to Gary in 1908, they called it the "Patch." It's where most of the saloons are, to **slake** the thirst of steelworkers on their way home from work. By the looks of it, you'd think the people here were a bunch of **alcoholics** just interested in **carousing**. When I was just a kid, my Dad used to send me to one of the saloons on Jefferson Street to bring home a bucket of beer. I learned how to twirl the bucket over my head, without spilling a drop – you know, **centrifugal force,** and all that. But, one time, I tripped over a crack in the sidewalk and spilled the beer all over the street. I went home crying and one of our **boarders** slipped me a nickel for another bucket. Luckily, Dad never found out about it or he would have tanned my hide.

"See that building on the right, the one with the pointed German-style turret? That's the Schlitz Building. It's kind of a gateway to the Central District. Another favorite of mine is the Buffalo Lunch, right there after the New York Central highline. It's run by a good friend of mine – Louis Peppoff. They serve great hamburgers and chili dogs, but no buffalo steaks. It's one of dozens of small eateries and taverns along Broadway that serve steelworkers on their way home from the mills, some nice, some not so nice. A lot of them are **garish** little dives you wouldn't want to bring your wife or girlfriend to. If you want **genteel** dining, or are a true **gourmand,** you need to go to Hotel Gary, or to Chicago, although the Dunes White House, Wilson's, and Jackson's Restaurant all have pretty good food. They're all east of here, on Dunes Highway.

"By the way, I shoulda told ya that Gary is laid out on a grid. The streets on the west side of Broadway are named after the Presidents in order of **succession**, followed by the Chief Justices of the U.S. Supreme Court. The streets on the east side of Broadway are named after the states of the Union, then the counties of Indiana. North to south are all the numbered avenues starting at the steel mills and going all the way to Glen Park, which is about four miles south of here. The arrangement makes it fairly easy to get around, even for newcomers like you.

"This here is 11th Avenue. The Gary Railways office and waiting room are over there on the left. See the tracks there? This is where the streetcars turn to go west down 11th Avenue, to the Tolleston section of town. There are dozens of small businesses in this area — saloons, small hotels, restaurants, bakeries, shoe repair shops, barber shops, Greek coffee houses, ethnic grocery stores, you name it. Some Central District residents live a **bohemian** lifestyle, including a group of **Gypsy** violinists who play every Friday night at Feczko's Tavern on Adams Street. And, unfortunately, there's a fair amount of **licentious** behavior that goes on here, as you might expect. And some of these coffee houses are just fronts for gambling establishments in the back room. If you're lookin' for a **reputable** bakery, try the **Balkan Bakery** at 13th and Adams. My friend, Alex Christoff, is the **proprietor**. And if you like great pumpernickel bread, try Richter's bakery, near 12th and Madison.

"Now, we're at 11th and Madison. That's the National Guard Armory, that brick building over there on your right. They have all sorts of events there — church carnivals, wrestling matches, dances, concerts, Boy Scout events, dinners, you name it. Up ahead on the right is the Spanish Castle, a fraternal club for people

from Spain. But, I'm going to turn here on Jackson Street, so you can see Froebel School and my church. Jackson Street is typical of the residential streets in the Central District, with sturdy brick homes or apartment houses. That's **Saints Helen and Constantine Greek Orthodox Church** coming up on your left. They even have Greek school there. There are lots of foreign churches in this neighborhood — Greek, Slovak, Hungarian, Spanish, Romanian, Lithuanian, and Russian. The Serbian and Polish churches are on the other side of Broadway.

"Here's my church on the right, the **Hungarian Reformed Church**. I grew up in this block, just six houses down from the church — 1336 Jackson.

My father came here from Budapest in 1910 and bought this three-flat apartment house in 1922. Now, my wife and I and our daughter live on the second floor, above my parents. They rent out the third floor to another Hungarian family. A lot of the ethnic families did the same thing. If they live in one flat and rent out the others, they can pay off the mortgage more quickly with the extra income.

"That's Froebel School on your right. They teach all grades here,

from kindergarten to high school, in the same building. If you're around during school hours, you can hear the Froebel High School marching band in the streets playing John Philip Sousa. They have a great band and orchestra director named Kenneth Resur. He's **irascible** at times, and doesn't take any guff from the kids, but he gets results. He also directs **U.S. Steel's Carillco Band**, which has the reputation of being the finest non-professional band in the United States. And, if you like to fish, the front lawn of the school is great for catching night crawlers after a heavy downpour. That's cuz the area used to be a swamp. But, don't try fishin' in the Grand Calumet River by the mills, unless you like your fish full of metal particles. You could probably catch 'em with a magnet. You're better off going out to Miller Beach, or Lake George in Hobart.

"This here is 15th Avenue. You can see the front of Froebel School real good – I mean, real well – from here. You'll have to excuse me. Sometimes I slip into the **vernacular**. My high school English teachers at Froebel would have a fit if they heard me say 'good' instead of 'well.' Adverb modifies a verb, or something like that. They were quick to correct us when we slipped up. But, not like the nuns. They'll whack you with a ruler on the knuckles if you use bad grammar.

"As I turn right, you can see the **Gary-Alerding Settlement House**, right here. It's run by the Catholic Church. It's named after Judge Elbert Gary and Herman Alerding, the former Bishop of the Fort Wayne Diocese that Gary's a part of. The nuns do a lot of good work for the immigrant families in the area. The kids hang out here after school and on the weekends. They can shoot pool, play basketball, ping-pong, have a Coke – you name it. And they have swell dances on Friday nights. The nuns also teach **catechism** classes.

They're pretty strict, but they have a good **rapport** with the kids and are not **averse** to playing pool or shooting baskets. These are street nuns, not the **cloistered** ones. And they're not overly **sanctimonious,** either, which makes it easier for them to relate to young people. Theirs is not an **ascetic** type of **discipleship**, but one that fully embraces the world. Besides, if things get **querulous**, they have the moral authority to **quell** any disturbance. But, that doesn't happen very often. These immigrant kids would never cross one of the nuns. If their parents found out about it, they'd get the tar kicked out of 'em. And, besides, if they're the **pugnacious** type, **Father Westendorf** is sure to recruit them for the **CYO** boxing team, or the **Golden Gloves.**

"That brick building on the right is St. Emeric's Hungarian Catholic Church and School. That's where the 'knuckle whackers' teach. Now, we're at Harrison Boulevard, one of Gary's major thoroughfares. That's Tyler Park across the street, or, I guess they call it Norton Park now. They just re-named it a few years ago, after our former park commissioner, Horace Norton. There's the park pavilion. When I graduated from Froebel in 1934, we had our class photograph taken in front of the pavilion.

"We're almost at Lincoln Street now. There's the Dixie Dairy. You can tell by the big columns out front shaped like milk cartons. On the right is St. Casimir's Roman Catholic School. That's for the **Lugans**... I mean the **Lithuanians**. Next to it is the convent for the nuns who teach at the school, and the rectory, where Father Vichuras lives. I used to deliver the newspaper to the rectory when I got my first neighborhood paper route. I delivered the *Chicago Tribune* between Grant and Madison Streets.

"Here we are: 1334 Lincoln. Say, it's right across the street from **St. Casimir's Church**. That should make gettin' to Mass pretty easy – that is, if you're Catholic."

"We may be a few minutes, driver. We want to pay our respects to Natalia's family."

"Sure thing, mister. I'll be waitin' right here. But, let me help the young lady with her luggage first."

Natalia was escorted to the door of a neat front-to-back brick bungalow by Ellen and her father. Natalia rang the door bell. A moment later, an **ebullient** middle-aged man with black mustache and a seemingly **urbane demeanor** came to the door.

"Don't tell me. You must be Natalia. And to finally meet you after all these years. Come in! Come in!"

Natalia's uncle led them into a small, but tastefully decorated, living room, filled with Russian icons and other cultural **artifacts** of the old country. The aroma of European **cuisine**, tobacco, and mothballs **permeated** the house.

A woman, presumably Natalia's aunt, emerged from the kitchen. They all exchanged warm embraces.

"Let me look at you, Natalia. You were just a child in the last photo I received from your father. You've grown into such a beautiful young woman, and so elegantly dressed."

"Uncle Stanislaus, I'd like you to meet my friends from Connecticut. This is Mr. Eric Anderson and his daughter, Ellen. I have them to thank for getting me here safely."

"Safely, you say? You will have to tell me all about that. I am so pleased to meet you both. Any friend of Natalia's is a friend of ours. You are most welcome to our home. I am Stanislaus Boroskova, but you can call me 'Stan.' And this is my wife, Veronika. Luckily, I was home this week. I've been working the midnight shift at the Tin Mill. Can we offer you some coffee and pastry?"

"Thank you very much, Stan. That's very kind of you, but we have to be getting along to our new apartment, and we don't want to keep our driver waiting. But, perhaps, we can come back another time. I am anxious to hear your stories of Russia," Ellen's father explained.

"Oh, can I tell you stories – mostly sad ones. Russia is certainly not the same place since the Bolsheviks took over."

With that, Ellen and her father kissed Natalia good-bye and promised to see her again very soon. Then, she and her father climbed back into their cab for the drive over to the East Side.

"Now where, folks?"

"We're going to 750 Carolina Street, near Emerson School."

"Sure, I know the area well. I have a friend who lives one block over, on Virginia Street. I can point out some more landmarks on our way, if you'd like."

"That would be swell," Eric replied.

"I'm going to go back down 15th Avenue, past Froebel School, to Broadway. You can get a better look at the school where I graduated. It's a beautiful building. It was the second high school built in the city, after Emerson. It opened in 1912, not long after the city was founded. We had a wonderful school superintendent here named William A. Wirt. He died four years ago. The 'Work-Study-Play' system of education was his **inspiration**. It became world famous. He thought us kids should have a well-rounded education, including art, music, athletics, industrial arts, and auditorium class, as well as the regular academic subjects. It was in auditorium that I learned about the great composers, and about parliamentary procedure. I even learned to sing a little – like all those college fight songs. You know: *Hail, Hail to Old Purdue, On, Wisconsin, Cheer, Cheer, for Old Notre Dame, Indiana, Our Indiana* – all places I could never afford to go, even if I had the ambition. But, I may be the most cultured cab driver in Gary.

"Many schools around the country copied what William Wirt did here. I just enrolled my little girl, Emily, in Mary Reising's kindergarten class. Her room is on the first floor. Her husband, Otto, teaches printing over at Horace Mann High School, on the West Side. I drove them both to the New York Central Station a couple months ago. I think they were going to visit relations out East.

"At the corner here, on Madison Street, is the Bailey Branch of the Gary Public Library. It's a short walk across the Froebel lawn from my place. This was actually the site of the earliest settlement in this area, the Gibson Inn. It's where stagecoaches used to stop on their way to and from Chicago, during pioneer days, and where the local **indigenous** tribes once roamed. This is where we bring my little Emily for story hours. That three-story building over there is the Miramar Ballroom. They have dances there with some of the big bands. Harry James was here a few months ago. Now, I'll drive you back over to Broadway."

"Driver, forgive me. I should have asked your name," said Ellen's father, apologetically.

"It's Toth... Victor Toth. It's a common enough name in Hungary, and there are a couple dozen Toths living in Gary. In fact, the former priest at St. Emeric's was a Toth. As I said, my parents live on the first floor of our building on Jackson Street. My uncle Lazlo lives next door to us."

"By the way, I'm Eric Anderson, and this my daughter, Ellen."

"Pleased to meet you both. Here's one of those Central District theaters I was telling you about – the Roosevelt. It shows mostly re-runs, and pictures with Negro actors. It's mostly frequented by the colored folks who live in the area. Unfortunately, you'll find that there's a lot of segregation in the city and the schools. Froebel is one of the few integrated schools in Gary, but most of the activities are still **segregated**. There are also lots of markets in this area, many catering to the foreign people. We shop at File's market, on Broadway. That's Hungarian. The File's live two doors down from us, on Jackson Street. Their daughter, Esther, teaches physical education at Emerson, or did, until she enlisted in the **WAVES** a few months ago.

"That's the Indiana Theater over there, near 11th Avenue, where we turned when we first came up this way. Oh, look, they're showing *Charlie Chan at Treasure Island*. I saw that picture at the Palace when it first came out a few years ago. That's one of the things I like about Gary. If you miss a picture the first time around, you just have to wait until it shows up at one of the **second-tier** theaters.

"Gary has lots of railroads passing through it. They built the **highlines** so that some of the trains wouldn't stop the traffic on Broadway. Here's the

Michigan Central tracks, followed by the New York Central **highline**. And here's the Wabash tracks, again, that run at grade level. I've already told you about the Palace Theater. Now, I'm going to turn east here on 7th Avenue. That big brick building you see there on the right is Memorial Auditorium.

It opened in 1927. The high school graduations are held there now, as well as lots of basketball games and other sporting events, concerts, and assemblies. The building across the street houses the police department, fire department, and the criminal court. It was once city hall, too, until they built the new city hall at 4th and Broadway, which opened in 1928. Now, we're coming up to Connecticut Street and Buffington Park, which has a bandstand for concerts in the summertime, a wading pool for the kiddies, and beautiful beds of irises, daffodils and tulips – that's the gardener in me. Across the street is the East Side Presbyterian Church. Now, we're at Virginia Street. Emerson School is the block after that. If you're coming from Emerson, it's an easy walk to Broadway and all it has to offer."

"Victor, do you happen to know when school starts in Gary," Ellen inquired.

"Sure. It starts the day after Labor Day. That would be September 8th."

"Thank you."

"Well, here's your street – Carolina. What was that number, again?"

"750 Carolina. But, would you please drive us around the school first?"

"Sure thing, Mr. Anderson."

"That's quite an impressive building. And the grounds are so nicely manicured. I'll bet any student would be proud to attend that school," Ellen's father remarked.

"I'll say. Emerson had the first **theatrical** stage of any school in the country and the first school swimming pool in the country. The principal – Everett Spaulding – is

a peach of a guy and the **epitome** of a gentleman. He's very even tempered and treats all the students fairly. When he visits the classrooms, he tells the kids about his farm and brings each of them a grape cutting to plant in their gardens. Now, how many school principals have you heard of who would do somethin' like that?"

Victor circled the large block that comprised the Emerson campus, which included the smaller elementary building next door and the industrial arts building across 6th Avenue. Ellen observed the school zoo she had read about in the *Calumet Region Historical Guide*, the gardens, and the athletic fields and running track behind the school. The football squad was out back, going through its late morning drills.

"That's Coach Art Rolfe – the guy with the baseball cap – over there, barking instructions. His team only lost one game last season. They beat my **alma mater** 21-0. The Blue Devils are going to have to work a lot harder this year if they hope to beat the Golden Tornado. It's not like they're not trying. Coach Kyle even uses the freshmen as tackling dummies to give the varsity practice."

As the cab circled the block to Carolina Street, Victor pointed to the row house across the street from Emerson.

"Would you believe that rowhouse was once Mercy Hospital? Of course, Gary was pretty primitive back then – just sand dunes and tumbleweeds. Now, the building contains apartments, and the hospital moved to the West Side."

A few moments later, Victor eased his cab to the curb in front of 750 Carolina. As he jumped out and helped his passengers with their luggage, Ellen stood and stared up at her new home away from home. It was a modest, two-story frame structure, with red tarpaper shingles befitting its working class neighborhood. The small front lawn was trimmed by a neatly manicured flowerbed dominated by petunias, gladiolas, and four o'clocks, and both annuals and **perennials**. The sound of children's voices punctuated the otherwise quiet morning air. They had arrived.

Settling In

"I can't thank you enough, Victor, for that informative introduction to Gary. It might have taken us weeks to learn what you **encapsulated** in little more than an hour. Here's a little extra for all your help."

"Thank you very much, Mr. Anderson. I was very glad to have been of service. Allow me to help you with your luggage, and that heavy trunk. I do hope your stay in Gary is enjoyable."

After carrying their bags to the front door, Victor got back behind the wheel and drove off in search of his next fare. With their luggage on the front porch, Eric rang the doorbell. A few seconds later, an **amply** proportioned middle-aged woman with black wavy hair opened the door.

"Mrs. Matheus, I presume? I'm Eric Anderson, and this is my daughter, Ellen."

"Välkommen, Mr. Anderson. Please come in. I've been waiting for you. Did you have a pleasant journey? I understand you came by way of the 20th Century Limited?"

"That's right, but our trip was a little more eventful than we had anticipated. I'll tell you more about that later."

"In the meantime, let me show you to your apartment. After you're settled, perhaps, we can have some coffee. I assume you like coffee?"

"You mean Swedish gasoline? Of course. That would be wonderful."

Mrs. Matheus led them up the staircase to the second floor apartment and into the front parlor.

"As I explained over the phone, this is a two-bedroom apartment, with bath, kitchen and living room. I think it should serve your needs for the next month or so. The kitchen has all the necessary cooking utensils, silverware, and other **amenities**. There are also linens for the beds, and towels. The icebox is fairly new and the gas stove works good. There's a bathtub, but no shower. I just freshened up everything yesterday. There's no telephone, but you are welcome to use mine whenever you like. It'll be nice to have some company around, now that my son, Ernest, has joined the **Seabees**."

"I think this will suit us just fine, Mrs. Matheus. Don't you think so, Ellen?"

"My, yes, it's a cute little apartment. I can't wait to get settled in."

After they had deposited their luggage in their respective bedrooms, Mrs. Matheus guided them down the back hall stairs and into her brightly decorated kitchen. Ellen observed two **Carl Larsson** prints hanging on the yellow walls, and a red Dala horse resting on a small shelf next to the kitchen table. She and her father took a seat.

"I see you like my Dala horse, Ellen. My little brother, Ernst, sent it to me

from Sweden last year. They've become very popular since making their **debut** at the New York World's Fair in 1939. They're made in the village of Nusnäs, on Lake Siljan, just outside of Mora. Ernst lived in Gary for ten years before returning to Sweden, after my father died. Two of his girls – Lilly Ann and Aina – were born here. In fact, they lived on Virginia Street, just a block from here. Do you have family in Sweden, Eric?"

"Yes. I have aunts and uncles and a Viking longboat full of cousins. We try to stay in touch, although visiting is certainly out of the question right now, what with the war and all. They live in Värmland. My mother's people came from Hagfors, my father's from Ekshärad. They took me to meet my relations when I was fifteen."

"Is that so? I was born in **Dalsland** – in the village of Dalen, Laxerby to be precise – but grew up right across the border in **Värmland**, in a little village called Bollsbyn, on Lake Ömeln. My mother still lives there, in the same house, with Ernst, his wife, Sigrid, and, now, three girls. I get homesick every so often when I think about it, but prefer living in America. There wasn't much opportunity for young people when I was growing up in Sweden, which is why so many of us came to America. My, it's going on thirty-three years since I arrived at Ellis Island – September 1909. I remember it like it was yesterday. It will be nice to have some Swedes living upstairs for a change. My last tenants were Finnish and spoke very little Swedish, but we got by."

"Well, you'll be happy to know that my Swedish is pretty good," Eric added, with a smile. "That's what my parents spoke in our home."

"What about you, Ellen? Do you speak Swedish?"

"Not much, but I'm learning. When I was growing up, my parents and their friends spoke Swedish when they didn't want me to know what they were talking about."

"Yes, I did the same with Ernest when we were having adult conversation. Do you take cream and sugar, Eric?"

"Just sugar for me. Ellen takes her coffee black."

"We have a Swedish Vasa lodge here in Gary. It meets every Wednesday evening on the second floor of the Lake Hotel on Washington Street. It's nice getting together with other Swedes on a regular basis, and speaking my native tongue. You're welcome to join us. Would you like some nice Swedish coffee bread?"

"Thank you so much," Ellen replied, her eyes brightening.

"So, what are your plans now that you've arrived in Gary?"

"Well, our first order of business is getting Ellen enrolled at Emerson High School. Then, I would like to pay a visit to Gary Armor Plate."

"That's right. You said so in your letter. Now, where is that?"

"It's off East Dunes Highway, near the Taylor Forge."

"I think I know the place. It's directly north of Union Drawn Steel. Ernest had a summer job there before enlisting in the Navy. That reminds me, there's a nice girl living next door who goes to Emerson. I believe she's your age, Ellen. Her name is Melanie McGuire. As I understand, she's a member of a club that escorts visitors around the school. So, she's just the person you need to show you around and tell you how to get registered. I was just reading in today's *Gary Post-Tribune* that incoming students are expected to register for classes by Wednesday."

While they were enjoying their coffee and Swedish coffee bread, Mrs. Matheus stepped over to the neighbor's house and invited Melanie over to meet her new tenants. A moment later, a **pert** and **vivacious** young girl with curly red hair and bright green eyes popped her head in the door.

"Hi, I'm Melanie. Mrs. Matheus tells me you're going to be staying in Gary for a while."

"Yes, hi, Melanie. I'm Ellen Anderson and this is my father, Eric. I understand you might be **amenable** to showing me around Emerson High School."

"Absolutely! I'd be happy to show you around. I know all the nooks and crannies in the building and can introduce you to the office staff and Mr. Spaulding. He's our principal. I'm free all afternoon. If you like, I can come back at one o'clock to pick you up. You'll probably want some time to freshen up."

"That'll be swell, Melanie. I'm looking forward to it," Ellen replied.

Ellen spent the next half hour getting herself settled into her bedroom, unpacking and putting her clothes away. Then, as she was plugging in her radio in the front parlor, she heard a knock at the back door. She scurried down the hall stairs and opened it.

"Hi, Ellen, are you ready to go?"

"Sure thing! Lead the way."

"Fantastic! You're going to love our school. The kids are great and we have wonderful teachers who really care about the students. There's a lot of school spirit at Emerson and a lot of **extracurricular** activities. I've been going to Emerson since kindergarten, first in the Little Building, next door, and then in the Big Building since the fourth grade."

As the girls approached Seventh Avenue, Ellen couldn't help but be impressed by the **regal** character of the imposing three-story brick structure and the ivy which graced its majestic **façade**. The gently terraced and well-manicured lawn was surrounded by a black iron fence and sheltered by stately elm trees. Brick **balustrades**, projecting out into the lawn, graced each end of the building and **accentuated** both sides of the front entrance. Except for the sound of boys' voices **emanating** from the athletic fields out back, the neighborhood was quiet and peaceful, as one would expect in those warm, **languorous** days of August before the opening of school. A few birds could be heard twittering in the trees overhead. Summer school was over and the office staff was busy getting ready for the new school year.

"That's Rubin's Grocery and Confectionary across the street. The kids hang out there at lunchtime and before and after school. They have a swell soda fountain. You can get hamburgers, hot dogs, milk shakes, and anything else your heart desires. They even make their own homemade ice cream sandwiches. You can buy all kinds of things there: groceries, newspapers, comic books, magazines, school supplies, work gloves, Peerless Potato Chips, wax lips, licorice ropes, penny and nickel candy,
and other **confections**. My Dad stops there every morning for the *Chicago Tribune*, a cup of coffee and a chocolate donut before he goes to work. Pop Rubin opens up at five in the morning to catch the mill traffic. He's been doing it for twenty years."

Climbing about a dozen steps to the front door, Ellen followed Melanie up another flight of interior stairs and down the hallway to the second floor office. At the counter, they were approached by one of the secretaries.

"Good afternoon, **Miss Link**, I have a new student for you. She's going to be my neighbor for a couple of months. Her name is Ellen Anderson and she needs to get registered."

"Welcome to Emerson High School, Ellen. I hope you're going to like it here. Why don't you come around the counter and have a seat at my desk. You can fill out a registration card, and then we'll get you signed up for your classes. Our school counselors are still on vacation, but you can look over this list of class offerings in their absence."

After completing the registration card, Ellen studied the list of classes. She selected Senior English with **Gladys Pierce**, Civics with **Henrietta Newton**, Physics with **Floyd Flinn**, Trigonometry with **Minnie Talbot**, A Cappella Chorus with **Grace Sayers**, Auditorium with **Gertrude Palmer** and **Melba Cromer**, and Physical Education with **Gertrude Reynolds**.

"That certainly looks like a full load," remarked Miss Link, as she looked over Ellen's selections.

"Your home room teacher will be Esther Tinsman, our biology teacher. She's one of our best teachers, or so all the students tell me. Of course, I don't see anyone on your list who's not first rate. Some of them have been here for fifteen years or more. In fact, I had some of them when I was a student here – Gladys Pierce, for instance. She was right out of Indiana University. I suppose you've already had biology, Ellen?"

"Yes, Miss Link, I took biology as a freshman, and chemistry in my sophomore year, at Stratford High School, in Connecticut."

"Connecticut? My, you're a long way from home. I've always wanted to go to New England. There's certainly a lot of history there. Anyway, classes start here on September 8th, the day after Labor Day. You'll be receiving an official class schedule in the mail next week. That gives you two weeks to enjoy what remains of your summer vacation. We're certainly glad to have you with us."

"Thank you, Miss Link, I'm looking forward to it."

"Miss Link, is Mr. Spaulding in his office? I'd like to introduce Ellen to him."

"No, Melanie, I'm afraid he's on vacation. Right now, I believe he's in Minocqua, Wisconsin with a fishing pole in his hands."

"Well, in that case, I'm going to take Ellen on a tour of the building, if that's all right?"

"Why, of course, Melanie. Ellen, I want you to know that Melanie is one of our most experienced student guides. She was trained by Mrs. Palmer of the Auditorium Department. She knows all the fascinating details about our wonderful school. You're in good hands."

One of the things that immediately impressed Ellen as they started walking down the second floor hallway was all the artwork that hung on the walls, most of it original oils.

"Emerson has been the **beneficiary** of original works of art donated by graduating classes since 1920," Melanie explained, "including several by Frank Dudley and other leading artists of the Indiana dunes. Here's Dudley's painting *The Trail of the Wind*, purchased by the Class of 1925. The art collection was originally Mr. Spaulding's idea. He had a strong belief that students should develop their **aesthetic** sensitivities in school. Today, the collection, which hangs in the second and third floor hallways, and some of the classrooms, is worth thousands of dollars. If you're going to be a senior, you may have an opportunity to choose a painting to be donated by our class. But, why don't we start our tour down on the first floor."

Melanie led Ellen downstairs and out the side entrance on Carolina Street. "See that date above the doorway – *1908*? It's an historical **anomaly**.

Excavation began in 1908, but the school didn't really open until 1909. It was probably one of the contractors who **presumptuously** decided to carve the year '1908' above the east and west entrances when the school was being built. The first class actually graduated in 1910. Miss Grieger, my American history teacher, told us about the error – she's a stickler for historical **veracity**. She even read us an article from the September 14, 1909 *Gary Post-Tribune*, about the school's opening, just to make a point about going back to original sources. Otherwise, she says, **negligent** errors will simply be **perpetuated** by those who don't bother to **verify** their facts, including journalists."

"I totally agree with you. People can be so **gullible** sometimes. They'll just parrot what other people tell them and accept it as gospel. And journalists, who should know better, often take short-cuts to meet their deadlines," Ellen added.

"Emerson was called a unit school because it educated all grades, from kindergarten to high school. Mr. Wirt, the first superintendent of schools here, thought that by placing all grades in the same building, the younger students would be inspired to graduate by the example of the high school students. You have to remember that, in 1900, only about six per cent of students were graduating from high school. Most quit early to go to work – not only farm children, but the children of recent immigrants. The typical student went no farther than the eighth grade. It was among Mr. Wirt's **innovations** to change all that.

"The first floor includes our school cafeteria, the home economics classrooms, the elementary classrooms, and the junior library, in this corner. Miss Nilsson teaches sewing in this room. I made two dresses and some skirts in her class last year. The library over here even has a fireplace because it was originally used as a kindergarten classroom, before they built the Little Building. They thought the fireplace would add a warm touch for children who were leaving home for the first time. At the back of the school are the boys' and girls' lower gymnasiums, locker rooms, and showers. It's through the showers that you can access the swimming pool. We had the first indoor school swimming pool in the United States. The boys and girls use it on alternate days. I hope you brought your bathing suit?"

"I sure did. I hope to go swimming in Lake Michigan before the summer's over."

"That's great! A bunch of us are going to the beach on Friday. You're welcome to join us. We take the bus to Marquette Park in Miller," Melanie explained, leading Ellen back up to the second floor.

"Here, on the second floor, you'll find the office, of course, the nurse's office, the language, history, commercial, biology, chemistry, and physics classrooms. Here's the entrance to the auditorium. Come take a look. We had the first theatrical stage built for a school building in the United States," Melanie explained, as she led Ellen down the center aisle toward the stage. It's also where we have auditorium classes with Miss Harrison, Miss Cromer and Mrs. Palmer. Mrs. Palmer helps us with our **elocution** and stage **deportment.** Miss Cromer plays the piano and leads us in singing. Miss Harrison is the head of the auditorium department. She's even written some of the plays we perform, including our annual Christmas pageant.

"The teachers run the auditorium classes according to **parliamentary procedure**. Each week, we elect a new chairman, and a secretary to keep the minutes. We learn the college fight songs, listen to recordings of the great composers, practice plays, hear from representatives of the community, and listen to reports about what the academic classes are doing. I don't think I would have ever developed a love for classical music, or the ability and courage to speak before an audience, had it not been for the **nurturing** atmosphere of the auditorium department.

"One of my favorite auditorium programs was when Dale Messick came here to speak. She's the cartoonist of *Brenda Starr, Reporter*. We learned from her how hard it was for a woman to achieve success as a cartoonist. In fact, that's why she uses the name 'Dale' instead of her real name 'Dalia,' because it sounds

more like a male name, and cartooning is a male-dominated profession. She even got up on stage and drew Brenda Starr for us on a giant sketch pad. She made it look so easy. She also told us she has a special affection for Emerson because her father taught drawing here for five years, starting when the school opened in 1909.

"If you follow me through this door off the stage, and into the boys' upper gymnasium, I can show you the band and orchestra rooms. We make lots of noise – I mean, music – so they keep us isolated in the back of the school. That's where I play my cello, with **Mr. Warren** and **Miss Kotora**, I mean

Mrs. Mistrovich – she just got married this year. Oh, shucks! The door's locked. The instrumental music department was recently **renovated** and I was anxious to show it off. I guess we'll have to wait until school opens to check it out. Under the circumstances, we can go out this way, to the second floor hallway."

Once in the west hallway, Melanie led Ellen down a flight of stairs and into the boys' lower gymnasium.

"Both the boys' and girls' gyms have a similar layout, with a basketball court on the lower level and a balcony with lockers on the upper level. Each one has a spiral staircase. That's Coach Rolfe's office over there, on the balcony, and there's the equipment locker where the football uniforms and sports equipment are stored. Follow me into the boys' locker room. I hope it's not in use. Football practice should have finished by now."

From the locker room, Melanie led Ellen through the doorway to the swim-

ming pool. What Ellen observed was a small pool by modern standards, but impressive nonetheless. Both the pool and the room housing it are finished in white ceramic tile, with stainless steel railings on either side.

"Here's our swimming pool – the first school pool in the United States. The boys and girls use it on separate days, although we're the only ones who wear bathing suits.

The boys swim **au natural**, if you know what I mean." Ellen smiled, innocently.

"Where does this door lead?" Ellen inquired.

"That door leads to the boiler room and the janitorial facilities. We're not permitted in there. The passageway leads under the school and exits in the first floor hallway, near the cafeteria. The boilers and coal storage are at the back of the building, adjacent to the swimming pool," Melanie explained.

"Let's go back to the second floor. I want to show you Miss Tinsman's room." They walked up the rear stairs and down the west hallway. "Room 204 is probably the most interesting one in the school, where most freshmen take biology. Miss Tinsman has been collecting stuffed animals and other **specimens** for more than thirteen years, including a twenty-foot tapeworm in a jar. Most of the animal specimens were former residents of the Emerson zoo. She knows a **taxidermist** out in Miller who does the stuffing. As you can see, there's a stuffed owl, a red fox, a possum, and a gray squirrel. There are also some of the best insect collections students have submitted over the years for their first grading period. By the way, I overheard that you're going to be in her homeroom. I had her for biology my freshman year. She's a very sweet lady, and reminds me of my maiden aunt, Mabel. She's a native of Dundee, Michigan and has been teaching in Gary since 1919. She came to Emerson in 1929. She has very high standards, but also has a **quirky** habit of making all the students with 'spectacles' sit in the front row. She lives in the Dalton Apartments on East Fifth Avenue, as do Miss Sayers, our choral teacher, and Miss Grieger, who teaches history. Now, I'll take you up to the third floor.

"The third floor has more classrooms, of course. Access to the auditorium balcony and training rooms is straight ahead, in the center of building. That's where Mrs. Palmer works on our **elocution**. The paintings near the central stairway and down the west side of the main hallway here represent the *Holy Grail Series* by the artist **Edwin Abbey**. These are copies of the originals in the Boston Public Library, and represent the Arthurian Knights of the Round Table and their quest for the Holy Grail. Each of the paintings you see throughout the school has an **edifying** story all its own. The school library is down here, on the

left. Now, follow me up to the fourth floor.

"The only classroom on the fourth floor is the drafting room. It was used for instrumental music until 1920 when they built the addition at the back of the building. Through this door on the right is the attic. It has a rifle range for the R.O.T.C. – that's the Reserve Officer  Training Corps. Here, you can see it, if I turn on the lights. With the war on, many of the boys have enrolled in R.O.T.C. The rest of the attic is for storage, mostly for drama department sets and costumes, and for old textbooks, school records, and furniture."

Back on the third floor, Ellen took a few moments to examine the three decades of trophies located in the exhibit cases in the east wing, including those awarded for track, basketball, state football championships, band contests, music memory, and chorus competitions. There was also a photo of Judge Gary's visit to Emerson in 1922, with the entire student body sitting on the front lawn.

"Is that the Judge Gary the city's named after?" Ellen inquired.

"That's right. Elbert Gary was the chairman of the board of the United States Steel Corporation. It was his decision to build the steel mills here and the board decided to name the city in his honor. He never lived here, but he visited on occasion. I believe this photo marks his only visit to Emerson.

"The Shops building is across the street from the athletic fields, on East 6th  Avenue. It was opened in 1925. It provides space for a variety of manual training classes, including aviation and auto shop, **foundry**, metal shop, carpentry, machine shop, and electric shop. A lot of the boys who go to work in the mills receive their **initial** training here. The building was originally a horse barn because they used horses to deliver coal for the boilers.

"You may have also seen our zoo, which was started by Mr. Spaulding in 1912, soon after the school opened. The students help pay for its maintenance by selling eggs to the people in the neighborhood. Oh, and I almost forgot the Little Building. It opened in 1926 and houses the kindergarten through third grade classes. Fourth graders move into the lower level of the Big Building."

As Ellen and Melanie left the building through the front entrance, Ellen couldn't help but feel a bit disappointed that her stay at Emerson would be of such limited **duration**. Much as she expected to miss her friends back home, particularly Ken, she was really looking forward to her time at Emerson. The length of her stay would depend entirely on the **duration** of her father's work at Gary Armor Plate.

"Thank you so much, Melanie. That was quite an **exhaustive** tour. I'm sure we'll be seeing a lot of each other. And I certainly plan to join you at the beach on Friday. I really appreciate your asking me."

Chapter 10

A Walk Downtown

When Ellen returned to her apartment, she discovered that her father had not yet retuned from Gary Armor Plate, and that Mrs. Matheus had gone to cook dinner for Dr. Bills, the West Side physician for whom she worked part-time. She left a note taped to the back door with Dr. Bill's phone number in case Ellen needed anything, and left her back door unlocked. With a few hours on her hands, Ellen walked upstairs, picked up her copy of Walter Krivitsky's book, and curled up in one of the overstuffed chairs that occupied the sun-filled front parlor. As she read of the **horrendous** acts of cruelty perpetrated by Stalin's regime, her thoughts returned to Natalia Boroskova and her courageous flight from her homeland. *What*, she thought, *has she told her uncle, and what revelations did he have to share with her?*

Shortly after five o'clock, her father came walking up the stairs and into the parlor.

"How was your day, Dad?"

"Great. Gus Bloomquist picked me up in his brand new Oldsmobile coupe and brought me back again. He also showed me where to catch the bus on 5th Avenue that will take me to the plant. I also have a much better understanding of what I need to **accomplish** while we're here. The drafting room has everything I need, and the employees couldn't be more helpful. I really can't say with any certainty how long we'll be here. It could be four weeks, or it could be eight weeks. I really don't know right now. A lot depends on **quality control**. I hope you're flexible, just in case my work keeps me here longer than I had anticipated?"

"After Melanie's guided tour of Emerson School, I feel very comfortable staying here as long as necessary. The important thing is that you complete your work successfully."

"That's great, honey. As a special treat, how would you like to eat at Walgreen's this evening – you know, the drug store next door to the Palace theatre that Victor Toth recommended?"

"I'd love it. I'm also anxious to see what the downtown has to offer. Perhaps, we can also take in a movie after dinner?"

"I anticipated that. Here, I picked up a copy of the *Gary Post-Tribune* at Rubin's. Why don't you check the movie listings?"

Ellen thumbed through the paper until she found the entertainment section.

"Let's see: *Mrs. Miniver*, with Greer Garson and Walter Pidgeon, is playing

at the Palace. *My Favorite Blond*, with Bob Hope and Madeleine Carroll, is playing at the State. The Gary has *All Through the Night,* with Humphrey Bogart and Conrad Veidt. That sounds like a re-run; besides, I already saw it in Stratford. The Grand is playing *Wake Island* with Brian Donlevy and Robert Preston. *The Little Foxes*, with Bette Davis, is playing at the Family. I vote for Mrs. Miniver. It's gotten excellent reviews, and besides, the plot is timely. It's about an English family during the **Battle of Britain** and the **blitz.** There's a seven o'clock show."

"That sounds fine."

"By the way, I see here that the RAF bombers have been hitting targets in western Germany and Holland. They also attacked a German convoy near the Frisian Islands. But, it also says that German **U-Boats** are still menacing Allied shipping, despite heavy aerial attacks on their boatyards and bases. And here's a somber note. A German bomb struck a shelter in East Anglia, killing a mother and all eight of her children. How sad!"

"I'm afraid we're going to be reading a lot more tragic stories like that one before this war's over," Eric replied.

It was just a brief ten-minute walk down 7th Avenue to Broadway. Buffington Park was practically deserted, with only a few children playing on the swings. At Memorial Auditorium, street vendors were hawking tickets and programs to evening wrestling matches, with the Polish Crusher and Yukon Eric as the headliners.

"Hey, my namesake's wrestling tonight – Yukon Eric. He's Swedish, you know, and comes from a long line of Swedish **brawlers**." Ellen figured her father was being **flippant**.

"I didn't know he was Swedish. Of course, I never even knew his last name."

"I'm not being **facetious**. His real name is Eric – Eric Holmback. His parents were born in Sweden."

Police cars were lined up outside of the Gary Municipal Building across the street, and several fire trucks were visible inside the fire station. At Broadway, the W. T. Grant store at the corner was still drawing customers. To Ellen, Broadway had a decidedly working class feel, judging by the **utilitarian** dress of the shoppers, some in their soiled work clothes who looked like they had just come from the mills. From the corner, Ellen and her father walked one block south to the Walgreen's at the corner of 8ᵗʰ Avenue, next to the Palace Theater. They paused briefly to look at the movie stills mounted in aluminum frames on each side of the entrance.

After a tasty dinner of meatloaf, peas, and potatoes, topped off with apple pie and a **liberal** helping of vanilla ice cream, Ellen and her father walked next door to the theater, arriving a few minutes prior to the start of the seven o'clock show. Everything that Ellen had heard about the Palace from their cabdriver, Victor Toth, was confirmed. The interior was an elegant blend of **Moorish** and

Italian architectural **motifs**, featuring rich, red carpets, wall niches with Greco-Roman sculptures, and a star-adorned ceiling. Shortly after taking their seats on the spacious main floor, the *MovieTone News*, narrated by Lowell Thomas, reported on the **devastating** land battle between Nazi and Soviet forces on the Eastern Front. This was **juxtaposed** with a **Robert Benchley** short, and a Woody Woodpecker cartoon. The feature attraction, *Mrs. Miniver*, was deserving of all the critical **accolades** it had received. It exceeded all of Ellen's expectations, with great performances from the entire cast, particularly Greer Garson and Walter Pidgeon. It made her all the more conscious of the daily sacrifices being made by America's British allies, both on the field of battle and on the home front. She was particularly impressed with the magnitude of the **evacuation** from Dunkirk that rescued over 300,000 British and Allied troops from German encirclement. With the newsreel and short subjects, it was nearly nine forty-five before they left the theater. On their walk home, Ellen told her father that she planned to pay a visit to Natalia Boroskova on Wednesday.

~~~~~~~~~~~

By the time Ellen awoke on Wednesday morning, her father was already in the kitchen having his breakfast when she poked her head around the corner.

"I thought I'd let you sleep in, Ellen. You had a long day yesterday and I thought you needed the rest."

"Thanks, Dad. But, I think eight hours is enough sleep for any person. I'm ready to get up and give Natalia a call. After breakfast, I'll ask Mrs. Matheus if I can use her phone."

"Fine. Then, I'll see you this evening after I get home from the plant. Here's ten dollars. Buy whatever you need for the **larder**."

After Ellen consumed a bowl of Shredded Ralston and a glass of orange juice, she returned to her bedroom and traded in her flowered housecoat for a light maroon pair of fitted gabardine trousers, paired with a white cotton button-front blouse. White socks and her black and white saddle shoes completed the outfit. Grabbing her purse off the nightstand, she walked downstairs and knocked on Mrs. Matheus' door.

"Good morning, Ellen. Did your father get off already? I thought I heard footsteps on the stairs."

"Yes, he left for work about twenty minutes ago. I'd like to use your telephone, if I may?"

"Why, certainly. It's there in the living room, on the end table. The telephone directory's there as well."

Placing the directory in her lap, Ellen flipped through the pages to find the name of Stan Boroskova. *Here it is*, she thought to herself, *Stan Boroskova, 2-1157.* Quickly, she dialed the numbers and waited for an answer.

"Hello? Boroskova residence. May I help you?"

"Yes, please, I'd like to speak with Natalia. This is her friend, Ellen Anderson."

"Oh, yes, Ellen, she's been waiting for your call. She's right here."

"Natalia?"

"Yes, hello, Ellen. I've been anxious to speak with you. I'd prefer to do so in person, however. We have so much to tell you. Are you free to meet us this morning? My uncle Stan can pick you up and bring you here. Would that be all right?"

"Why, sure."

"Where are you living, again?"

"I'm at 750 Carolina Street, near Emerson School."

"She's at 750 Carolina, Uncle Stan."

"Uncle Stan says we can pick you up in about ten minutes. Is that enough time for you to be ready?"

"Yes. I'm already dressed. I'll be on the front porch in five minutes. Just tell him to look for a girl in maroon slacks and a white blouse."

"No problem. I'll be with him. We'll see you in a few minutes, then."

"Thank you, Mrs. Matheus. I'll be going out for a while. Don't worry about me. I expect to be back sometime this afternoon, though."

Almost to the minute, Uncle Stan and Natalia pulled up in front 750 Carolina and Ellen climbed into the back seat.

"So, are you all settled in to your new apartment? It's certainly convenient to your school."

"Yes. It's very comfortable. And I've already registered for classes and had a tour of the building with Melanie McGuire, the girl who lives next door."

As their car turned left at Seventh Avenue, Natalia explained:

"Uncle Stan's going to show you how to get to our house by streetcar, in case he's working."

Driving south on Broadway, he turned right at 11th Avenue.

"This is the way the streetcar goes, Ellen," instructed Uncle Stan. "When you're on Broadway, just make sure you catch the Tolleston line. That will take you west on 11th Avenue. You know your Presidents, of course. Just get off at Pierce Street – 11th and Pierce. From there, walk south until you come to Norton Park. At the park, turn right and stay on 13th Avenue until you come to Lincoln Street. Our house is in the middle of the block, right across from **St. Casimir's Lithuanian Church**, if you remember. It's that simple. Here, I'm coming to Pierce Street now and there's the park up ahead. Just follow my route. Before I had an automobile, this is the way I walked home from the **Sheet & Tin Mill**."

"That's pretty easy. I can remember that," Ellen replied.

After Uncle Stan parked his car in the driveway, the three entered through the backdoor and walked into the living room.

"Have a seat, Ellen. Can we get you something to drink?"

"Not right now, thanks. I've just had break-fast. Perhaps later."

Ellen's eyes wandered across the room, where Russian figurines and works of art were much on display, including an antique Russian **icon**. Much like Mrs. Matheus, Stan and his wife had decorated their home with **mementoes** of their homeland. Such was the **psychological** longing for that which they had left behind in Russia, probably forever.

"Uncle Stan and I had a long talk last night about the situation in the Soviet Union. Right now, of course, the people are in a life and death struggle against the Nazi war machine. But, when that's over – and we're both convinced that it's only a matter of time – Stalin will reassert his **dictatorial** control over the whole of the Soviet Union and, perhaps, Eastern Europe. Uncle Stan is in communication with a number of former Soviet citizens who have managed to flee to the West, just as we have. They fear that once the Nazis are defeated, a new wave of **repression** will sweep the country, with grave **repercussions** for many of those who have had contact with the West.

"One of the refugees with whom he has spoken now lives in Gary. We'll call him 'Boris,' for now. Several others are in Chicago. One is a defector from the Soviet army who, after several months in a German prison camp, was exchanged for captured German soldiers. But, rather than welcoming these men home, Stalin had them sent to the **Gulag**. To his **perverted** way of thinking, they were **irreparably tainted** by their contact with Western influences. It was on the way to a slave labor camp east of the **Urals** that Boris escaped and made his way to the United States."

"What Natalia tells you is true. The situation inside the Soviet Union is a nightmare. Everyone is suspect. And it all boils down to Stalin's **paranoid megalomania**, and the **fanaticism** that Communism breeds. He doesn't trust anyone. One could be head of the **NKVD** one day, and the victim of a bullet to the back of the head the next. I came to Gary in 1923, following the defeat of the **White Russians** by the **Bolsheviks**. I was originally a supporter of **Tsar Nicholas**, but championed democratic reforms that would have allowed

him to hold on to power. That all went out the window after he and his family were murdered by the Bolsheviks in 1918."

"What kind of political platform did the White Russians have, other than opposition to the Bolsheviks?" Ellen inquired.

"Generally speaking, the White movement had no set political beliefs or **ideology**. Some members were **monarchists**, others republicans, rightists, or **Kadets**. They were united in their **nationalistic** spirit and in their opposition to **Bolshevism** and the Red Army, although I am ashamed to say that our ranks also included a number of **anti-Semites** who persecuted the Jews. I began to sympathize with the Kadets, which had been a liberal leaning, Constitutional Democratic Party during the period of the **Russian Empire**. Since immigrating to the

United States, and becoming a citizen, however, I found myself most in **alignment** with the ideals of your **Republican Party**. The **Democratic Party** in the United States is just moving in the direction of Communism, though much more slowly than that of the Bolsheviks, perhaps to a form of **democratic socialism**. There are forces in the Democratic Party that wish to assert total dominance of the government over the lives of the people. Certainly not to the same degree as Stalin, but through what might be described as a **soft tyranny**. Although I don't think President Roosevelt is a Communist, there are Communists in his administration who are seeking to bring about that result."

"What are the political leanings of the Russians now living in Gary?" Ellen inquired.

"On balance, they are of a **classical liberal** mindset and opposed to big government in all its **manifestations**, including **socialism**, **fascism**, **progressivism**, and this **statist liberalism advocated** by Roosevelt. They are also a deeply religious people who also oppose Communism because of its **atheistic tenets**. A small number are sympathetic to the Soviet Union, however. Some are even ardently **pro-Stalinist**. Why, I cannot **fathom**. I think they have blindly accepted the Communist **propaganda** without analyzing its terrifying consequences, or coming to grips with the millions who have been slaughtered in its name. Some are like the *New York Times* reporter, **Walter Duranty**, who pens those glowing **encomiums** to the Soviet Union. He **rationalizes** the wholesale slaughter of innocents with such phrases as 'you can't make an omelet without breaking a few eggs.' Those who try to **exonerate** Duranty and his ilk are simply **abetting** the terror.

"Another characteristic of the Soviet sympathizers in this country is that they tend to be new arrivals, **disaffected** with life in America. They are so caught up in the **ideological ferment** that has many Europeans in its grip that they assume the same conditions prevail here, including the strong class divisions that characterize European society. Over time, however, many of them come to the realization that our **republican** institutions and **free market capitalism** work wonders for the common man who is willing to put his shoulder to the wheel and take advantage of the opportunities this country affords them. When those opportunities **manifest** themselves, they usually become ardent defenders of democracy and capitalism. And, if they do not, their children do.

"A few years ago, we had a school superintendent in Gary – William A. Wirt – who testified before Congress that he had heard people at a Washington, DC dinner party openly expressing sympathy for Communism. This was during the period of the **Popular Front**, when the Soviet Union maintained an outward stance of hostility toward Nazi Germany, and sympathy for Communism was at its height in the West. Many in your intellectual classes were drawn to Marxist-Leninist ideology or to the front groups **cynically** created by the Communists to lure them, sort of like the way a spider lures a fly. Secretly, of course, Stalin sought a **rapprochement** with Germany to secure the Soviet Union's western border and direct the Nazi's attentions against France and England. In Wirt's view, the Communists had also infiltrated the Roosevelt administration with the intent of collapsing the American economic system. This is what he heard **articulated** at that dinner.

"After Wirt went public with his **revelations**, a congressional committee, chaired by **Congressman Alfred Bulwinkle**, was assembled to conduct an investigation of his charges. Not surprisingly, the committee's Democrat majority came to the defense of the Roosevelt administration and rejected Wirt's charges of Communist **infiltration**. It was exactly the kind of response that one might have expected. Charges made against the administration were likely to be viewed through a **partisan prism** as an attack on the Democratic Party. Thus, rather than viewing the charges objectively, and seeking to root out Communist influences, they only succeeded in summoning up a defensive posture against Roosevelt's critics. But, to those of us who have an intimate familiarity with Communism and its **subversive** agenda, Wirt's charges were all too true. There are, in fact, hundreds of Communists and **fellow travelers** working inside the New Deal at this very moment. And it's not a **benign** presence either, reflecting our temporary alliance with the Soviet Union against the Nazis. Their aim is to influence the post-war world in which the Soviet Union faces off against the United States and its allies. The Soviet spymasters are amazed at how **apathetic** and naïve most Americans are, and how **vulnerable** to **covert infiltration**. It's a situation they would never tolerate inside the Soviet Union, with its police state and the **pervasive** surveillance of the citizenry. I fear that unless there's blood in the streets, Americans won't feel a **compelling** reason to take action."

"Isn't this the William Wirt who designed the 'Work-Study-Play' system of education used in the Gary Schools?" Ellen inquired.

"The same. He was Gary's first superintendent of schools and one of the leading figures in the history of modern American education. His system served as a model for more than 500 school systems across the country. He was also an outspoken advocate for free market capitalism and a vigorous opponent of President Roosevelt's attempts at economic planning. Sadly, he died in 1938, some say because of the strain **exacerbated** by all the negative publicity he received from Roosevelt's defenders. This is a favorite tactic of the left. Anyone who speaks out forcefully against them is **demonized** to **diminish** their **credibility** and influence, and the communists like this just fine."

"Does William Wirt have any family left in Gary?"

"Yes. His widow, Mildred Harter Wirt, still lives here. She's the supervisor of the Auditorium Department for the Gary Public Schools, and is influential in the national auditorium movement. She taught auditorium at Froebel School before becoming an administrator."

"Do you happen to know where she lives?" Ellen inquired.

"It's my understanding that she lives in the Ambassador Apartments on Monroe Street, near Jefferson Park. You can check the telephone directory."

"I'd love to have a talk with her sometime. Perhaps she can shed further light on William Wirt's charges of Communist infiltration into the Roosevelt administration. But, what about the book you brought here from London, Natalia? Has your Uncle Stan had an opportunity to examine it?"

"I've turned it over to one of my close associates in Tolleston, a Russian ex-patriot who has a photographic studio and the equipment to read the microfilm," explained Uncle Stan. "He stayed up half the night and brought me copies of the documents this morning. They're most **enlightening**. That's what we wanted to share with you."

Chapter 11

Subversives in Their Midst

"Not many people would comprehend the gravity of these documents, Ellen, but they are probably the most important **cache** of top secret material **extant** in the West since the Bolsheviks came to power, many implicating Soviet **operatives** in the United States government. While they date from 1938, they appear to confirm some of what we have learned from our own **surveillance** efforts in Gary and Chicago. I would not be surprised if some of these same people are now engaged in stealing American military secrets. If that's the case, we have to do everything in our power to **frustrate** their efforts."

"I read about the experiments **Niels Bohr** was conducting with **nuclear fission** at Princeton University a couple of years ago. Could this in any way be related to that?"

"Quite possibly. I must say, you are a remarkably well-informed young woman. Yes, it was that announcement that led a number of scientists to believe that fission might be a possible source for **nuclear power**. However, they feared that what they had discovered was also on the radar of Nazi scientists, who might seek to **militarize** the technology. If so, it could potentially change the course of the war, and allow the Nazis to bring the rest of the world under their **hegemony**. In 1939, **Albert Einstein** and **Leo Szilard,** two **eminent** physicists, wrote a letter to President Roosevelt warning him of the military threat posed by German atomic research, and urging him to support an American effort to develop an atomic weapon. That led the President to fund a crash program at Columbia University, where **Enrico Fermi** was already engaged in atomic research. From Columbia, Fermi went to the **University of Chicago**, where, rumor has it, they have begun working on the construction of the first **nuclear pile** in an underground laboratory beneath Stagg Field. We believe that Soviet operators are in Chicago at this very moment in an effort to learn the details of those experiments. And we are extremely hesitant to dismiss these threats as **apocryphal** because the stakes are simply

West Stand Stagg Field University of Chicago.

too high.

"Incidentally, the general public has no knowledge of these developments. American scientists have stopped publishing articles in the scientific and popular literature regarding atomic research for fear that our enemies will **glean** critical information from them. However, one of our own Chicago associates has been able to **discern** the general thrust of their work, and believes the Communists are attempting to **infiltrate** the project."

"Nuclear pile? I don't know that term." Ellen inquired.

"A nuclear pile is a **primitive** type of nuclear reactor designed to create a

sustained **fission** reaction. I know, it's rather technical mumbo-jumbo to the **uninitiated**, and I don't pretend to know more than the basics myself. Ultimately, however, the goal is to **exploit** the power of the atom to produce a weapon of **incalculable** force."

"It sounds like we're in the thick of a **conspiracy** with tremendous national security **implications**," Ellen suggested.

"Very much so. In fact, these documents have identified a Russian-born scientist sympathetic to the **Stalinist regime** who may have access to this program. Others are German nationals who were educated in the United States and took up permanent residence here a number of years ago. According to these documents, and other information we have gathered recently, there are three or four men with scientific training either working directly with the Chicago experiments or in close collaboration with those who are. We believe that the Communist cell in Gary is supporting these efforts. So, in the event that the Chicago operators are **neutralized** by the authorities, the secrets can be passed on to their **confederates** in Gary, or elsewhere."

"But, why don't we turn this evidence over to the **F.B.I.**?" Ellen suggested.

"At first glance, that would seem to be a logical course of action. But, the situation is a little more **ambiguous** than that. The fact of the matter is that we are concerned about **double agents** in the **F.B.I.** who might **compromise** the investigation and turn over what information we have to the Soviet Union. Why, just last month, information that was passed on to a local **F.B.I.** agent may have been the cause of the death of one of our associates who lived on Idaho Street in Aetna, a few miles from here. The agent simply disappeared without a trace. Besides that, if the Russians find out what information we have, it will blow our cover and make penetration into their cells far more difficult.

"Surprisingly, the **F.B.I.** has not devoted sufficient resources to investigating the Communist threat. As late as 1940, the **F.B.I.** didn't even have a Soviet squad; and Russian was treated as an **exotic** language in the universities and libraries, more often grouped with Oriental studies. Even the **House Committee on Un-American Activities** has limited **expertise** in **Sovietology**. As **displaced** Russian patriots, we not only have a **sophisticated** understanding of the Communist threat, but a **visceral** desire to root out these Communists and protect the United States because we understand the realities of that threat better than the vast majority of Americans. But, we can't allow our **animus** against these **malefactors** to **thwart** our ultimate goal of protecting our most sensitive military secrets."

"But what on earth are they doing in Gary in the first place, Mr. Boroskova?"

"It would appear that several have family here, who may or may not be **implicated** in their acts of **subversion**. But, beyond that, most of the Eastern European nationality groups in Gary harbor at least some Communist or socialist **sympathizers** who got their political education in Europe. You might find some of these activists on street corners peddling the *Daily Worker*, the Marxist newspaper. These are most commonly the members of the local Communist Party USA who are engaged in more or less public activities. Working in the shadows are the underground operatives, some of whom are not even known to the open party members. Being more heavily involved in propaganda or espionage activities, they are typically assigned cover names by their Moscow handlers, and keep a low profile. Also, Gary is sufficiently distant from

Chicago – about thirty miles – that it provides a safer **refuge** in the event that the **F.B.I.** gets suspicious and begins arresting the members of the Chicago cells. I would not be surprised if the Communists are also interested in the **armaments** being manufactured in Gary, or in our steelmaking processes. It's our role to **mitigate** these threats."

"Do those documents tell you where any of them are living?" Ellen inquired.

"Yes, they do. And, this is among the most exciting **revelations** on the **microfilm**. We have what we think is a nearly complete roster of all the Soviet **operatives** in the United States, with their addresses, as well as those operating in Europe and the Far East. These appeared in internal operational documents to which only high-level diplomatic officials had access, Natalia's father among them. They were no doubt used by diplomatic or **consular** officials to keep in contact with local **agents**. They may be a bit dated, and are all in Russian, of course, but that provides no barrier to me, Natalia, or our associates."

"Is there anything Natalia and I can do to **expose** these spies?"

"Yes there is. But, I must **admonish** you to exercise the utmost **discretion** and not **divulge** anything of our conversation. Natalia is still in serious danger. Going public, or informing the authorities **prematurely**, would only endanger her, and our mission. Even if the Soviets knew that she had already **disclosed** all her secrets, they would have no hesitation in having her killed, or kidnapped, as a warning to those who might follow her example. Stalin has hit squads throughout the West to **exterminate** turncoats, like **Walter Krivitsky**, or enemies, like **Leon Trotsky**."

"You have my word, Mr. Boroskova. Your secrets are safe with me. I wouldn't want any harm to come to Natalia."

"Good. Then, there are some tasks you can **tackle**. I want you two to keep a close eye on the newspapers, particularly the *Gary Post-Tribune*. We believe the Soviets, through the local members of the Communist Party USA, are engaging in a variety of criminal acts to fund their **subversive** activities, based on the **spate** of burglaries on the West Side in recent months. Why, just last week, the Gary police picked up a Russian man as he fled from a home near 7th and Taft, on the West Side – that's the most **affluent** neighborhood in the city. When they located his car in the alley, they found that he had attempted to **abscond** with jewelry, silverware, and antiques, just the kind of items a burglar could sell or pawn for some quick cash in the Chicago area. Of course, his nationality may be just a coincidence – after all, people of all races and nationalities commit crimes. Or, it may be part of the Communist conspiracy. But, it's worth checking out. What we want to do is isolate the names in these documents and put them under surveillance. You can also check the police logs for patterns of activity and the names of the **alleged perpetrators** to see if there is any overlap. The police station is not far from your apartment, Ellen."

"That's right. In fact, my father and I passed it last evening on our walk to Broadway."

"You and Natalia might also investigate whether any of these individuals have families living here, including children from whom you can **extract** information. All of these operatives live in the Central District, where they are less **conspicuous**. After all, there are many eastern and southern Europeans living in this area: Lithuanians, Hungarians, Greeks, Italians, Macedonians, Croats, Romanians, Czechs, Slovaks, as well as Russians. It is common to hear European languages or **dialects** being spoken on the streets of the Central District, or when frequenting the local business establishments, or coffee houses."

"What about the Lithuanian Church right across the street?" Ellen added.

"It's interesting that you should mention that. The Lithuanians are, in the **aggregate**, **fervent** and **implacable** anti-Communists. After all, their independence was taken from them by the Soviets in June of 1940, probably as part of some secret agreement with Germany to divide up Eastern Europe. The country was then forcibly occupied and a **puppet government** established. The Soviets lost no time in rounding up those who might pose a potential threat to their regime, including intellectuals, politicians, teachers and priests. Many were shot or shipped to Siberia. Paul Baukus, one of our close **confidants**, is a member of St. Casimir's. But, there are a couple of church members who are Stalinist sympathizers and are simply

using the church as a cover. Paul is monitoring their activities. Several other Russians are also using the cover of the church to disguise their true sympathies. At least one belongs to our church, St. Mary's Russian Orthodox, at 17th and Fillmore. Another belongs to St. Nicholas Carpathian Church which is located at 14th and Johnson, right behind our home. In fact, you can see the back of it through our kitchen window. There's even a small group that hangs out in Norton Park that we've had under **surveillance** since early spring. Most afternoons, some of them can be observed playing chess or cards near the pavilion. Part of our job will be sorting out the Soviet agents from the sympathizers, or **fellow travelers**, as they're called, and those who are merely innocent Russian **nationals**."

"Uncle Stan suggests we develop friendships with some of the children of these Soviet agents, like those attending Froebel School," Natalia interjected. "He also suggests that I register for classes at Froebel as a way of meeting young people in the neighborhood. I was planning to do that regardless. While I do have the **equivalent** of a high school diploma from the Soviet Union, I could certainly benefit from classes in American history and government to familiarize myself with your American traditions, the **United States Constitution**, and other foundational principles. I have much to learn about your country."

"That's right, Ellen. I'm going to give you and Natalia a list of suspected Soviet agents in the city, drawn from these documents. Don't let it out of your possession or share it with anyone."

Ellen scrutinized the names on the sheet of paper Mr. Boroskova handed her. There were seven names:

Dimitri Poliakov, 1522 Van Buren
Yevgeny Alexandrov, 1333 Adams
Alexei Kropotkin, 1342 Jackson
Mikhail Ivanski, 1209 Johnson
Ignace Eisenberg, 1121 Jefferson
Galina Borovsky, 1573 Fillmore
Boris Sokolov, 1176 Tyler

"I see that they all live west of Broadway, and, **ironically**, on streets named after American presidents. And, they're in a relatively narrow range of avenues from 11th to 16th," Ellen observed. "That should make it a little easier to track them down, provided they're still living at these same locations."

"That's right. As I explained, the Central District is home to dozens of nationalities, many of them southern and eastern European – a **fertile** ground for recruitment. Names like these won't stand out as much here as they would on the East or West Sides of Gary. You and Natalia can **compile** a **dossier** on each one of these people, first, by verifying that they're still living at these addresses and, if not, trying to determine where they've moved. Of course, it's always possible that one or more of them has adopted a **pseudonym**, making your task more **onerous**. In that case, you may have to approach your job from a more **oblique** angle."

"My, but the time has flown. Natalia, why don't we start our investigation tomorrow morning. I've got to be getting back home. It's nearly three thirty. You don't have to drive me this time, Mr. Boroskova. I'd prefer to take the streetcar to get better **acclimated** to the city. Why don't I meet you here at ten o'clock tomorrow morning, Natalia?"

"Fine. I'll be waiting for you."

After saying her 'goodbyes,' Ellen took off in the direction of 11th Avenue. At Van Buren Street, she heard the 'clang' of a streetcar in the distance. As she walked, she reflected on the **sage** knowledge and advice of Natalia's Uncle Stan. By the time the streetcar approached, she was standing in front of Central

Florist, at the corner of 11th and Jackson. Climbing aboard the trolley, she dropped a dime in the box and took a seat. There were only a few passengers on the car when she boarded: two older ladies, and a **pregnant** woman. A young woman with a child also boarded at Jackson Street.

"Oh, how **cunning**! How old is your little boy?" Ellen asked.

The woman, a beautiful brunette in a flowered housedress who appeared to be in her late twenties, smiled. "He just turned four in July. His name is Cordell, but we call him 'Corky.'"

"Oh, just like in *Gasoline Alley*," Ellen replied.

"That's right. His Uncle Ernie gave him the nickname. I'm just glad he didn't call him Skeezix."

"Cordell... hmmm. He wouldn't be named after the Secretary of State, Cordell Hull, by any chance?"

"As a matter of fact, that's where his father and I got the name," the woman replied.

"What's that pin on your shirt, young man?"

"That's my 'Corky' pin. I got it in Pep cereal."

"That's pretty neat, finding a pin with your name on it in a box of cereal."

"You bet!"

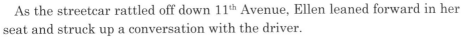

As the streetcar rattled off down 11th Avenue, Ellen leaned forward in her seat and struck up a conversation with the driver.

"Been driving long?"

"Six years. Since 1936, in fact, soon after I graduated from Froebel High School. My Dad's a motorman, too, so I had an in with Gary Railways. It's a great job. Sorta like gettin' paid to enjoy your hobby. I've always been fascinated with trains and streetcars."

"I think it would be great fun to drive a trolley. I'm going to the Gary Public Library, but I think I'll ride to the end of the line and come back, if you don't mind. I'm new to town and I'd like to see a bit more of the city."

"You can ride as long as you like, miss. It's no skin off my nose. Besides, I kinda like the company."

"Do you usually drive the Tolleston trolley?"

"No, they move us around, so we're familiar with all the lines. This week I'm assigned to the Tolleston run."

"What's your favorite?"

"Well, you could've asked what was my favorite run. That was the Valpo line. Valpo's about twenty miles southeast of Gary. Many of my passengers were students at Valparaiso University. It was the most scenic run – mostly countryside – but it wasn't very profitable, which is why Gary Railways discontinued it in 1938. The same thing happened earlier to the Miller line. It just **epitomizes** the future of transportation in Gary. It's just a matter of time before they discontinue the trolleys altogether. The company has already replaced some of the lines with busses. In a few more years, I'll be just a bus driver – mark my word – and streetcars will be **obsolete**."

After a brief stop at the Public Service Building at 11ᵗʰ and Broadway, where

Gary Railways maintained an office, the car proceeded through the Broadway business district, picking up and discharging passengers with greater frequency. The young mother with 'Corky' **disembarked** in front of Sears, Roebuck. As the car neared the steel mills and administration building at the north end of Broadway, it reversed directions on the track loop on the west side of the street. Its arrival also

coincided with the four o'clock shift change at U.S. Steel that suddenly **disgorged** a **torrent** of workers from the massive plant. Within the span of a few minutes, Broadway was **inundated** with **pedestrians**, many of whom climbed

aboard the **idling** trolleys or busses. Since the other female passengers had already **disembarked** in the business district, Ellen found herself the only female on a car filled with dirty, exhausted, and hungry steelworkers, most with lunch-buckets in hand. She found herself the object of a lot of roving eyes.

"Most of these guys are happy to be working again. The Depression hit us pretty hard in Gary. A few years ago, there were long lines at the employment office and most job seekers were simply turned away. It's too bad it took a war to get production moving again."

"Did you ever work in the steel mills?"

"As a matter of fact, I did, shortly after graduation. There weren't many jobs in those days, and the lines at the employment office were so long you could never hope to get hired. But, one day, my friend, Al Zvingilas, and I went fishing at the lagoon – that's out near Miller Beach. We stayed out so

Scene Marquette Park Gary Ind 6-12

late that we decided to sleep on a dune, under the stars. By the time morning came, Al got the idea of hiking through the dunes to the Coke Plant, and, once inside the plant, to the Broadway employment office. There were no fences to keep us out. They probably thought no one would be crazy enough to walk three miles

through the sand dunes to get inside. They didn't know Al and me. We were first in line when it opened at eight o'clock. We both got hired and were assigned to the Wheel Mill. No one caught on to our **ruse**. I felt a little guilty about it, but not too much. I was just happy to be working."

"But, you didn't stay?"

"No. I worked there about a year before getting hired by Gary Railways as a relief driver. When one of the drivers retired, I got hired full time. My Dad had a hand in that because he was friendly with one of the managers. The pay's not as good as the mills, but it's a lot more fun."

"Well, I suppose it's time for me to get off. Can you tell me where the public library is from here?"

"This is 5th Avenue. The Gary Public Library is two blocks west of here. This is Lytton's Department Store. The library's between Adams and Jefferson Streets. It'll be on your right. You can't miss it."

"Thanks for the ride. By the way, what was your name?"

"Smelko... Tom Smelko. What's yours?"

"Ellen Anderson, from Stratford, Connecticut. Perhaps, I'll see you again sometime," she said, stepping down to the street.

Rather than heading straight home, Ellen was anxious to examine the current city directory for the names on her list of local Communist agents. She knew about city directories because her grandfather kept a copy of the *Bridgeport City Directory* in his office. She knew that they not only listed residents by their last name, but also who lived at each street address. As she strolled along 5th Avenue between Broadway and Jefferson Street, she noted a number of small eateries and businesses lining both sides of the street, including the Sip and Bite restaurant, the Malis Fruit Market, and the Gary Billiards Club. After passing the Flamingo Lounge, where the arresting aroma of fresh pizza

assaulted her nostrils, she found herself across the street from both the Gary Public Library and the Y.M.C.A. The library was set back from the street, behind a neatly manicured lawn. Passing through its **ornate** carved entry doors, she climbed the stairs to the reference desk. A middle-aged gentleman with wire-rimmed spectacles looked up and smiled.

"May I be of some assistance?"

"Yes. I'd like to see your current *Gary City Directory*, please."

"Certainly. We have one for 1941. I hope that will do?"

"What about 1942?"

"They didn't publish a 1942 directory. They don't do them every year. We keep the 1937, 1939 and 1941 behind the reference desk. Older ones are in the Indiana Room. Perhaps the telephone directory will help if you're looking for a current listing, but, then, many people don't have telephones. In that case, the city directory should be more complete."

"I think I'd better have a look at both," Ellen replied.

Ellen took the city directory and the telephone directory to one of the large oak tables that filled the library's main reading room. She removed the list of names from her purse and placed it next to the volumes.

"Let me see now: Poliakov..."

Flipping pages and running her finger down the alphabetical column of names in the city directory, she spotted an Igor Poliakov at 1522 Van Buren, but no Dimitri. Making some notations on the paper, she moved on to the next name:

Alexandrov, Yevgeny. Finding no person with that name, she tried the street listings for Adams Street. There it was: *Y. Alexandrov (Ludmilla) lab USS 1333 Adams.* Checking the key, she ascertained that he was a laborer at United States Steel. Of the remaining five names, Ignace Eisenberg was listed at 1121

Jefferson, but without occupation. Boris Sokolov, at 1176 Tyler Street, had only a current telephone listing. There were no listings in either book for Alexei Kropotkin, Mikhail Ivanski or Galina Borovsky. She made further notations with her pencil. Tucking the piece of paper back in her purse, she returned the books to the reference librarian, thanked him, and headed for home.

On her way home, she spotted an A & P grocery store near 5th and Broadway and remembered her assignment to stock up on provisions. By the time she got home, her arms were fairly aching from carrying two heavy bags of groceries. She wished she had her little red wagon, or one of those wheeled wire baskets she observed some little old ladies pulling down Broadway.

Carolina Street was deserted as she approached the house. She shifted both bags to her left arm, braced them against the house, and unlocked the back door. The house was quiet, with no sign of her father, or Mrs. Matheus. Anticipating her father's **imminent** arrival, however, she began to prepare some tuna patties, mashed potatoes, and green beans, while setting the kitchen table. A few moments after five o'clock, she heard those familiar footsteps on the stairs.

Chapter 12

Revelations Over Dinner

"Atomic secrets? Soviet espionage? Are you serious? What have you gotten yourself mixed up in? I thought you were going to avoid excitement on this trip?"

Ellen's father helped himself to another tuna fish patty as Ellen re-filled his glass with lemonade. He was always **amenable** to Ellen's, or Edna's, tuna patties.

"What could I do, Dad: 'throw Natalia to the wolves' – your words? It seems like this case just fell into our laps and, as it turns out, has serious national security implications. Natalia's Uncle Stan, who is a White Russian, is very much involved in counter-espionage work. He filled us in on all the details. Gary is home to a Communist cell that is working in **conjunction** with other Soviet spies in Chicago. He doesn't have any concrete evidence as yet, but he believes that it's their goal to infiltrate the atomic research going on at the **University of Chicago**. The documents that Natalia smuggled out of the Soviet Union provide a complete roster of the Communist spy network in the United States. We believe that at least a half dozen are still living in Gary."

"This sounds dangerous. Shouldn't it be obvious that if their goal is to steal atomic secrets, they'll stop at nothing to get what they want, even kill those who stand in their way?"

"Don't worry, Dad. Natalia and I plan to exercise **prudence**. We don't plan to confront any of them directly. We'll leave that to her Uncle Stan and his **compatriots**, or to the authorities. Our mission is simply to do background research in the library and at the police station. We plan to be very **surreptitious**."

"Well, just so you confine your activities to the library."

"In fact, that's where I was this afternoon – at the library. Can I interest you in a piece of blueberry pie, and coffee?"

"I don't mind if I do."

After dinner, and after sharing the dishwashing chores with her father, Ellen retired to the front parlor and, again, **immersed** herself in Walter Krivitsky's book. She read:

> *The agents of Stalin's secret cabinet spied upon the former opposition leaders, whether these were in jail or still in high office. They were gathering 'evidence' for all eventualities. The entire **Bolshevik Old***

*Guard was constantly watched by a **veritable** army of informers and **stool pigeons**. An **indiscreet** remark was sufficient to make a case of **heresy** against the speaker. A spell of silence at the wrong occasion when, for instance, everybody was offering praise to Stalin, was enough to justify suspicion of disloyalty.*

Reading Krivitsky's words aroused Ellen's **reflective** side. She remembered that Natalia's father had been a member of the **Bolshevik Old Guard**. *Had he simply been around too long? Did he know too much? Was he a potential threat to Stalin, or was he a completely innocent victim of the culture of **duplicity,** and false **accusation** that the system **engendered**?*

In the morning, after breakfast, and after her father had left for work, Ellen walked to Broadway to board the Tolleston streetcar. Pedestrians were little in evidence before the stores opened. The streetcar was occupied by just a couple of westbound passengers. Norton Park was virtually deserted and only the squawking of a small flock of Blue Jays punctuated the morning stillness. Natalia was waiting for her on the front steps as Ellen approached the Boroskova home on Lincoln Street.

"Ellen, I'm so glad to see you. Come in and have a seat. Uncle Stan's still asleep. He's working midnights this week and just got home about eight thirty. Aunt Veronika's in the kitchen."

"Good morning, Ellen, can I bring you a cup of hot Ovaltine."

"That would be lovely. Thank you, Mrs. Boroskova."

"I've been trying to figure out how we can investigate the names on our list of Soviet agents to determine if they're still living where they were in 1938."

"I had the same thought, Natalia. After leaving here yesterday, I went to the library and searched the city directories. I've already had some success. Let me see... Yevgeny Alexandrov is still living at 1333 Adams Street, and Boris Sokolov is still at 1176 Tyler. Ignace Eisenberg is at 1121 Jefferson. There's an Igor Poliakov at 1522 Van Buren, but no Dimitri. I suppose it's possible that some of them are using **aliases**. If we can catch the mailman on his rounds, I'm sure we can find out where Dimitri Poliakov has gone. The other three may still be around, but there's no record of them in the city directories."

"Here's your Ovaltine, Ellen, and some ginger snaps."

"Oh, thank you, Mrs. Boroskova. That's very thoughtful."

"I think that's a great idea about speaking with the postman," Natalia replied. "If we could manage to gain his confidence, we may be able to learn where Dimitri Poliakov has moved. And if he's no longer in Gary, perhaps the mailman can help us obtain his forwarding address."

"Another thought came to mind," Ellen continued. "What if one or more of these agents has left the Communist Party and is no longer working for the Soviet Union? And what if we could find that person and gain his or her confidence?"

"That might be difficult," Natalia replied. "The Soviet Union doesn't deal lightly with **defectors**. Look what happened to Walter Krivitsky. More than likely, if they have left the party, they would prefer to keep a low profile and not call attention to themselves. They might even be living under assumed names. Otherwise, they could be marked for **assassination**. That's probably why you didn't find some of them in the city directories. I know that if I left the Party, I'd move to Idaho or some other remote place, and change my identity."

"You're probably right," Ellen responded. "But, if we could find just one, it would give us some invaluable insights into their operations. I have a suggestion. Do you remember that settlement house run by Catholic nuns at 15th and Van Buren? Our cab driver, Victor Toth, pointed it out to us when he first brought us here." Natalia nodded. "We could ask the nuns what time the postman makes his rounds, and wait for him. I'm hoping he can tell us what has happened to Dimitri Poliakov, the one who once lived at 1522 Van Buren."

"That sounds like an excellent idea. We could head over there as soon as you've finished your Ovaltine."

"My cup's empty. Let's go!"

"Aunt Veronika, Ellen and I are going for a walk. We'll be back later this afternoon."

In a flash, the girls were out the front door and walking briskly down 15th Avenue, passing St. Casimir's Lithuanian School, the Norton Park Pavillion, and St. Emeric's Roman Catholic School. The Bishop Alerding Settlement House was situated on the corner of 15th Avenue and Van Buren Street, a block from the Froebel School grounds. When they reached the entrance to the Settlement House, Ellen knocked firmly on the large wooden door. A few moments later, a nun in traditional

black **habit** opened the door and greeted them.

"Yes, girls. May I help you?"

"Yes, good morning, sister. My name is Ellen Anderson and this is my friend Natalia Boroskova. Natalia is a recent Russian immigrant."

"Russian, you say? Perhaps you would be interested in our English class for recent immigrants, Natalia. Sister Beatrice always has room for one more."

"That's very kind of you," Natalia responded, "but I'm quite fluent in English. I attended school in England for seven years. Actually, we came for a different reason. We need to speak with the postman who makes deliveries in this area. Can you tell us when he delivers your mail?"

"Well, I can't say for sure, but I believe he generally comes in the morning, some time between eleven and twelve o'clock."

"That's all we needed to know."

"Why don't you wait on the steps of St. Anthony's Chapel, around the corner. It's nearly eleven o'clock now. He should be coming along shortly."

"Thank you, sister…"

"It's Sister Rita."

"Thank you, Sister Rita. We hope to see you again soon. I understand you have dances here on Friday nights."

"That's right. You're most welcome to join us. They're very popular with the boys and girls in the neighborhood. Goodbye, now, and God be with you."

Ellen and Natalia rounded the corner and sat on the steps to St. Anthony's, the small chapel that formed a part of the Settlement House complex, and which fronted on Van Buren Street. The street was lined with attractive, mostly single-story, brick homes with neatly manicured lawns and flowerbeds, reflecting the immigrant families' pride of ownership. Basketball courts occupied the lot immediately adjacent to the chapel.

"So how did your uncle get so involved in counter-espionage work?" Ellen inquired.

"Uncle Stan is very **prescient** about what he sees as the coming war between the Soviet Union and the United States. Unlike most Americans, he understands the threat of communism and the steps the Communists are taking to undermine this country. He saw, as I did, what the Bolsheviks did to the Soviet Union. Now, he's doing all he can to aid **dissidents** who flee the Soviet Union and to counter Soviet influence in the United States. He's committed to undermining their propaganda and espionage efforts. The information I brought on the microfilm was of **incalculable** value to him and his fellow Russian patriots. I'm going to do all I can to help him," Natalia explained.

"It's clear that the Soviet undercover apparatus in the United States is looking beyond the war's end and the defeat of Nazi Germany, and views the

United States as its next target," she continued. "Uncle Stan says that your government is too consumed with the current war effort, or too indifferent, to be fully **cognizant** of the threat the Soviet's pose. And Americans are just too isolated from the **conflagration** in Europe and the **ideological** conflict that propels it to take the steps necessary to protect themselves. He says that the ocean that protects you also isolates you from these harsh realities."

"Here's the mailman, now," Ellen exclaimed, as she saw him cross 15th Avenue in their direction. The two girls stood and approached him.

"Excuse me, sir, but can you help us find a missing person? My name is Ellen Anderson and this is my friend, Natalia."

"George Mistrovich. Pleased to meet you. Who is it you're looking for?"

"Dimitri Poliakov." Natalia replied. "He used to live at 1522 Van Buren, but seems to have dropped out of sight. We thought you might be able to help us locate him."

"Sure, I know that name. He had his mail forwarded to Chicago a few months ago, but he still visits his brother Igor at that address. I've seen him hanging around the place on a few occasions. Why don't you simply ask his brother?"

"We hesitate doing that right now. Do you know where in Chicago his mail is forwarded?" Ellen persisted.

"Why do you want to know? I'm not sure if I'm permitted to give you that information. Of course, if you want to reach him, you can always write him a letter and it'll be forwarded to his new address."

"Frankly, we believe that Dimitri Poliakov is a Soviet agent engaged in espionage against this country. We're trying to help Natalia's uncle trace him before we turn the information over to the F.B.I.," Ellen explained.

"The F.B.I., you say? I'd be happy to help the F.B.I. and put these commies behind bars. I guess that explains why you didn't simply ask his brother where he's moved."

"That's right," Ellen continued. "We have no idea where his sympathies might lie."

"I can check his forwarding address back at the main post office downtown. How can I get in contact with you?"

"I live at 1334 Lincoln Street, with my uncle, Stan Boroskova," replied Natalia. "Here, I'll write it down for you. Your head's probably filled with thousands of addresses in a profession like yours. And if you don't mind, there are a few other Soviet agents we are trying to locate. We'd be most grateful if we could call on your assistance in the future. I'm sure you must know this neighborhood like a book."

"You've got that right. I've been delivering mail in this neighborhood for more than eleven years. Eventually, the names and addresses become imprinted on the brain. I'd be glad to help you. I've got family in the Ukraine and know all about the brutal Stalinist regime. My uncle used to have a farm there, but his land was **confiscated** and turned into a **collective** farm. After that, he was **allotted** only a small plot of land for a vegetable garden. They called him a 'Kulak' because he had a pig and a few chickens. I suspect that many of his neighbors were sent to Siberia for resisting the **collectivization**. I simply can't be **indifferent** to what you are trying to accomplish, but let's keep it between us. I could get in trouble for violating post office rules."

"George, you're a peach. We understand. Anyway, now you know how to get in touch with Natalia."

As George waved them 'goodbye' and continued on his appointed rounds down Van Buren Street, Ellen suggested investigating the next name on their list.

"How about this name on Adams Street? According to the Gary City Directory, Yevgeny Alexandrov and his wife, Ludmilla, live at 1333 Adams," Ellen explained. "I think we should check it out."

"Let's go," Natalia replied.

After the girls rounded the corner, they followed 15th Avenue to Jackson Street, then crossed the front lawn of Froebel School. The park-like grounds

were shaded by the **arboreal** splendor of towering elm trees. The impressive three-story structure, designed by St. Louis architect William Ittner, was the dominant architectural **edifice** in Gary's Central District, yet strangely silent in the glow of midday. Crossing the grassy **expanse** to Madison Street, they followed 15th Avenue to Adams Street. From there, it was a short walk to the European Coffee House, a small Greek-owned establishment at 1335 Adams, in the middle of a congested and generally **mundane** and **utilitarian** business block. The adjacent doorway at 1333 seemed to suggest that there were apartments upstairs. Entering the small vestibule at the bottom of a flight of stairs, Natalia examined the names on the two mailboxes. A musty odor permeated the hallway.

"Here it is – Alexandrov, Y." Natalia exclaimed, before covering her mouth with her outstretched palm. Their mission having been quickly accomplished, the girls decided to check out the adjoining coffee house for further evidence of his presence. They entered and took seats against the back wall of the small establishment so as to command a better perspective on those coming and going.

"What can I get for you ladies?"

"Two coffees, please, and two chocolate frosted donuts," Ellen instructed the waiter, a small, dark-haired man with mustache who spoke broken English.

"You wanna some cream and sugar?"

"Yes, thank you," replied Natalia.

"I'll have mine black." Ellen added.

"I took the liberty of ordering you a chocolate doughnut, Natalia. I hope that's all right. I have a **penchant** for chocolate myself."

"As do I. But, chocolate was quite the luxury in the Soviet Union. We were lucky to get a piece of fruit on occasion."

A half dozen tables filled the interior of the small shop, three of which were occupied by older men – probably Greek – of **swarthy** appearance, some of whom were playing cards and smoking exotic-smelling European cigarettes. The café was rather **austere** and the air permeated by the **pungent** aroma of the men's cigarettes.

A few minutes later, the waiter was back with their coffee and donuts.

"Ees der any anything elsa you like?"

Ellen thought for a moment. "Yes, there is one thing. Do you have any apartments for rent?"

"No, I'ma sorry. We have only two apartment in dis building. Mr. Bikos – he's the owner – lives in one, and Mr. Alexandrov lives in the other," the waiter replied.

"You don't mean Yevgeny Alexandrov?"

"Ya, dat's him, but he goes by 'Gene.'"

"How long has he lived here? The reason I ask is that he's an old friend of my family," said Natalia.

"Ees dat so? He's lived upstairs as long as I been here. Dat's six years dis October."

"Does he still work in the mills? And what about Ludmilla?"

"Yea, he works in da big mill. His wife works the lunch counter at Kresge's five and dime, downtown."

"Does he have any other family in Gary? Our families knew each other back in the old country, in Russia."

"Ees dat so? Not dat I know, but he has Russian friends who meet him here. Sometimes, de go to da park and play chess. Other dan dat, he pretty much keeps to hisself."

"If you don't mind, I'd prefer that you not mention us to Mr. Alexandrov. We want to surprise him the next time we're in the neighborhood," Natalia requested.

"Sure. I understand. I keepa your secret," the waiter replied.

As she sipped her black coffee and munched on her chocolate doughnut, Ellen leaned back in her chair and **pondered** the mystery that confronted them. About ten minutes later, after perusing the morning edition of the *Chicago Tribune*, the door to the café opened and two powerfully built men of medium height entered and took a table near the window. Both appeared to be in their fifties.

"Where's Gene these days?" shouted one of the men to the waiter.

"He's workin' days. He might stop in for dinner. His wife doesn't always feel like cookin'."

"Tell him that Mike and Iggy were here. He'll know what it's about."

"Sure ting, gentlemen," replied the waiter, who cast a knowing glance in the girls' direction.

The men conversed, but at a pitch too low to be **audible**, despite Ellen and Natalia's best efforts to eavesdrop. What they did manage to hear was in Russian, and then only Natalia could **decipher** it.

"Did you hear one of them say 'Iggy?' That could be a nickname for Ignace, one of the other names on our list: Ignace Bronstein. I have a suspicion that those men are connected to this group in some way. Why don't we follow them when they leave," Ellen suggested.

"I was going to suggest the same thing," Natalia replied. "This may be a lucky break for us."

While the girls waited for the men to finish their coffee, Ellen continued to entertain herself by perusing the *Chicago Tribune*. A few minutes later, as she lowered the newspaper, she observed the two men pay the cashier, leave the café, and turn north on Adams Street. Hurriedly, she and Natalia approached the counter and paid their check. Out on the sidewalk, they could **discern** the two men a half block away, turning west at 13th Avenue.

"Hurry, Natalia," Ellen urged. "We don't want to lose them."

Walking briskly, the girls observed the men crossing to the north side of 13th Avenue and heading up Jefferson Street. They followed on the opposite side of the street until they observed them enter the doorway of a two-story brick building with the numbers '1121' above the doorway.

"Bingo! What did I tell you?" Ellen exclaimed. "'Iggy' is Ignace Bronstein, the fifth name on our list. I'd call that a pretty successful morning. Three addresses confirmed, or nearly confirmed, in two hour's time."

Chapter 13

A Day at the Beach

It was Friday morning. Ellen's father had just left for work when she heard a knock at the back door. She ran downstairs and opened the screen door to find Melanie McGuire standing on the back porch.

"Good morning, Ellen. Did you forget? We're going to the beach today."

"No, I didn't forget, but thanks for reminding me. What time do we leave?"

"A bunch of us girls are planning to catch the ten fifteen bus on Fifth Avenue. Can you be ready in an hour?"

"You bet! After staring at the steel mills all week, I'm anxious to see what the lake looks like behind all those depressing factory buildings. Say, would you mind if I invited a friend to come along? She's new to this country and I'm sure would appreciate being made to feel welcome."

"Sure thing! Where is she from?"

"The Soviet Union."

"The Soviet Union! How exciting! How did she ever manage to leave during wartime?"

"It's a long story, but I can let her tell you all about it when she joins us. She's staying with her uncle on Lincoln Street, in the Central District. I'll give her a call and tell her to meet us here by ten o'clock."

Mrs. Matheus was in her kitchen having coffee when Ellen knocked on the door. The smells of bacon and hot cinnamon buns **permeated** the kitchen.

"Come in, Ellen. What can I do for you?"

"I'd like to use your telephone, Mrs. Matheus, if I may?"

"Why certainly, dear. You know where it is."

Ellen walked into the front parlor and dialed the Boroskova residence.

"Hello, Mrs. Boroskova. Is Natalia home?"

"Yes, Ellen, she's right here, helping me with the dishes."

"Hello, Ellen?"

"Natalia, how'd you like to go the beach today with me and some Emerson High School girls?"

"That would be wonderful, but I'm afraid I haven't got a bathing suit."

"Don't worry about that. We'll bring along an extra one. Can you meet us at my place by ten o'clock?"

"Sure. I'll have Uncle Stan drive me over."

"Good. We'll see you then. And, let me suggest that we say nothing to

Melanie and her friends about our activities," Ellen cautioned.

"Absolutely. There's no telling how far idle gossip will travel. We can't afford to be careless. What's that they say about 'Loose Lips Sink Ships'?"

It was a bright, cloudless morning as Ellen stepped out into the sunlit street and gazed at the compact two-story red-shingled dwelling next door that was occupied by the McGuire family. Just as she momentarily turned away, she heard a screen door bang against a doorframe, breaking the stillness of the morning air and releasing Melanie McGuire onto the front sidewalk. Within minutes, three other girls emerged from houses in the same block, each with a beach bag, and one with a portable radio in hand.

"Ellen, I'd like to introduce my friends Mary Sullivan, Lorraine Robbins, and Virginia Kelley," as she pointed to each girl in turn. "Girls, this is Ellen Anderson, my friend from Connecticut. She's going to be living in Gary for a few weeks while her Dad is doing some work for Gary Armor Plate."

"I'm pleased to meet all of you," Ellen replied. "I've asked a friend of mine to join us, but she'll need a bathing suit. She should be here any minute."

"I've got an extra one she can borrow," said Melanie. "I'll be back in a jiffy."

A few minutes later, a late model blue Packard sedan pulled up in front of Mrs. Matheus' residence, and Natalia poked her head out of the passenger side window.

"Ellen. Uncle Stan has offered to drive us all to the beach."

"That's swell. But, are you sure he has room for everyone?"

"I believe so. It'll be tight, but we can fit four in the back seat and two in the front," Natalia suggested.

The girls climbed into the spacious 1940 sedan and settled into the soft maroon cushions. Soon, they were on their way to Miller Beach.

"Girls, I'd like to introduce my friend, Natalia Boroskova. She's a recent immigrant from the Soviet Union I met on the train to Gary. And this is her Uncle Stan."

"Pleased to meet you both. My name is Melanie McGuire, and I'd like to introduce Mary Sullivan, Lorraine Robbins, and Virginia Kelley."

"I'm happy to meet all of you. It was so nice of you to invite me," Natalia replied. Stan echoed his niece's sentiments.

"Ellen said you needed a bathing suit, Natalia. Why don't you put this one in your bag. It's my sister June's, but it should fit you well enough. You can change in the bathhouse."

"Thank you so much. I've haven't had a chance to go shopping since I arrived."

Uncle Stan turned his car around and drove north on Carolina Street. The Emerson football team was out doing **calisthenics** on the edge of the running track behind the school. He drove past the Emerson Shops building at the corner of Sixth and Carolina, then turned right at Fifth Avenue, near the East Side branch of the Gary Public Library. As their car sped down Fifth Avenue and left their East Side residential neighborhood behind, Ellen observed several smaller manufacturing plants on both sides of Dunes Highway, including the Gary Screw and Bolt Works, Union Drawn Steel, and observed a sign pointing to Gary Armor Plate, where her father was temporarily employed.

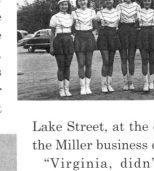

Another mile down the road was Ted's Drive-In, a roadside eatery famous for its smartly dressed carhops in short red satin skirts, majorette hats, and white cowboy boots. Also on the south side of the highway, and just outside the small residential community of Aetna, was Wilson's restaurant, famous for its barbeque. A few minutes later, their car was crossing the South Shore tracks at

WILSON'S BAR-B-Q . . . U. S. Hwys. 12-20 . . . Gary, Indiana

Lake Street, at the entrance to the Miller business district.

"Virginia, didn't you say you've been horseback riding at the Mountain Ridge Riding Stables?" Melanie inquired.

"Oh, sure. I've been there dozens of times. My Dad loves to go horseback riding. He grew up in McCook, Nebraska where his family raised horses, so riding comes naturally to him. I even have a favorite horse – 'Dusty.' Humpy White – he's the owner – always has 'Dusty' saddled for me when we ride. There are miles of trails through the dunes. We should all go riding there one of these days. It's such fun riding through the dunes."

"Perhaps, Ellen and Natalia would like to join us," suggested Melanie.

"We'd love it," Ellen exclaimed.

From Grand Boulevard, their vehicle proceeded north to Marquette Park, where a statue of the priest and explorer, Father Jacques Marquette, greeted them at the park entrance. Uncle Stan continued around the park loop and deposited the girls in front of the impressive two-story Municipal Pavilion and Bathhouse, with its red tiled roof and **colonnaded façade**.

"Thank you so much, Mr. Boroskova. We really appreciate the lift. We can catch the bus home from here," Melanie explained.

"You're quite welcome, girls. It was nice of you to let Natalia join you."

As Stan Boroskova's car drove off, the girls entered the bathhouse to change

into their bathing suits. Emerging a few minutes later on the other side of the bathhouse, they sank their feet into the clean, warm sand that hugged the sparkling shores of Lake Michigan. Only a few isolated white clouds disturbed the otherwise clear blue sky, while small whitecaps lapped against the **pristine** shoreline. To the west, the smokestacks of U.S. Steel loomed impressively in the distance. Farther still, to the northwest, the outline of the Chicago skyline could be **discerned** through the haze. To the east, compact beachside cottages hugged the rising dunes. More than a hundred beachgoers, mostly young people, children, and their parents, were spread out across the sand between the bathhouse and the shoreline. Others staked out positions in the shade of the towering poplar trees that grew in the sand dunes some distance from the shoreline, and whose leaves fluttered in response to the gentle **zephyrs** off the lake.

The girls chose a spot about twenty feet from the water's edge and laid out their blankets and towels. They chipped in to rent a couple of large beach umbrellas to provide much needed protection from the late summer rays. A bottle of sun tan lotion was quickly circulated. A short distance from their outstretched blankets, the bronzed body of a strapping lifeguard – a member of the Horace Mann swim team – sat perched atop a white-painted lifeguard station. Wearing dark sunglasses and an inverted sailor cap, his nose was painted white with suntan lotion. He surveyed the **bevy** of beauties that surrounded his observation platform with **rapt** attention, including one particularly **voluptuous** brunette from Lew Wallace High School, while **simultaneously** struggling to maintain an alert gaze on those who had ventured into the water.

Portable radios could be heard across the sand, their speakers blaring the sounds of Glenn Miller's *I've Got a Gal in Kalamazoo*, Tommy Dorsey's *Tangerine*, and the Andrews Sisters *Don't Sit Under the Apple Tree*. Seagulls wandered randomly across the sand, scavenging for scraps of bread or pieces of Cracker Jack thrown to them by children. While the girls talked mostly about boys, the upcoming football season, and their chosen fall classes and teachers, their concerns seemed somewhat **vapid** and **trivial** to Ellen and Natalia who, by now, saw the world through a more **sobering prism**.

Melanie recognized some of the boys from the Emerson Class of 1942 stepping quickly over the hot sand, including cheerleader and boys' treasurer, Tom Croll, and class vice president, Spiro Cappony, both of whom had recently enlisted. Ed Burns, president of the Board of Control, and one of the friendliest students at Emerson was there as well. Diane Orlich, Mary Miller, Mary Gregor and several other girls soon joined the swelling Emerson contingent. Members of the Class of 1941 were there as well, including Matt Bleicher who was chatting it up with the girls. Later, Tiffany Moss arrived with Junior Foley, Emerson's softball pitching ace. It was an enjoyable and relaxing day, both in the water and out. Children and teenagers constructed **elaborate** castles in the soft sand near the water's edge, while **undulating** waves threatened, and periodi-

cally undermined their fragile creations. By and large, it was a **garrulous** crowd. Boys from other Gary high schools stopped by to talk, or flirt. A group of girls from Froebel High School were spread out on the sand in close proximity to the girls. Virginia Kelley, who, like Melanie, was an Emerson cheerleader, recog-nized one of them as a member of the Froebel High cheerleading squad.

"Sophie? I don't know if you remember me," Virginia inquired.

"Of course. We met at the Emerson-Froebel basketball game in January."

"Sure. Memorial Auditorium. And I'll never forget that two-point loss in overtime back in '41. That Davage Minor sure had a great jump shot. We just couldn't contain him. But, did you hear? We got a new basketball coach this year: **Bill Klug**. He's a Horace Mann graduate. We're expecting big things from him. We hear he's quite the defensive **strategist**."

Ellen, who couldn't avoid eavesdropping, felt com-pelled to join in the conversation.

"Hi, Sophie. My name's Ellen Anderson, and this is my friend Natalia Boroskova. Natalia will be attending Froebel this fall. She's a recent Russian immigrant and is just getting **acclimated** to life in Gary. Perhaps you can tell her a little about Froebel."

"Why, sure. I'm pleased to meet you both. My name's Sophie Charnetsky. I've been going to Froebel since kindergarten. Where do you live, Natalia?"

"Near 13th and Lincoln, across the street from St. Casimir's Church."

"Sure, I know that church. My cousin attended St. Casimir's Catholic School through the eighth grade. Where in Russia do you come from?"

"From the outskirts of Moscow. I lived with my cousin after my parents died. I feel so fortunate to be in the United States after living in the Soviet Union. Life there was **horrendous**, particularly since the war started."

"I can only imagine how bad it must be there. We have family in Poland, so I know what you're talking about. Well, Froebel's a wonderful school. It opened in 1912, three years after Emerson. It's a real melting pot of nationalities, and is the city's only racially integrated school. Just about every European nationality is represented. We have great teachers and an excellent athletic program. And, Kenneth Resur, our band and orchestra director, is first-rate. I play first violin in his orchestra."

"Yes, I've heard all about him. I play the violin, too."

"I'd like you to meet Sonia Petrovich. Her family comes from the Ukraine, but they came here before the last war, as did most of the immigrant families in Gary."

"That's right," Sonia added. "We came here before the First World War, from a village near Kiev. And a lucky thing it was, too. We lost several family members when the Bolsheviks took over. Our people didn't take kindly to what soon became a Communist **dictatorship**, particularly after they **confiscated** our farms. They were forced to **forage** for food to stay alive. Some of their neighbors were carried off by Soviet troops."

"Do you have family in Gary, Natalia?" Sonia inquired.

"Yes. I'm living with my aunt and uncle. I just moved into the neighborhood on Tuesday and you are the first Froebel students I've met. I plan to enroll for my senior year. I hope we can become better acquainted."

"Sure thing. We'll all be seniors, too. I'd like to introduce Helen Feczko, Toula Betsos, Sophie Pradus, Mary Drakulich, and Stella Markovich. We've been best of friends since grade school, but always have room for one more. We'd be happy to show you around the school and help you get enrolled. We also know all the best dance spots – the Miramar Ballroom, the Spanish Castle, the National Guard Armory, the Settlement House, and the Elks Club."

"That's very kind of you," Natalia replied. "Melanie here just helped Ellen get enrolled at Emerson on Tuesday."

"Sophie, do any of you live near 15th and Van Buren?" Ellen inquired.

"I don't, but Helen lives in the same block."

"Really? Do you know the Poliakovs, Helen?"

"Not very well. I'm acquainted with their daughter, Stasha, but we haven't been in any classes together. She's only a sophomore. I have talked to her at some of the Settlement House dances, though. Why do you ask?"

"Well, I hope you won't think my request **presumptuous**, but I'm trying to locate her uncle, Dimitri. He once lived with her family, but has since moved to Chicago – at least, I believe he's moved to Chicago."

"Yes, I remember him. But, I haven't seen him for months. I'd be happy to make some **discreet** inquiries for you next time I see her."

"That would be great," Ellen replied, "particularly if you don't arouse suspicion. You might just innocently inquire on the **pretence** that you used to talk to him in the neighborhood, but haven't seen him around for a while," Ellen suggested.

"Sure. I can do that. How do I get in contact with you?"

"Well, I'm living on the East Side, but Natalia lives at 1334 Lincoln. Here's her phone number: 2-1157," which she jotted down on a piece of paper.

"Great! I'll call you if I learn anything."

In addition to good conversation, the girls spent a fair amount of time cooling off in the water, which was at an **optimum** temperature for swimming. Their appetites were **satiated** with food from the concession stand, which offered a **plenitude** of beach fare: hot dogs, hamburgers, Peerless Potato Chips, Waverly pop, and assorted ice cream treats, including sherbet push-ups, ice cream sandwiches, and  drumsticks. It was a **surefire** menu for **gluttony,** and stomachaches. As the afternoon **waned**, however, and as the sun drifted lower in the western sky, the girls packed up their towels and blankets, wiped the sand from their feet, said 'goodbye' to their new friends from Froebel, and returned to the bathhouse to change back into their street clothes for the bus ride back to Gary.

Shortly before five o'clock, a Gary Railways bus pulled up in front of the bathhouse and the girls climbed aboard. Taking their seats near the front, Melanie directed Ellen's and Natalia's attention to the Marquette Park Pavilion that rested on the shore of the nearby lagoon, attractively ringed by sand dunes.

"That's where we held our junior and senior proms last year," Melanie explained. "I was dating a senior boy at the time, Ted Cunningham. He's since enlisted in the Navy."

Suddenly, their conversation was interrupted by unsettling news from the front of the bus.

"Have you girls heard the news?" the driver exclaimed. "Thieves broke into Emerson High School last night and made off with the art collection, or at least a substantial part of it. Here, you can read all about it in the afternoon *Post-Tribune*." He passed the paper to Ellen, who fixed her attention on the front page story, while the others girls looked on.

Thieves broke into Emerson School late Thursday evening and made off with an estimated $20,000 in artwork that graced the walls of the school's second and third floor hallways. According to principal, Everett Spaulding, the collection, which included works by such noted dunes artists as Frank Dudley and Charles Dahlgren, was donated by graduating classes over the past 22 years. "It's an **irreplaceable** loss," said Spaulding, "not only in monetary terms, but to the legacy left by former Emerson students." School secretary, Maureen Link, a 1928 Emerson graduate, also **lamented** the loss. "Since 1912, the graduating classes have been donating works of art to the collection, and since 1920, the classes have raised the funds to acquire original oil paintings. It's one of Emerson's proudest traditions that set us apart. I only hope they can be recovered and the **miscreants** brought to justice."

According to Gary Police, tire tracks discovered at the rear of the school suggest that the thieves **presumably** removed thirty-three paintings through the school's rear boiler room sometime between midnight and 3:00 a.m. The police, who are in the process of interviewing neighborhood residents, presently have no clues as to the whereabouts of the collection or the individuals responsible.

THE GARY POST-TRIBUNE

VOL. XXXIII, NO. 284   TWO SECTIONS   GARY, INDIANA, FRIDAY, AUGUST 28, 1942   FINAL EDITION   PRICE THREE CENTS

EMERSON SUFFERS MIDNIGHT ART HEIST

An Irreplaceable Loss for School

FIGHT FOR NEW WORLD ORDER, YOUTH IS TOLD

Axis Offers Only Death, Roosevelt Asserts; Praises Soldiers

Meatless Day In Each Week Looms-F.D.R.

Movie 'Tough Guy' To Spur Bond Sale

Cagney to Tour Mills Friday Before Public Appearance Here

Hope for New Life

To Meet Star

Public Appearance

BRAZIL YOUTHS RUSH TO JOIN FIGHT ON AXIS

Concentration Camps Bulging; Many Flee To Uruguay

HAIL OF BOMBS SLOWS AXIS IN DESERT CLASH

Rommel's Drive Fails To Make Headway, British Assert

U. S. Planes Smash Attack on Darwin

Four Bombers, Nine Zero Fighters Shot Down by Allied Fliers in Brilliant Defense; Dual Chinese Offensive Threatens Japs

BRITISH GREET GREATEST U.S. TROOP CONVOY

Transports Put In at Many Ports; Navy Guards Route

JAP BASES MENACED

Chapter 14

An Irreplaceable Loss

After the Miller bus dropped them off at 5th and Carolina, the girls ran most of the way to the school, where dozens of bystanders had already gathered on the front sidewalk, and in front of Rubin's confectionary. A police barrier had been erected at the base of the front steps, limiting public access, with several uniformed officers standing guard to prevent curiosity seekers from entering the building. The mood was a **somber** one, almost bordering on the **funereal**, and reflecting the magnitude of the loss. Ellen approached one of the uniformed **sentries**.

"Officer, can you tell me when the building is likely to reopen?"

"I can't say for sure, miss. Perhaps tomorrow, once Sergeant Billick and the other detectives have completed their investigation. Until then, only the office staff will be permitted inside."

Ellen and the other beachgoers huddled outside the school's black iron fence, watching for signs of activity and talking with neighborhood residents who continued to linger, their faces **manifesting** a common sense of grief. Some were almost **apoplectic** over the loss. Apparently, the office staff had already left for the day, but a few police officers remained inside the building. Several others were out back making plaster impressions of tire tracks, presumably those of the vehicle used to spirit the paintings away from the school.

"Who would do such a thing?" lamented Frances Monfort, a former student, and artist herself, who, Ellen learned, was a member of the Class of 1929.

"That collection had a value far more than monetary. It was one of Emerson's most important traditions. It'll take years to **efface** the memory of this horrible tragedy. I can't imagine starting from scratch to replace it."

Ellen approached another woman, possibly in her late thirties, who stared somberly at the school from the sidewalk.

"Excuse me, ma'am, are you an Emerson graduate?"

"You bet! Pauline Hilton, Class of 1925." She extended her hand to Ellen.

"I was a member of the gift committee that donated four paintings to the school, including Frank Dudley's *Trail of the Wind* and Arvid Nyholm's *Lamp*

Effect. Our class held an art exhibition that raised over $1,700 to acquire them. I suspect they are among the missing."

"There's Miss Tinsman and Miss Sayers, two of our teachers," Melanie observed. "They live on 5th Avenue, in the Dalton Apartments."

"Hello, Miss Tinsman, Miss Sayers."

"Hello girls. Isn't this a tragedy?" Miss Sayers lamented.

"It certainly is. We can't imagine who would want do such a thing."

"Who are your friends, Melanie? I haven't seen them around the school before," said Miss Tinsman.

"This is Ellen Anderson. She's my new next door neighbor. She's here temporarily from Connecticut. And this is Natalia Boroskova, who just immigrated to this country from the Soviet Union."

"Will you both be attending Emerson?" Miss Sayers inquired.

"I will," Ellen replied, "but Natalia lives in the Froebel district and will be enrolling there. I understand that I will be in your homeroom, Miss Tinsman and in A Cappella choir with you, Miss Sayers."

"That's wonderful. You're going to love Emerson. It's just a shame that your arrival had to coincide with this unfortunate tragedy. I'm sorry you won't be able to appreciate what a wonderful art collection we had."

"I would love to get my hands on a list of the stolen paintings," Ellen suggested. "I wonder who might have a list of the missing pieces?" she **mused**.

"You would have to speak to Miss Link in the office about that. She's Mr. Spaulding's 'Gal Friday,' and keeps faithful records of such things," Miss Tinsman replied. "Well, we must be off to dinner. I look forward to seeing you in my homeroom, Ellen."

"Thank you, Miss Tinsman. I can't wait for school to start."

As the two teachers walked off in the direction of the Dalton Apartments, Ellen turned to Melanie and her Carolina Street friends.

"We have to try and imagine what the thieves would do with the stolen property," Ellen suggested. "They certainly wouldn't try to **fence** the paintings in the Gary area. It would make more sense for them to take them to Chicago, or some more distant **metropolis** where art **connoisseurs,** or even **dilettantes,** are in greater **abundance**. There must be hundreds of art or antique dealers in the Chicago metropolitan area alone. I have a feeling this is more than a random act of burglary. A theft of this nature took planning, probably by an organized gang of professionals with the ability to **fence** the stolen items. And they're unlikely to do that in Gary."

"Say, I just remembered. There's a list of the collection in *The Gold and Gray Book*, our student handbook," Melanie observed. "I'll dig it out when we get home."

As the curiosity seekers began to drift away, Ellen, Natalia and Melanie walked to the rear of the school by way of the sidewalk between the Big and Little Buildings. Like the front entrance, the side entrance was similarly cordoned off to the public. They found the rear of the school entirely abandoned, however, with no sign of a police presence. The monkey bars, swings, and merry-go-round stood silent in the sandy rear playground. Even the animals in the Emerson zoo were **eerily** quiet. Oddly, a light burned in the band room, halfway up the iron fire escape.

"Who could be up there at this hour?" Melanie audibly **pondered**. Suddenly, the girls observed a boy's face peering out of the band room window.

"Why, that's **Hank Gordon**, the concert band president and drum major," exclaimed Melanie. "What's he doing up there? I thought only school staff were allowed in the building."

"Perhaps, he'll let us in?" Ellen suggested.

"I don't think that would be advisable," Melanie replied. "We could get in trouble."

"Now, if you were a burglar," Ellen inquired, "how would you go about removing the paintings from the building?"

"I would remove them through that rear service entrance, probably where the coal deliveries are made," Melanie suggested. "After all, it's the only place where a truck can be **unobtrusively** backed up to the building, as the *Post Tribune* suggested."

"Exactly. That's why we need to get into the boiler room. Perhaps we can find a clue there that might lead to their recovery."

"Hank!" Melanie waved to the face in the window.

Hank Gordon opened the door to the fire escape and peered down at the girls.

"I was just getting ready to leave, Melanie. I've been helping Mr. Warren get the band instruments ready for the opening of school."

"We need to get inside for a few minutes. Can you let us in?"

"I don't know. The police instructed me to stay back here in the music rooms. The rest of the school is closed." He thought for a moment, **mulling** over the **propriety** of admitting the girls.

"We'll be just a few minutes," Melanie insisted, throwing him her most enticing smile.

"Well, I suppose it will be all right. Come on up."

Ellen, Melanie and Natalia ran up the iron fire escape to the band room,

"Thanks, Hank. We'll be back in a few minutes," Melanie exclaimed. Once in the band room, the girls moved quickly to the interior stairway that led to the boys' upper gymnasium. With Melanie leading the way, the three girls scurried across the gym floor and poked their heads into the second floor's west corridor. Seeing no signs of police activity, they ran down the stairs and into the boys' lower gymnasium.

"Hurry. This way," Melanie urged, "before we're discovered."

The door leading to the shower room and swimming pool lay across the basketball court and near the iron spiral staircase. Melanie opened the door and peaked inside.

"The coast is clear. Somebody left the lights on."

The interior locker room consisted of several rows of lockers utilized by members of the football team. The shower room lay just beyond.

"Here's the door to the boiler room," she whispered.

"It's dark in there. Too bad we didn't bring a flashlight."

"Leave the door ajar." Ellen suggested. "Hopefully, the light from the locker room will be sufficient for us to see our way around."

"I've never been in here before, but I understand that this corridor extends all the way from the first floor hallway to the back of the building," Melanie observed. "So, what are we looking for?"

"Anything that might reveal the presence or identity of the thieves, or the paintings they removed," Ellen suggested.

Moving cautiously over the irregular basement floor, Ellen listened for any sounds of the police that might compromise their mission. She assumed that the police had already examined this portion of the school. Feeling her way along the walls of the narrow corridor with her hands, she found an unlocked wooden door whose handle yielded easily to her effort. She flipped on the adjacent light switch and illuminated a small janitor's office. **Fortuitously**, a flashlight lay on top of the oak desk.

"Look what I've found," she whispered to Melanie, who was trailing a few yards behind her. The two girls quickly located Natalia who had taken off exploring in the opposite direction, with Ellen systematically shining the torch across the darkened floor.

"Keep your eyes open for anything that might be of importance, no matter how small or insignificant," Ellen urged.

Mostly, the floor was **devoid** of anything that might be considered useful. The cement surface, discolored by thirty years of grime, yielded only an occasional nail or wood fragment. Without warning, a rat scurried down the hallway, brushing Natalia's sneaker. She cupped her hand over her mouth, suppressing the urge to scream. When they had gotten to the end of the corridor, near the engine and coal storage rooms, they came up against a windowless steel door, secured with a padlock, that provided access to the coal trucks and other utility vehicles. The **noxious** smell of the school's furnace and coal supply permeated their nostrils.

"Well, we've reached the end of the line and I haven't seen a thing," Ellen lamented.

Wait, just a minute," Melanie exclaimed. "What's that? Shine the flashlight on the floor there."

Reaching into a small hollow where the cement floor met the brick wall, she retrieved a fragment of a dirt-smudged card. Ellen shined the flashlight on the unexpected **boon** and picked it up.

"This may be just the clue we've been looking for," Ellen suggested. "It looks like a business card. Too bad that half the address has been torn off. It doesn't look very old. Hopefully, we can **decipher** it."

ports

niture

gton Street

, Indiana

"Whatever it is, we'd better get out of here before the police catch us," Melanie advised.

Hastily beating a retreat out of the darkened corridor, back into the brightly lit locker room and across the gym floor, the girls ran up the stairs to the second floor.

"Jim, did you hear footsteps back there?" shouted one of the police detectives, rounding the corner near Esther Tinsman's second floor biology room.

"No, but perhaps you'd better check it out, just to be sure."

By the time the officer had made his way down the west corridor, Ellen and her chums had already escaped across the boys' upper gymnasium and back into the band room. Hank Gordon was still waiting for the girls at the door to the fire escape. A few seconds later, after making their way down the iron staircase to the schoolyard below, Hank secured the door and followed them down. As the four young people walked to Carolina Street, Ellen whispered to Melanie:

"Let's not say anything to your friend about our discovery. We should thank him for his assistance, but keep the find to ourselves." Melanie shook her head in agreement.

"We didn't find what we were looking for, Hank," Melanie explained, "but we want to thank you for your help. We have to be getting home now."

The girls each gave him a kiss on the cheek. It was all the reward the **flustered** young man needed. He looked like he had just died and gone to heaven.

"You're certainly welcome. Anytime I can be of assistance..."

As the girls walked down Carolina Street, Ellen and Natalia realized that it was time to bring Melanie into their confidence, realizing that they might need her help in the days ahead. They both understood that, as Gary **neophytes**, they lacked the detailed knowledge of the city to aid them in their **quest**.

"Melanie: Natalia and I have something to share with you, but it will have to wait until tomorrow. We have to be getting home, and I've promised my father to have dinner on the table when he gets home from work. Can we agree to meet tomorrow morning at ten o'clock in Norton Park? It's not far from Natalia's uncle's home. I can pick you up at nine fifteen and we can take the streetcar there. Will you join us? And, don't forget to bring that Emerson student handbook you mentioned – the one with the inventory of paintings."

"Sure. I'm honored that you want to take me into your confidence. You've certainly peaked my curiosity."

"Oh, and one more thing. Please don't tell anyone what we've been up to – not even your parents. There'll be time enough for that, later."

"You have my word, Ellen."

As Natalia headed up Seventh Avenue to Broadway, and the Tolleston streetcar, Ellen and Melanie continued on to their respective residences. Mrs. Matheus was already home, busily preparing dinner in the kitchen. She greeted Ellen as she stepped in the back door.

"Dr. Bills didn't need me today, so I've made you and your father some of my special Swedish meatballs in cream sauce. It's a secret recipe I got from my mother." She handed Ellen a warm Pyrex dish covered in aluminum foil.

"That was awfully thoughtful of you, Mrs. Matheus. I just love Swedish meatballs, or should I say Svenska köttbullar?"

"Ah, you know some Swedish. Think nothing of it. It's so nice to have some Swedes living upstairs for a change." Ellen gave Mrs. Matheus a warm hug across the shoulders, then climbed the rear stairs to their apartment with the meatballs. A few minutes after placing the dish in the oven, Ellen heard her father on the back stairs.

"Ellen, I'm home. What's for dinner? I'm famished."

"Svenska köttbullar!"

"You don't say?"

"Only, I didn't make them. Mrs. Matheus made them. She says it's her mother's secret recipe. I'll heat up the leftover mashed potatoes in the Frigidaire, and a can of peas. It'll only take me a few minutes. Why don't you go freshen up."

A few minutes later, they were both sitting down at the kitchen table.

"Say, these meatballs are delicious! It must be the cream sauce. I'll bet your mother would love to get her hands on the recipe."

"I'm sure I can coax it out of Mrs. Matheus before we leave for home."

"So, how was your trip to the beach today?"

"It was swell. It's a wonderful beach, and the water was just the right temperature for swimming. I also met a lot of great people, including some students from Emerson and Froebel. We were there nearly seven hours."

"Seven hours! I hope you didn't get sunburned. You don't look sunburned."

"No. I took precautions. We all did. We tried to stay out of the direct sun, used suntan lotion, and rented some beach umbrellas."

"Say, what's all the **commotion** over at the school? Are there some doings going on tonight?"

"No! Haven't you heard? Thieves broke into the school last night and stole the Emerson art collection."

"What! How did they do that? Aren't there any night watchmen?"

"Apparently not. The police think they broke in between midnight and three o'clock in the morning, in other words, after the janitors had left for the night. They made off with more than thirty original oil paintings, all of which had been donated to the school by graduating classes. The police are working with Mr. Spaulding – he's the Principal – to come up with an inventory of the stolen items. According to the *Post Tribune*, they're valued at more than $20,000. Can you imagine? And I just got to see a few of them briefly on Tuesday, when Melanie gave me a tour of the building."

After dinner, Ellen relaxed in one of the overstuffed chairs in the front parlor and examined the business card fragment the girls had found in the Emerson basement.

This shouldn't be too difficult to decipher, she said to herself. *What else could it be but a furniture store on…Washington Street? There can't be any other street in Gary ending in 'gton.' But, where on Washington?*

She quickly ran down the rear stairs and asked to see Mrs. Matheus' telephone *directory*.

"Sure, Ellen. Help yourself."

Ellen sat on the **davenport** in the front parlor and flipped to the Classifieds in the back of the book.

Here they are. Let's see… Florists… Funeral Directors… Furnaces… Furniture Dealers – Retail.

Running her finger down the list of about twenty furniture dealers, she found it – Crimean Imports… 1334 Washington Street. *That's it,* she thought. The evidence was clear and **unambiguous**. *No question about it.*

THE GOLD

AND

GRAY BOOK

E

EMERSON SCHOOL
GARY, INDIANA

Chapter 15

Sharing Secrets

After her full day at Miller Beach, and the ensuing excitement of the Emerson art heist, Ellen was asleep by nine o'clock. When she awoke fully rested the following morning, she had **ample** time to prepare breakfast for her father and herself.

"I'm planning on spending a half day at the plant today," Ellen's father explained over a breakfast of orange juice, eggs, buttered toast, and coffee. "Based on your **revelations** last night, it sounds like you and Natalia now have two mysteries to solve. I just hope you'll be careful and keep yourself out of dangerous **entanglements**."

"Dad! You should know me by now. I'm very cautious, and so is Natalia. Neither of us believes in taking unnecessary risks."

"Well, I know you well enough, but I don't know about Natalia. She's already taken some serious risks just making her way to the United States. Just promise me you'll be careful."

"We'll be careful, Dad."

Shortly after her father left for work, Ellen heard a knock at the back door. It was Melanie.

"I had trouble getting to sleep last night. All I could think about was what you had to tell me. So, what's this all about?"

"I promised Natalia I wouldn't say anything until we meet her at Norton Park."

"O.K. I suppose I can wait a few more minutes, but the suspense is killing me."

With that, the girls grabbed their purses and headed off to catch the Tolleston streetcar in front of the Coronet Shop at Seventh and Broadway. Ellen could tell that Melanie was dying of anticipation. As the girls boarded the streetcar, Ellen was surprised to see her **affable** friend, Tom Smelko, behind the wheel.

"Hi, Tom! Remember me?"

"Sure. You're Ellen Anderson, the girl who's a long way from home. Connecticut – right?"

"That's correct. Boy, you've got a good memory."

"I never forget a pretty face," he replied with a wide grin. "Don't worry, I'm married."

The girls got off at Eleventh Avenue and Harrison Boulevard, and walked a block and a half to the Norton Park Pavilion. There, sitting on a park bench under a large Catalpa tree, was Natalia. It was nine forty-five. The park was otherwise deserted.

"It looks like we're both early birds," Ellen remarked. "Why don't we sit at that picnic bench over by the railroad tracks. That way, no one can eavesdrop on our conversation."

They found a table in an oak grove close to the chain-link fence separating the park from the Pennsylvania Railroad tracks.

"So, what's this all about?" Melanie asked.

"First, I want you to swear to utmost secrecy. You're probably not going to believe some of the things we're going to tell you, but they're all true. What's more, many lives are at stake if the information we know gets into the wrong hands. You can't even tell the members of your own family, at least for now. Do we have your solemn promise?"

"Absolutely. I promise not to share it with anyone."

"As Natalia has already explained, she's a recent immigrant from the Soviet Union. But, what she hasn't told you is that her parents were both executed by Stalin's regime and that she made her way to this country all alone, at great personal risk. She brought with her **invaluable** documents that implicate a number of Soviet spies who are engaged in espionage in this country, including some who are living in Gary. She's staying with her Uncle Stan, a White Russian who's an active anti-Communist."

"White Russian? What's a White Russian?" I thought that was a kind of cocktail?"

"No. No. A White Russian is someone who opposed the Bolshevik, or Communist, takeover in Russia. In other words, not a Red. The White Russians fought the Bolsheviks during the Russian Civil War, from 1917 to 1923. After their defeat, and the consolidation of the Soviet Union under Lenin's **dictatorial** rule, many fled to Western Europe, or the United States, including Natalia's Uncle Stan. They are ardently anti-Communist, and among the most **fervent** opponents of Soviet influence in the United States, and Europe generally," Ellen explained. "They harbor no **illusions** about the temporary alliance of necessity with the Soviet Union to defeat Nazi Germany, but remain **gravely** suspicious of their ultimate intentions."

"That's right," Natalia explained. "My Uncle Stan fought with General Wrangel during the Russian Civil War. Since escaping to this country, he has been an **indefatigable** opponent of the Communist menace in this country. He and his friends are dedicated to exposing Communists who are engaged in **subversive** activity. Ellen is helping me track several Communists in Gary who may be engaged in activities hostile to American security interests. Uncle

Stan believes that some of the burglaries taking place in Gary are the work of these Communists who need money to finance both their underground activities and their propaganda **apparatus**. They receive financial support from the Soviet Union, but are expected to raise their own funds as well."

"What's particularly **vexing** is that the theft of the Emerson art collection may be related to this pattern of criminal activity," Ellen suggested. "And the police are probably totally unaware of it. While they may be investigating individual acts of burglary, they are undoubtedly unaware of how they are connected. That's why I was so anxious to get inside Emerson yesterday, to see if we could find any clues that might suggest a link."

"So you think that business card may be of significance?" Melanie asked.

"Possibly. That's what we hope to find out," Ellen continued. "I did a little research last night and discovered that the fragment we found is from a furniture store called Crimean Imports, at 1334 Washington Street. Of course, there's no proof that the card was left there recently. I don't think the thieves would be naïve enough to fence the paintings in Gary, but it's just possible that Crimean Imports could be implicated in the burglary. It certainly bears further investigation."

"I know that if I were them, I'd get the paintings out of Gary at the first opportunity," Natalia suggested.

"Incidentally, Melanie, all of the Communist **agents** we have identified so far live in the Central District, in an area bounded by Broadway and Hayes Streets, and by 11th and 16th Avenues. Some may have moved out of the area since first taking up residence here, however. Uncle Stan says that some of them hang out in this very park, where they play chess or cards."

"This is truly unbelievable. To think that Communist spies are operating in Gary, under our very noses." Melanie exclaimed. "So, is there anything I can do to help you?"

"You can help us by doing some **surveillance** work. Our first step is to pay a visit to Crimean Imports and see if we can detect anything about their business that might suggest **complicity** in the theft of the paintings," Ellen suggested. "By the way, did you bring along that Emerson handbook you mentioned yesterday."

"Yes, I did."

"May I see it?"

"Of course."

Melanie reached in her purse and removed a small gray booklet entitled *The Gold and Gray Book*, printed for Emerson School in 1933.

"Gold and gray are our Emerson School colors. The gold is for the sand dunes and the gray for the steel mills," she explained.

Ellen thumbed through it. The booklet provided detailed descriptions of Emerson's facilities, course offerings, class schedules, activities, and procedures. But, more importantly, it included a complete list of art works donated to the school by graduating classes from 1912 to 1931. There were separate lists for reproductions, photographs, and, most significantly, original oil paintings. She took particular note of the oil paintings and the prices paid for them:

PICTURES PURCHASED FROM ART EXHIBIT EARNINGS

1. After the Snow - Albert Krehbiel - 1920 - $200.00
2. Autumn Morning - Carl R. Kraft - 1920 - $1,200.00
3. Autumn on the Creek - Charles Dahlgren - 1923 - $250.00
4. Blue and Gold - Carl R. Kraft - 1920 - $150.00
5. Calves in Pasture - Eugenie Glaman - 1920 - $125.00
6. Cattle Near a Wood - Eugenie Glaman - 1920 - $200.00
7. Desdemona's Palace - Oliver Grover - 1922 - $250.00
8. Fleecy Clouds - Karl A, Buehr - 192 - $150.00
9. Fluttering Leaves - Lucie Hartrath - 1921 - $350.00
10. In the Dunes - F.C. Peyraud - 1920 - $200.00
11. In the Hot House - William Clusman - 1920 - $150.00
12. In the Pasture - Karl A. Beuhr - 1921 - $225.00
13. Lamp Effect - Arvid Nyholm - 1925 - $350.00
14. Leafy Screen - Edgar Cameron - 1920 - $175.00
15. Marine - Frederic Tellander - 1925 - $500.00
16. Overlooking Quebec - John F. Stacey - 1920 - $350.00
17. Surf and Rocks on the Pacific - Anna Lee Stacey - 1920 - $250.00
18. The Home of the Moose - J. A. Spelman - 1925 - $600.00
19. The Pet Chicken - Ada W. Shulz - 1924 - $225.00
20. The Sentinels - Lucie Hartrath - 1920 - $250.00
21. The Trail of the Wind - Frank V. Dudley - 1925 - $300.00
22. Wheatfield - Allen Philbrick - 1920 - $200.00
23. Winter in Brown County - Charles Dahlgren - 1920 - $150.00
24. Wood Interior - Karl A, Beuhr - 91920 - $150.00
25. Hans Brinker and the Silver Skates - Jessie Wilcox Smith - 1929 - $350.00
26. Hurry Up Jim - George E. Albright - 1930 - $250.00
27. The Pool, Montreuel, Summer - George Ames Aldridge - 1930 - $600.00
28. Gary at Night - Alexis Jean Fournier - 1930 - $500.00
29. Night - Frank V. Dudley - 1930- $1000.00
30. The Song of the Forest - Adolph Heinze - 1930 - $350.00
31. The Big Oak - J. W. Vawter - 1930 - $175.00
32. March Storms - Carl Hoerman - 1930 - $500.00
33. Segovia Spain - Charles Killgore - 1930 - $800.00
34. The Carmen Gate - Charles Killgore - 1930 - $75.00
35. In Mexico - Charles Killgore - 1930 - $75.00
36, Shelter - Paul Sargent - 1930 - $200.00
37. Autumn Days - J. A. Spelman - 1930 - $400.00
38. Lumberville - E. W. Redfield - 1931 - $2,600.00
　　　Total　　　　　　　　　　$14,093.00

She observed that, between 1920 and 1931, a total of thirty-eight oil paintings were donated to the school, at a cost of over $14,000. The most significant of these were Carl R. Kraft's *Autumn Morning*, valued at $1,200, Frank V. Dudley's *Night*, valued at $1,000, and E. W. Redfield's *Lumberville*, purchased by the Class of 1931 at a cost of $2,600. Many others were valued at amounts of $500 or more.

"This is extremely helpful. Do we know how many more paintings were acquired since 1931?" Ellen asked.

"I can't give you a **definitive** answer – a few, I believe. Perhaps, Miss Link can be of some assistance on that score. She keeps very good records of such things for Mr. Spaulding. After all, it was he who **initiated** the art collection in 1912, and Miss Link's been working for him since she graduated, in 1928. However, it's my assumption that the Depression put a **damper** on such gifts after 1931. Why, Emerson even stopped producing yearbooks after 1932, and didn't do another until 1938. Few students could afford to buy them during the Depression years."

"Well, at least we can use this as a checklist of the most notable items in the collection." Ellen suggested.

"I also have some good news to report," Natalia added. "Remember our friend, the postman, who promised to check on Dimitri Poliakov's forwarding address? Well, he stopped by our house yesterday while we were at the beach and gave this address to Aunt Veronika. He's living at 5468 S. Woodlawn Avenue in Chicago."

"I know that neighborhood," Melanie replied. "That's in **Hyde Park**, just north of the University of Chicago. If I'm not mistaken, it's not far from the **Oriental Institute**, which contains a world-class collection of Near Eastern artifacts, and **objets d'art**.

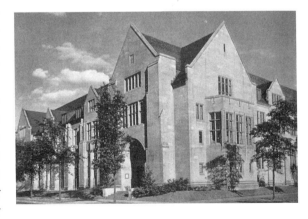

My father took my brother, Ted, and me there last year. Ted's interested in becoming an **Egyptologist**."

"While it's purely **speculative** at this point, Uncle Stan believes it's **feasible** that the Communists may be trying to **infiltrate** the top-secret research being conducted at the University of Chicago and share it with the Soviet Union. That could explain why Dimitri Poliakov is now living near the University."

"Natalia, don't you think that anybody involved would have to obtain high level security clearance from the government?" Ellen inquired.

"Certainly. But, that would only be the case for those on the inside – you know, scientists, and the like, who would have to be above suspicion. It would not apply to those on the **periphery** – the **couriers**, **conduits**, and other party members, whose task it is to gather the information and pass it on to those who can spirit it out of the country. That task may fall to the underground network of agents, or to **consular** officials stationed in Chicago who have the benefit of **diplomatic immunity**. All they need is one **mole** on the inside who can pass along the critical information."

"It seems clear that we're going to have to make a trip to Hyde Park and **ascertain** the whereabouts of this Mr. Poliakov," said Melanie.

"Of course," Ellen replied. "But first things first. Right now, we need to check out Crimean Imports. In fact, I suggest we pay a visit to the store right now on the **pretext** that we need to buy some used furniture."

"Then, let's go," Melanie urged.

Chapter 16

Exploring the Central District

The sky had turned an **ominous** shade of gray, heightening the **aura** of mystery that pervaded the Central District south of the Wabash tracks. Crimean Imports was situated in a **drab** and **down–at-the-heel** business district in the 1300 block of Washington Street, sandwiched between the Kallavryta Coffee House and the Steel City Hotel. Unlike Gary's downtown business district, the area between Broadway and Madison Street in Gary's **Central District** was working class and heavily **ethnic**, its streets harboring an **eclectic** mix of European coffee houses, **ubiquitous** tap rooms, restaurants, bakeries, small hotels, laundries, billiard parlors, ethnic groceries, hardware stores, **cobblers**, and other establishments serving its **multicultural** and **multiracial** population.

Also occupying the same block as Crimean Imports were the Oriental Café, the Hellas Coffee House, the American Serbian Athletic Association, the National Bottling Works, and the Ristoff Tavern, most apparently with apartments upstairs. The street **exuded** an atmosphere more typical of the fringe of a **cosmopolitan** European city than an American one. Indeed, visitors would be hard pressed to hear any English being spoken in the **polyglot** Central District, particularly where fellow nationals congregated. They would be more likely to hear Greek, Hungarian, Serbian, or Polish being spoken than English, particularly among the adult foreign-born population.

Walking briskly from the Norton Park Pavilion, the girls traversed the front lawn of Froebel School, and passed the popular Miramar Ballroom at the corner of 14th and Madison, before locating Crimean Imports in the middle of the 1300 block of Washington Street.

Superficially, the store looked relatively **innocuous**. The **expansive** plate glass windows on either side of the recessed entryway displayed a **diverse** array of new and used furniture, European and American antiques, lamps, figurines, paintings, console radios, and gramophones. A bell attached to the front door announced their arrival. A portly, middle-aged gentleman with dark hair, and eyebrows resembling a pair of oversized brown caterpillars, hovered **inscrutably** at a distance while the girls meandered through the aisles between Queen Anne highboys, Chippendale chairs, French Empire bureaus, and more **pedestrian** items of uncertain **provenance**. The paintings they casually observed were of no particular note, most merely reproductions of European masters – Constables, Turners, Renoirs, Gainsboroughs, Rembrandts, and a smattering of Dutch landscapists. The few original oils they observed appeared to be of **negligible** worth.

"May I be of some assistance?"

"Why, yes, we were looking for a chest of drawers and a dining room table and chairs. Nothing too expensive." Ellen suggested. "We're on a limited budget."

"That depends on what you mean by 'not too expensive.'"

"Well, let's say, under fifty dollars."

"We have items in every price range. Perhaps this table and chairs would suit your needs. It was recently acquired at a West Side estate sale. They're not antiques, but are a real bargain at $45.00. We also have this nice chest of drawers for $25.00, but I'll let you have them both for $60.00."

"Do you have any other items not on display here, perhaps in your back room?"

"No, we have limited storage space here. I'm afraid everything we have is here in the showroom."

"They're very nice, but we'd like to discuss it privately, if you don't mind."

"Certainly." He stepped away while the girls conversed, quietly.

"I suggest we tell him we're still looking, but would like his business card should we decide to buy them later," Ellen whispered. "As for paintings, I don't see anything original here. We'd best leave it at that. If we start asking about original art work, it might just arouse suspicion. Besides, oil paintings would be a bit of an extravagance if we've already told him we're on limited budget."

"You're right, Ellen," Melanie replied, to which Natalia nodded in agreement.

Ellen approached the gentleman. "I think we'd like to keep looking, but may we have your card should we decide to take you up on your offer?"

"But, of course," the man replied, pulling a business card from his front shirt pocket.

After thanking him for his time, Ellen led her friends out the door and to the corner of 13th Avenue, outside the Oriental Café.

Ellen handed the business card to Melanie and Natalia.

"The name is Russian, as I suspected, and his card has two addresses. The second must be his home address."

"I believe you're right, Ellen. I've been in Aetna many times and I'm sure there are no furniture stores on Arizona

> Konstantin Ivanov
>
> Crimean Imports
>
> Antiques & Furniture
>
> Bought and Sold
>
> 1334 Washington Street   900 Arizona Street
>
> Gary, Indiana

Street. I think the only business in Aetna is a small grocery store on Aetna Street itself," Melanie explained.

"I don't trust him," Natalia suggested. "I think his professional **demeanor belies** something more **sinister**. And it's not just my feminine **intuition**. One thing I **gleaned** from **perusing** the store was the fact that there's obviously more storage space in the back room than he's letting on. The display room is definitely not as deep as the lot on which the store sits, suggesting a more **capacious** storage area in the back. In fact, I **discreetly** paced it off while I was in the store. The showroom couldn't have been more than ninety feet deep. If I pace off the distance from here to the alley, we can determine the approximate depth of the backroom."

Beginning at the corner, Natalia began pacing:

"One, two, three, four..."

Once she had reached the alley, she began to calculate the distance.

"If my paces are about three feet, then I would estimate the depth of these lots at about a hundred and fifty feet. Deducting for the sidewalk and the front display window, that leaves about forty-five feet for storage in the back. Mr. Ivanov wasn't being truthful. That should tell us something."

"But what if he's stashed the paintings at his home?" Melanie suggested.

"That's certainly a possibility, provided he's got the room," Ellen replied. "We won't know that until we can make a trip out there and investigate. How far is it to Aetna, Melanie?"

"It's about three miles from here, as the crow flies. We passed it on our way to Miller Beach, if you recall. Aetna Street is just a couple of blocks east of Wilson's restaurant and Ted's Drive-In – the place with the carhops. The bus passes it on Dunes Highway. We can catch the Miller bus at Fifth and Broadway."

"I don't know about you, but I'd like to check out the alley behind the store first," Natalia proposed. "I'd like to know if they keep a delivery truck out back and, if so, what it looks like."

Walking into the alley behind the Oriental Café with some **trepidation**, the girls scanned the back doors of the Washington Street businesses for the rear entrance to the furniture emporium. A light panel truck, without distinguishing markings, was parked outside a large service door and an accompanying entryway, both with the words "Crimean Imports" painted on them. On the opposite side of the alley was the back of the Balkan Bakery that fronted on Adams Street.

"Natalia, I want to take an impression of one of these tire tracks. Do you have a piece of paper?"

"Yes, I think I've got some paper in my purse. It's folded. Is that O.K?"

"That should work well enough," Ellen replied.

Unfolding the paper and taking a pencil from her purse, Ellen placed the paper against the tire tread and rubbed the flat edge of the pencil lead across the paper until an impression of the treads appeared. Suddenly, without warning, a man in blue overalls and gray cap emerged from store's rear entrance. After lighting a cigarette, and climbing into the cab, he started the engine. Undetected for the moment, the girls barely had time to duck into a narrow gap between the furniture store and an adjacent coal storage bin. Their **anxiety ebbed** only when they saw the truck pull out of the alley and turn west on 14th Avenue.

"That was a close one. Let's get out of here before someone else surprises us," Ellen urged. The cloudy sky had **metamorphosed** into a light drizzle as the girls made their way to Broadway.

"We can catch the streetcar at the Gary Railways office at 11th Avenue," Melanie suggested, "and get a transfer for the Miller bus at 5th and Broadway."

"Let's go," Natalia replied.

The Gary Railways office was located in a three-story brown brick building on the northeast corner of 11th and Broadway. Streetcars, or busses, coming from Glen Park, Tolleston, Hobart, Valparaiso, and Crown Point stopped there before proceeding to Gary's downtown business district, and the mill gates. The girls waited patiently until the next streetcar from Tolleston made the turn from 11th Avenue and stopped alongside the station. Finding seats in the middle of the coach, the girls rode it as far as 5th Avenue, where they disembarked in front of Schulte's Cigar Store, and a small newsstand that occupied the corner. They waited for the next Miller bus in front of the ND Lunch, a **nondescript** greasy spoon whose hamburger griddle was visible through the front plate glass window. It was just past noon when the Miller bus pulled up in front of the eatery. They took seats in the back, near the rear door.

"Do you see that apartment building in the next block," Melanie interjected. Those are the Dalton Apartments. Three of our Emerson teachers live there: Miss Tinsman, who teaches biology; Miss Grieger, who teaches history; and Miss Sayers who teaches choral music. I've had all three. Several other Emerson teachers live downtown: Mrs. Pierce, one of our English teachers, lives in the Ambassador Apartments on the West Side, near Jefferson Park, as does Henrietta Newton, who teaches American history and civ-

ics. Melba Cromer, our auditorium teacher and pianist, lives in Hotel Gary."

"There's Hannan's drugstore where we sometimes go for lunch," Melanie exclaimed as the bus passed Virginia Street.

The girls rode the bus two miles east on Fifth Avenue that became Dunes Highway along the way. They got off at Aetna Street and East 9th Avenue, just north of the Wabash Railroad tracks. The wide cement street was mostly deserted. A 1938 Oldsmobile was parked in front of Wesley Vantrease's grocery, a two-story brick building on the east side of the street. A few shoppers were observed leaving the store, arms laden with bags of groceries. A few children loitered outside, eating ice cream bars, or reading comic books. On the west side of the street stood the former Wabash train station that had been converted into a residence, now occupied by **octogenarian** and former Aetna Powder Plant employee, Bill Sanderson. From there, the street was **devoid** of human habitation, trailing off into sand dunes, oak and poplar trees, and tumbleweeds.

Aetna was a **dormant** little village whose **antecedents** lay in the **munitions** industry of which it had once been a part. While located within the Gary city limits, it was isolated from the rest of the city by small factories, sand dunes, marsh, and scrub vegetation. Founded in 1881 as the site of the Aetna Powder Company, the community originally produced gun power and **nitroglycerine**

for **agricultural** and industrial purposes. During World War I, it was acquired by the Aetna Explosives Company and became a leading source of gun cotton used by the Allied armies in France. At its peak, the plant employed over 2,000 men, a few of them living in Aetna, the remainder commuting from Miller, or Gary proper. Following the **Armistice**, however, the plant was shut down due a decline in demand for its products and pressures from city officials and residents who feared **recurrence** of the **volatile** explosions that had once rocked the city's foundations and shattered plate glass windows up and down Broadway. Shortly thereafter, the plant buildings were dismantled and carted away. What little remained was partially buried beneath a layer of shifting sand. Within a few years following the plant's closing, the village comprised just a few dozen dwellings and less than 200 inhabitants, most of them living between Idaho and Arizona streets. Most of the students living in Aetna attended Miller School on Lake Street, or the recently opened Wirt High School. The remainder attended Emerson.

"That must be it," shouted Melanie, as the girls approached Arizona Street. Only five houses could be observed in the vicinity of Arizona Street, four on the south side of East 10th Avenue, and one on the north side whose garage faced the street. This single story brick house was bordered on the north

side by an extensive lawn that abutted the Wabash Railroad tracks, and was shielded from East 10th Avenue by a tall row of hedges. A roadside mailbox read 'Ivanov.'

"I know that house. The old Aetna Powder Plant office was located in there. My grandfather used to punch his time card in that house when he worked there. In the 1930s, it was called the 'Mickey Mouse Theatre.' That's when Betty Lyman converted it into a **venue** for her theatrical workshop and puppet shows. It was part of the **Federal Theatre Project**, of the **Works Progress Administration** – you know, one of President Roosevelt's **New Deal** programs to get the country moving again. They also put on plays, and orchestra and choral concerts. I came here at least a half dozen times with my parents. My mother was determined to expose me and my sister to culture. I distinctly remember the Disney characters painted on the walls of the theatre. I assume that's what Ivanov's now using for a garage. I was only in the residence once, as I recall. It was small, with a kitchen, living room, several bedrooms, and a screened-in front porch. I'm assuming the garage would be the only possible place for storage."

"I have an idea," said Ellen. "Presumably, Mr. Ivanov is still at his store. What we have to determine is if he has anyone living at his home when he's gone – a wife, perhaps, or a housekeeper. I suggest we knock on the door and say we are looking for Annette Carlson – I just made the name up. If they tell us that no one by that name lives there, we leave. If no one answers, we try to get into the garage and see if there's anything inside which might **implicate** Mr. Ivanov in the theft. Are you game?"

"I'm willing. How about you, Natalia?"

"After what I've already been through, nothing could **faze** me. However, I suggest that one of us serve as a look-out in case Mr. Ivanov comes home **prematurely**."

The girls slipped through the hedges on the west side of the house and approached the front entrance. The house was **eerily** quiet in the heat of midday. Finding the screen door locked, they proceeded to the east side entrance and knocked on the wooden screen door. **Fortuitously**, there were no dwellings to the east that might threaten to expose their presence. **Eliciting** no response, they knocked several more times. Silence. Ellen peaked in through the kitchen window. She tried the door. Not surprisingly, it was locked. Nevertheless, she breathlessly anticipated what their entry might **portend**.

"Just a minute. Let me try my **skeleton key**," said Ellen.

"A skeleton key? Where on earth did you get such a thing?" Melanie asked, **incredulously**.

"I got it from a Stratford locksmith who lives on my street. It's a long story."

Inserting the key in the lock, Ellen turned it this way and that until it yielded to her efforts.

"There! We're in!" she whispered.

"Amazing!" Melanie exclaimed.

Standing in the dwelling's **utilitarian** kitchen, the girls **pondered** their next move.

"Melanie, while Natalia and I search the garage, you need to find a window where you can keep a lookout for any vehicles approaching the house. If anyone does come, knock on the wall three times, and we'll meet at the screened porch and escape across the front lawn. I'll unlock the front screen door in advance to **facilitate** our escape. We can dash through those hedges leading to the grocery store. First, let me re-lock the kitchen door. That way, the only thing disturbed will be the front screen door. If we don't tamper with anything else, Mr. Ivanov might not even notice that it's unlocked. Most likely, he'll think he failed to lock it himself."

"Pretty foxy, I'd say. What crime school did you attend, Ellen?" Melanie quipped.

"It's pretty much just common sense. That and what I've learned from reading police manuals and detective novels."

"O.K. You know your assignments. Natalia, come with me."

The garage, which had sufficient space for two vehicles, was **accessible** off the kitchen. It appeared to have been converted from whatever theatrical purposes it had once served, although the Disney murals were still clearly **discernible** on the walls. The lack of windows, however, made investigation difficult without a flashlight, although some light filtered in from the kitchen. But, for the obvious automotive tools and a small workbench, the space was largely empty, with no signs of any hidden paintings or other contraband. The garage **exuded** a chemical **odor**, as if it had recently been **fumigated**. Ellen noticed what appeared to be a narrow closet along the interior wall. It was also locked. Again, using her skeleton key, she succeeded in opening the door. The space was even darker than the garage, making investigation difficult.

"We'll have to feel with our hands," Natalia said.

Once their eyes had adjusted to the dim light, they discovered only a few small wooden boxes that contained coffee cans filled with nails and screws.

"Come quick! You've gotta see this!" shouted Melanie from across the house.

Quickly re-locking the closet door, Ellen and Natalia ran into the house, through the living room, and into what appeared to be the master bedroom. Melanie pointed to the wall above the headboard.

"Would you look at that!"

Ellen and Natalia fixed their eyes on the painting that hung above the headboard, in full view. The brass plaque at the bottom of the frame read: *Autumn Morning* by Carl R. Kraft.

"Wow! Is that what I think it is?"

Ellen reached in her purse and pulled out the *Gold and Gray Book* that Melanie had handed her that morning. Flipping to the inventory of paintings in the back, she quickly found No. 2: *Autumn Morning* by Carl R. Kraft, purchased in 1920 at

a cost of $1,200.00. The evidence was clear and **unequivocal**.

"Mr. Ivanov thought he was being clever, but even the cleverest of thieves can sometimes make **fatal** errors in judgment. What **temerity**! Even if he kept only one painting for himself, it's enough to put him behind bars, either as an art thief, or an **accessory after the fact**."

"Let's bring it to the police," Melanie suggested, "and turn him in."

"Absolutely not! We don't want to be **impetuous** and give any indication that he has been discovered. It might compromise our recovery of the rest of the collection. It's **imperative** that we just leave it where it hangs. We're after bigger game. Not only Mr. Ivanov, but, I suspect, his Communist buddies."

At that very moment, the girls heard a car door slam in the driveway, followed by footsteps crunching on the gravel driveway.

"Quick! We've gotta get out of here!" Ellen urged.

Within a few seconds, the girls flew out of the bedroom, through the living room and out the unlocked front screen door. Running as fast as their legs would carry them, they raced across the lawn and through the hedges at the boundary of the property, emerging behind the Aetna Street grocery store. **Fortuitously**, no one had observed from whence they had come. But, now, they had **incontrovertible** evidence that Mr. Ivanov was implicated in the theft.

"Ice cream, anyone? I'll stand treat," Ellen said, with a **mischievous** grin across her face.

Chapter 17

Afternoon at the Boroskova's

By the time Ellen arrived home that afternoon, she found a letter from Ken waiting for her on the back steps. She hurried upstairs, unlocked the door to their apartment, ran into the parlor, and plopped down in one of the comfortable armchairs. She tore open the envelope and began reading:

Dear Ellen,

I hope you are well and enjoying Gary.

*Things are relatively quiet here. Mr. Mueller and I have been busy transporting a number of rare **tomes** he acquired at two estate sales. There are lots of interesting items, including a first edition of Blackstone's Commentaries on the Laws of England, published in 1765-1769, and Hutchinson's Historical Essay Concerning Witchcraft, published in 1718. The book on witchcraft came out of the old Benjamin mansion, which has a beautiful oak paneled library on the first floor. What Mr. Mueller can't sell at his store, he plans to **catalog** and sell on the **antiquarian** book market. He's teaching me a lot about rare books.*

I looked in on your mother on Wednesday. She said your grandmother was feeling better, but still needed looking after.

*Betsy and Linnea asked me to the movies on Saturday. We're going to see the new Alfred Hitchcock movie, "Saboteur," with Robert Cummings, at the Stratford. Would you believe, it's about **sabotage** at an aircraft factory in California? Too bad they didn't hear about our case sooner or they could have filmed on location in Stratford.*

I hope you are behaving yourself and staying out of trouble. Write soon. I can't wait until you're back home.

Love,

Ken

Ellen's father returned from Gary Armor Plate about three o'clock and suggested they have dinner at the YWCA Cafeteria on East 6th Avenue. That evening, while relaxing in front of the radio, they received a phone call from Natalia's Uncle Stan, inviting them over on Sunday afternoon, after church.

~~~~~~~~~~~~~~~~

By the time Ellen awoke on Sunday morning, her father was already relaxing in the living room, with a cup of coffee and the Sunday funnies in the *Chicago American.*

"Well, would you look at that. Flash Gordon and Dale Arden have been captured by Ming the Merciless who plans to turn them over to the Lizard Women unless Dale consents to be his bride. I've heard of shotgun weddings, but this sounds more like a raygun wedding. 'To be continued next week.' Figures."

"Sounds pretty **ominous**. Don't you just hate it when you have to wait all week to find out what's going to happen? I remember when you read me the funnies every Sunday before I was able to read them myself. I really miss those **frivolous** days."

"So do I. Say, I was going to suggest that we go to the First Methodist Church this morning. You know, the beautiful church behind Hotel Gary. For a treat, we can have breakfast at the hotel after that."

"That would be swell, Dad. Then, I'll save my appetite for after church."

The First Methodist Church (popularly known as City Church), at 6th and Washington Street, was an **auspicious** environment for Ellen and her father to attend their first church service in Gary. The stained glass windows and vaulted ceilings of the **gothic** style structure added an impressive architectural **ambiance** to worship, **complemented** by the rich sounds of the Ferris Tracker pipe organ that **reverberated** throughout the **cavernous sanctuary**. The **ecclesiastical** environment was certainly **atypical** for Gary, which generally boasted less **grandiose** and more **prosaic sanctuaries** for the faithful. Ellen found it a fitting setting in which the **repentant** could seek **divine absolution,** and became lost in the **ineffable** beauty and **ethereal** mood of the **spiritual** experience. City Church was indeed an impressive physical **manifestation** of the **munificence** of its **reverent** parishioners.

The hymns were all familiar ones Ellen had sung at the First Congregational Church in Stratford: *Come Thou Fount of Every Blessing, Rock of Ages, The Old Rugged Cross,* and *What a Friend We Have in Jesus.* In his **eloquent** sermon, entitled 'Shadows,' Pastor William Clark urged his parishioners to focus on the things of **eternity**, rather than the **ephemeral, fleeting**, and **evanescent** preoccupations of the present day. The pastor's spirited and **erudite** presentation also **exhorted** them to **expiate** sin and resist **debauchery** in their lives. The organ **postlude** – Charles Widor's *Toccata from his Symphony No. 5* – was one of Ellen's favorites, and concluded with a mighty **crescendo** that **reverberated** off the limestone walls and **vaulted** ceiling. In **deference** to the organist, Dwight Davis, who was obviously a **consummate** musician, Ellen and her father sat in their pew long enough to hear it in its entirety, and stayed afterwards to **compliment** him on his playing. After church, they were invited by several members of the **congregation** to Hotel Gary's Blue Room for a **sumptuous buffet** breakfast consisting of eggs, waffles, bacon, fruit, orange juice, and other delicacies, and to enjoy each other's **conviviality**.

Ellen's father had been looking forward to the opportunity of conversing with Natalia's Uncle Stan since their brief meeting the day of their arrival in Gary. After breakfast was concluded, their first **inclination** was to wait for the next streetcar in front of Ridgely's Drugstore at 6th and Broadway. It being Sunday, however, they soon discovered that the next Tolleston trolley was not scheduled for another forty minutes.

"What do you say we walk, Ellen? We can get there on foot faster than waiting on the trolley, and, besides, I kinda' need the exercise."

"Sure thing, but instead of going down Broadway, why don't we walk to Jefferson Park and take Madison Street south from there. It's also a through street to the Central District."

"O.K. You lead the way."

Madison Street was just four short blocks west of Broadway. Jefferson School, which opened in 1908, and was the first permanent school building in Gary, was located in the 600 block of Madison. Across the street, an impressive white limestone-clad water tower commanded the northern half of the

park. Ambling leisurely south on Madison Street, they paused, briefly, at the Coca Cola Bottling Plant near 10th Avenue, looking through the large plate glass windows and marveling in fascination as the bottles wound their way down the assembly line in the process of being filled and capped. Then, after passing under the New York Central railroad highline and over the Michigan Central tracks, they found themselves at the corner of 11th and Madison where they were greeted by the Indiana National Guard Armory on the right and, across the street, a Mack Truck showroom. Crossing to the south side of 11th Avenue, they encountered a variety of local

business establishments, including Mailath's Pharmacy, Club SAR, and the West End Lunch, before turning left at the Lach & Stalinovich Funeral Parlor at Jackson Street.

The residential block below 11th Avenue contained a mixture of one-, two- and three-story houses and apartment buildings, **terminating** in the twin-domed Saints Constantine and Helen Greek Orthodox Church at the corner of 13th and Jackson. Riding his tricycle on the sidewalk in front of the church was Corky, the little boy Ellen remembered from riding the streetcar a few days before.

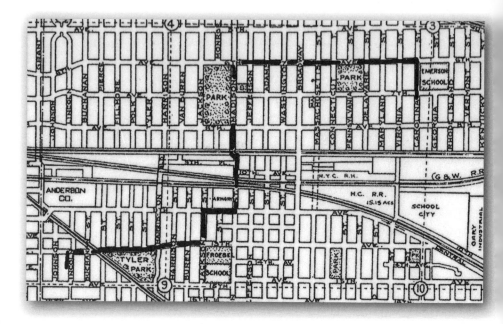

Across 13th Avenue, Froebel School's athletic fields and running track were sprawled across several acres of clay and sand. On the opposite corner from the Greek Church stood the Hungarian Reformed Church, where the last of the Sunday morning parishioners were leaving the building and getting into their automobiles, or walking home. From the church, the pair walked west, again, down 13th Avenue to Norton Park, and to Lincoln Street. The Boroskova home, a neat front-to-back brick bungalow, with a well-manicured lawn, privet hedge, and gladiola beds, awaited them. Stan and Veronika were sitting on the shaded front porch as they arrived.

"Your flowers are gorgeous," Ellen exclaimed.

"Thank you," replied Veronika. "I've been **propagating** gladiolas since we first moved here in 1927."

"Well, greetings and **salutations**. Did you walk all the way? We could have picked you up," Stan said.

"That's all right. The **brisk** walk did us good. We stopped to watch the Coca Colas being bottled," Ellen's father explained.

"Oh, you came by way of Madison Street?"

"Yes, rather than wait an hour for the next Tolleston streetcar on Broadway, we took a **circuitous** route in order to see a bit more of the city. It was a nice walk. I must say, there certainly are a lot of churches in this area."

"That's for sure. You can blame it on all the ethnic groups in Gary. Each one serves its own **parochial** interests and has to have its own church, and in its own language. Well, come in! We stopped by the Balkan Bakery after church and picked up some pastry."

Ellen and her father were **cordially** escorted into the living room and offered a chair.

"With this heat, I thought you would prefer lemonade to coffee," Veronika suggested.

"Oh, yes, lemonade would be refreshing," Ellen replied.

"So, where did you two go to church this morning?"

'The First Methodist Church on Washington Street," Eric replied.

"Oh, that's a beautiful church! So you're Methodists, then?"

"Not really. We're Congregationalists back home, but the Congregational Church in Gary is a bit of a hike, at 6th and Johnson, so we chose a church closer to our apartment. In this case, geography won out over **theology**. And what about you?"

"We belong to St. Mary's Russian Orthodox Church at 17th and Fillmore. In fact, many of those in Gary of Russian **extraction** are members of St. Mary's. We have a wonderful pastor – Reverend Kedrovsky. He was born in Russia, but came to this country in 1909. The church is only about four blocks from here. We could drive, but prefer to walk. He delivers the most **flamboyant** sermons, not like the **soporific** ones some ministers deliver that can put you to sleep. He also has a **prodigious** memory for biblical passages."

As Veronika brought them each a cold glass of lemonade and placed a tray of pastries on the coffee table, Ellen looked around the room. It was obvious that Veronika was a **fastidious** housekeeper, and presented a gracious and **felicitous** manner with guests. Their home was **impeccably** decorated and tastefully furnished. The living room was done in an elegant French **faux** wallpaper in light blue with a **superimposed** gold **damask** design. A Russian **icon** hung on the wall, and a red and blue Persian carpet graced the floor. There was a davenport covered in a maroon **damask** fabric, two matching Queen Anne wing chairs, end tables on each side of the davenport, and a glass-covered coffee table in front of it. An elaborate Sheraton mahogany **breakfront** contained an impressive collection of books on Russian history and politics.

"Is that a genuine **Roerich**?" Eric inquired, standing to admire the painting at close range.

"It certainly is. I acquired it from a Chicago art dealer about three years ago. It cost me two month's salary, but I promised Veronica it wouldn't become a habit. So, I take it you're familiar with his work," Stan replied

"I certainly am. I had the opportunity to visit his skyscraper museum on Riverside Drive shortly after it opened in 1929, and was blown away. He's a **visionary** and **prodigious** artist."

A curio cabinet displayed a variety of Russian artifacts and **mementos**.

"I see you're admiring our carpet, Ellen?"

"Yes. It's gorgeous, Mrs. Boroskova. I assume it's a genuine Persian carpet."

"It is. We bought it from Youshia Elisha, an Assyrian gentleman who sells the most beautiful Persian carpets out of his home in Glen Park. He was born in Persia, but his children were born here. He has two sons, Charles and Walter, and a lovely daughter named Louise. Interestingly, they're Presbyterians."

"I thought most Persians were Muslim," Eric inquired.

"Well, that's correct, but Assyrians are an **indigenous** Aramaic-speaking people, with their own unique language, culture and heritage which goes back centuries. They're part of the Christian minority in Persia, as are the Armenians, both of which were persecuted and forced to **placate** the Muslim majority. Some became Presbyterians as a result of **evangelistic** efforts by Presbyterian missionaries, and were **savvy** enough to immigrate to this country to escape further religious **persecution**. Theirs was certainly an **unconventional** religious **odyssey**. So, tell me, Eric. What brings you to Gary?"

"My father's toolmaking business has a contract with Gary Armor Plate, to design **prototypes** for artillery and tank components. I expect to be here for a month or more to make sure the **calibrations** are exact. I'm the lead tool designer."

"Sounds pretty important. How long have you been doing war-related work?"

"Not all that long. Since shortly after Pearl Harbor – March of this year, to be exact. Most of our contracts are now war-related. But, I've been a tool designer for more than twenty years."

"Well, my work isn't anything so sophisticated," Stan replied. "I'm working as a **scarfer** at the Sheet and Tin Mill. We use blowtorches to burn off the impurities from the surface of steel slabs before they're sent to the rolling mill to be made into sheet metal. The **compensation**'s excellent, and **commensurate** with the number of slabs we process. We work in **tandem** with the crane operators. They unload the slabs from the railroad cars, then flip them over after we've finished with one side. Once the other side is done, they're ready for the rolling mill. We're quite **proficient** when we work as a team, although we do have to contend with the normal **vicissitudes** of the steel making industry. The **War Production Board** is leaning heavily on U.S. Steel to ramp up its production. After all, if we don't produce the steel, the planes and military vehicles don't get made. It's not only our soldiers in the field who are going to win this war, but American steel production that will help smash the Nazi and Japanese war machines."

"I'd love to get a tour of the plant one of these days," Eric replied.

"So would I," echoed Ellen.

"That might be difficult. They've beefed up security a lot since America entered the war, and **promulgated** regulations that bar access to non-employees. There's a lot of concern about sabotage."

"Well, that's understandable. We had problems of our own in Stratford, where Nazi agents were engaged in **espionage**, but thanks to some **diligent** detective work, they were **apprehended**." Not wishing to embarrass Ellen, her father simply threw a knowing 'wink' in her direction.

"So, now that you've learned about Natalia's experiences, I thought I'd tell you some of my own inside the Soviet Union."

"We've been looking forward to it," Eric replied.

"Of course, you have to understand that this was more than twenty years ago. Ironically, I grew up in an **apolitical** environment. My father was the proprietor of a small **dry goods** store where he and my mother worked, and where I helped after school and on weekends. Like my parents, I was initially sympathetic to the Tsarist government, not because I was particularly **enamored** of royalty, but because I feared the alternative. In **retrospect**, the Tsar was a relatively **benevolent autocrat** compared to the **genocidal** and **vindictive** Bolsheviks. When the **nascent Revolutionary** movement erupted in February 1917, we had hopes that a democratically-elected government could be established in place of the Tsar, or under which the Tsar could retain merely the ceremonial **trappings** of his office. But, this was not to be. After Tsar Nicholas **abdicated** in March 1917, Alexander Kerensky emerged as the dominant figure in the **provisional** liberal-socialist **coalition** government. But, he **bungled** things badly and was soon forced out by the Bolsheviks."

"How so?" Eric inquired.

"Well, by this time, the Russian people had turned against Russia's involvement in the war. More than two million Russians had already died in the conflict, more than four million were wounded, and significant numbers of soldiers had deserted. Despite these **horrendous** losses, Kerensky visited the front and urged the Russian troops to continue the fight. But, ultimately, he was unable to provide a justification for **prolonging** the war, other than fulfilling Russia's **dubious** obligations to the Allies, and the fear that a failure to do so would cause England and France to cut off vital food and other supplies. The Russian Army had some initial successes, but was eventually **rebuffed** by a strong Austro-Hungarian and German counter-attack. By this time, our soldiers were **dispirited** and their ranks plagued with desertion, **sabotage**, and **mutiny**. The **dissemination** of Communist literature by the Bolsheviks only **exacerbated** the situation, sewing widespread discontent and making Kerensky's position even more **precarious**. Kerensky didn't help things either by **brazenly** taking authority away from officers and giving it to **revolutionary** soldier committees. He also isolated **conservatives** with his policy of '**no enemies to the left**,' which only emboldened the Bolsheviks and **dissuaded** others from supporting him.

"There is much evidence to suggest that the German authorities facilitated the return of Lenin and other Russian exiles through Germany to Russia in a sealed one-carriage train in the hopes that their presence would undermine the existing government and **hasten** the **disintegration** of the Russian war effort. At Lenin's request, the carriage was protected from interference by a special grant of extraterritorial status. Whether true or not, the **gambit** paid off, but did not **forestall** eventual German defeat.

"By October, Kerensky's **dithering** had cost him most of his support in **Petrograd** – now Leningrad. The **denunciation** of his administration by the Bolsheviks was merciless. After the Reds took control of the government in the October **coup**, he escaped to Pskov and raised an army of loyalists. After their defeat, however, his **putative** support **dissipated** and brought his administration into widespread **disrepute**. In a political **quandary** about his future political **viability**, he subsequently fled to France. In July 1918, came the **demise** of Czar Nicholas Romanov and his entire family, who had been under house arrest for more than a year. They were **summarily** executed by Bolshevik soldiers, **allegedly** on orders from Lenin himself.

"Under **Leon Trotsky**'s leadership, the Red Army was increasingly willing to employ **devious** and brutal tactics. And, to **buttress** its authority, it **initiated** the mandatory **conscription** of peasants and workers, making it a **formidable** foe on the battlefield. **Devoid** of moral **scruples**, they enforced their control by taking hostages and **methodically** shooting those who **balked** in order to make others **tractable**. They even took whole families hostage to ensure obedience. They became a **scourge** across the Russian landscape and set a pattern for the **egregious** violations of human rights that followed."

"But I thought the Communists were attempting to usher in a workers' state?" Eric replied, with a touch of humorous sarcasm.

"That was the **rhetoric**. The Bolsheviks initially promised to **enfranchise** the **restive civilian** population, to modernize Russia's **primitive** and **antiquated** industrial sector and **archaic** agricultural methods, and to **assuage** the people's biting poverty, but Lenin had other ideas. Sure, he wanted to modernize the Russian economy, but under the **authoritarian** and **ruthless** rule of a **vanguard** of paid professional revolutionaries. There was only one election for the **constituent assembly** – the first in Russia's 900-year history – on November 25, 1917, at which the Bolsheviks garnered only 25 percent of the vote. But, that assembly met only once, in January 1918. Lenin subsequently issued a **peremptory** decree dissolving it and used heavily armed guards to prevent it from **reconvening**. The failure of a public uprising by more **moderate** forces to protest Lenin's **dictatorial** actions sealed Russia's fate. It was a **bellwether** of what was to come. After that, Russia remained under the control of Lenin and his **henchmen,** who engaged in **summary executions** of their political opponents."

"Where were you living while all this was going on, Stan?" Eric inquired.

"I was living in Kirovsk – about thirty miles east of Petrograd, now Leningrad. I was still a student at a local trade school, and too young to be **conscripted** when war broke out in 1914. But, in 1917, I was ordered into service. Luckily, I wasn't sent to the front, or I might have been killed fighting the Germans, along with so many others. There was considerable **carping** in the ranks. My unit was not sympathetic to the Bolsheviks, but it was nevertheless caught up in the **frenetic maelstrom** of political and economic forces that was sweeping through Russia at that time. While I wasn't a **monarchist**, I feared the **chaos** that would follow if the Tsar was **deposed**. Naively, I hoped for some kind of peaceful transition to a democratic government under the **Duma**, which is what we called our **constituent assembly**. But, that was a **chimerical** illusion. After all, we had no democratic tradition in Russia upon which to draw. The Bolsheviks were better organized and took full advantage of dissatisfaction with the Tsarist government to carry out a **defamatory** campaign against it, and take control over the fragmented and easily controlled masses. In their ignorance, the people had no idea that the Bolsheviks would lead them down a path far more destructive and **ruthless** than that which they had known under the Tsar. And Lenin, who was possessed of a **charismatic** personality, successfully inflamed the passions of the mobs with the most **strident polemics** and **incendiary** language. The Bolsheviks even **defiled** the homes of aristocrats and people they deemed to be capitalist **exploiters**.

"Soon after the October Revolution in 1917, however, the country grew more **fractious,** and anti-Bolshevik forces began to **coalesce** in opposition to the new government. It was a **nebulous** and loosely organized **confederation** of landowners, republicans, conservatives, middle-class citizens, reactionaries, pro-monarchists, liberals, democratic reformists, army generals, non-Bolshevik socialists, and even some **hedonists** who had grievances with the new regime. This **amalgam** of **disparate** political factions was voluntarily united only in its opposition to Bolshevik rule. The Bolsheviks weren't the only ones engaged in forced **conscription,** however. The **White Army** also used both forced **conscription** and **heinous** acts of terror to grow their ranks when they were unable to **goad** the **beleaguered** peasants into enlisting. The civil war made everybody more **callous** and insensitive to the normal rules of civilized behavior. And foreign influence, driven by fear of the Bolsheviks, also played a part. Both France and Great Britain sent troops to Russian ports and engaged in violent **confrontations** with Bolshevik forces. They also provided essential arms and other supplies to the White movement."

"I can remember Winston Churchill declaring that "Bolshevism must be strangled in its cradle," Eric added.

"Yes, Churchill had the **prescience** of mind to **assess** the threat of Bolshevism from the outset. That's why he **vilified** the Bolsheviks and urged England and the other Allied governments to support the White Army. Our principal **fidelity** was to Generals Yudenich and Denikin, as well as Admiral Kolchak. While the armies they commanded controlled large **swaths** of Russian territory for most of the civil war, they were ultimately defeated by the better organized Bolsheviks and the **anarchists** in the **Black Army** who were not **averse** to **flagrant** abuses of the civilized rules of warfare, an **infamy** for which they can never **atone.** The remains of the White forces, commanded by General Wrangel, attempted to defend the **Crimean Peninsula**, but our cause ultimately became a **fiasco**. We were forced to **forsake** our **fatherland**

and evacuate to **Istanbul** in November 1920, although fighting continued for three more years in the Far East."

"And where were you during the civil war?" Eric inquired.

"I was attached to General Denikin's White Army for nearly two years. Frankly, I'm lucky to be alive. I survived a number of **harrowing** engagements with Bolshevik forces, including our **abortive mobilization** against Moscow. And, once, in the Ukraine, I was cornered by Bolshevik troops in a peasant cottage. We hid in a cleverly disguised root cellar before being rescued by our own **counter-offensive**. I also survived continuous **artillery** barrages, tank battles, and months of street fighting. The **paucity** of food was also **deleterious** to my health. You would not believe the level of hardship we endured for months at a time. After our defense of the **Crimean Peninsula** collapsed, our army was totally **enervated** and **reticent** about continuing

the fight. I was able to escape to Istanbul with the **remnants** of our forces. All of our efforts had been for **naught**. It was the **nadir** of my young existence."

Natalia, who had been listening intently to her Uncle Stan's **monologue**, asked: "My father told me that you hired on as a **stevedore** in **Odessa** before you went to Baltimore. Is that right?"

"Not quite. I hired on in **Istanbul**. Odessa was overrun by the Reds before I could do that. Besides, the region was in such chaos that normal shipping schedules were **disrupted**. Most shipping lines were **reticent** to send ships there for fear their goods would be confiscated by the Bolsheviks. Nor would I have left my comrades at that critical time anyway. We were committed to staying together until we crossed the **Black Sea**. When I did make my way to Baltimore, I jumped ship. I soon learned of job opportunities in the Gary steel mills and arrived here in 1921."

"You know, what's got me puzzled is the attraction of communism," Eric inquired. "How can anyone subscribe to its doctrines, particularly in the West? I can understand those in the Soviet Union who are forced to support the Communist government under threat of imprisonment or death, or poor peasants who are offered **illusory** hopes of a better life and are **devoid** of realistic alternatives, but why would someone in this country, or France or England, become a Communist? It's a **paradox**, isn't it?"

"It's a mental **pathology**, really, masked by a **façade** of idealism and **al-**

truism," Stan explained. "Communists are so **odious** and so committed to their **abstract** dreams of a **utopian** future that they will **countenance** all manner of horrors to bring it about. But, it is, at its root, a **pernicious contradiction**, this idea that slaughtering innocents can lead to a society where all will eventually live in peace and brotherhood.

"Europeans are already consumed with political **ideology**, as the current **conflagration** will attest. Much of it is a product of their history, the **class structure**, **resentment** against the **aristocracy**, the **animosities** fueled by war and its aftermath, and an **irrational** impatience with economic progress under free market capitalism. The Communists believe that by imposing their Marxist doctrines on society, they will be able to hasten the creation of a **utopian** society – the 'workers paradise,' as Lenin called it. Some develop an almost **idolatrous** attraction to the state as a form of **secular** religion, making their minds **impervious** to reason. They are simply unable to **comprehend** the inherent **contradictions** in Marxist **dogma**. Lenin was an **enigmatic** leader and an **audacious** politician who ultimately had a **baleful** impact on the course of Russian, and world, history. Ultimately, he had nothing but **contempt** for workers whom he viewed as pawns in his grand scheme. As a middle class intellectual, he thought he knew best how people should live their lives. Ultimately, the Communists were totally **disingenuous** and their ideology just a smokescreen for a **virulent** and **repressive** dictatorial regime.

"At its core, Bolshevism is also characterized by a base **vulgarity**. Like Lenin before him, Stalin is similarly concerned only about his own personal political **aggrandizement**. Under his **regime, extolling** the leader has become the highest form of patriotism. The American experiment in ordered liberty is an **affront** to everything in which the Communists believe. Our freedom and economic success are **unprecedented** in world history, yet the Soviets persist in this unattainable dream that their system will somehow be an improvement. Ironically, the Bolsheviks initially asserted **egalitarian** ambitions, but, once **entrenched** in power, quickly replaced these empty **platitudes** with rule by an **elitist** minority.

"Remember that the Russian people had never known true liberty as we have it in the West. The vast majority were uneducated peasants, accustomed to being ruled by a Tsar, under the **yoke** of the aristocracy, and exhibiting a **servile** mindset. After all, **serfdom** was only abolished by the Tsar in 1862, and many peasants remained virtual serfs under the control of large landowners. For many Europeans as well, freedom and democracy were relatively recent **phenomena**. This made them more susceptible to control by others and to the lure of ideology. The Russians just traded one **sovereign** for another, but, in this case, they got one whose evil knows no bounds.

"The **irony** is that, under the czar and the aristocracy, the peasants were tied to the land. Now, under the Soviet regime, they are tied to their collective farms or factories, as the case may be. At least under the czar, they had hope for escape, or emigration. Now, under Stalin, that hope is virtually **foreclosed**, and any attempt to relocate without permission will result in the loss of employment, shelter, and income, if not forcible relocation to **Siberia**, where survival is **tenuous** at best. And, who in his right mind would even attempt it if he has a family to support?"

"It all seems rather **perplexing**. After all, didn't Marx predict that the state would ultimately wither away?" Ellen **interjected**.

"That's more of the **chimerical utopianism** that **infused** the Communist movement and drew several million **acolytes** to its cause. There isn't the slightest chance that Stalin, or any of his successors, will ever **relinquish** power voluntarily. He's got the Soviet Union firmly in his grip and his **edicts** have already resulted in the **extermination** of millions in an effort to enforce his will. In my view, he's even worse than Hitler, because his regime of terror is **devoid** of limitation. His **directives** are enforced by the fear he has been able to **engender** in the Russian **populace**, even among innocent people who may support the regime and the communist ideology. In this **contemporaneous** political environment, no one can speak **forthrightly**, or with **candor**. Nor can they **circumvent** his will. Why, Stalin would have his own brother **liquidated** if he thought it would help **perpetuate** the regime and the climate of fear that keeps him in power."

Chapter 18

Horrors of the Soviet Regime

"What I don't fully **comprehend** is how, during the Purges, Stalin and his **minions** were able to force innocent men and women to confess to crimes they didn't commit," Eric inquired.

"Once they brought them to the **Lubyanka** in the infamous **Black Marias**, it wasn't really so difficult for an **execrable** and **amoral** regime **devoid** of **scruples** that had the ability to break a man in body and spirit. According to Krivitsky, men who were otherwise sane and healthy could be brought to a state of mental confusion and emotional **despair** by a **sophisticated** process of **interrogation**. First, they applied mental and physical **duress**, utilizing teams of interrogators who forced prisoners to stand on both feet for fifty hours, or more, and then on one foot for ten hours, under blinding lights, while deprived of sleep. Then, after **writhing** in pain for hours, the prisoner begins to **hallucinate**, his legs swell up, his face turns black, and he collapses. Then, he is put in **restraints** and thrown into an overcrowded cell where he cannot rest properly. After regaining consciousness, he is hauled out for another round of interrogation. If the subject continues to resist, the brutal methods will be alternated with softer forms of treatment – polite conversation, tasty morsels of food, gentle persuasion.

"By this time, the subject is emotionally desperate and physically **debilitated**. If he continues to resist, or proves **evasive**, his interrogators will employ both prods and incentives to **coerce** a confession. He will be presented with false confessions, manufactured testimonies, and **incriminating** evidence to demonstrate the hopelessness of his **predicament**. Even before his arrest, he is **shunned** by his associates and made to feel that no one will come to his defense. He faces **calumnies** from every side. Once under arrest, **stoolies** and **agent provocateurs** are placed in his cell to trip him up and **demoralize** him. His only hope, then, is to throw himself on the mercy of the court, which is made up of a variety of political **reprobates** eager to **curry** favor with the regime, or **burnish** their reputation with the Leader.

"In some instances, the interrogators **tempered** their **brutality** with vague promises of **clemency** or **lenient** treatment, even **reprieve**, provided the prisoner confesses. Usually, these promises were made in private sessions, and included the assurance that relatives and friends would be spared. If all these techniques failed, the final course would be to **castigate** and threaten harm to loved ones. After 1935, the death penalty could be applied to children as young as twelve, and the confinement of children in labor camps was legalized. Younger offspring could be placed in state orphanages. After all this, is it any wonder that even the strongest and most **imperturbable** prisoners were willing to **abase** themselves and **concede** their guilt before their **tormentors** by confessing in open court? And once a death sentence is pronounced, it's almost never **revoked**. Eventually, the prisoner comes to an **ignominious** end, usually in the form a bullet to the back of the head, with no one to sing a **dirge** or deliver a **eulogy** over his lifeless body, which is **unceremoniously** tossed in an unmarked grave along with thousands of others. **Compassion** was simply not a part of their vocabulary.

"Here's a book by Eugene Lyons you will find very enlightening, Ellen. *Assignment in Utopia* is Lyons' first-person account of his six years in the Soviet Union as a correspondent for **United Press International**. Listen to what he wrote in 1937 about the Soviet secret police:

> *One need not be guilty of an overt act to have his house searched, himself stuck away in a foul cell, his family terrorized. An **anonymous** denunciation by someone who **coveted** his room or his job might do it, or the fact that he had been seen playing chess with someone else who was denounced. Perhaps his name was listed in the address book of a suspected person, or a second cousin by marriage, in the course of interrogation, had mentioned the relationship... I knew dozens of men and women who lived in a state of **chronic** terror, their little suitcases always packed, though they worked **diligently** and avoided even facial expressions which might cast doubt on their loyalty. To awaken in their own beds in the morning was a daily miracle for such people. The sound of a doorbell at an unusual hour left them limp and trembling.*

"These are the kinds of people we are up against, they and their **sycophants** in the West. I think you would enjoy reading it, too, Eric."

"Thank you, Stan. It's certainly difficult for those of us in the United States to **comprehend** the depth of human **depravity** and **reprehensible** conduct exhibited by the Bolsheviks," Eric observed. "But how do you explain the appeal of communist ideology to those in the West who seek to undermine their own governments?"

"Well, it's not because of ignorance. It's a myth that Western intellectuals sympathized with the Soviet Union because they were **oblivious** to the true nature of the Bolshevik regime. Most of the **atrocities** perpetrated by the Communists were fully reported in the West. I've made an effort to monitor the news out of the Soviet Union since immigrating to the United States and can testify to this. Take Sergey Melgounov's book, *The Red Terror in Russia*, which has become a **seminal** work in the field. As early as 1925, he exposed the arrests and summary executions of any who opposed the regime. Or take the English journalist, Malcolm Muggeridge, who published his *Winter in Moscow*

in 1934. That brave man did much to **debunk** the glowing portraits that many journalists, like I. F. Stone and Walter Duranty, were painting of the Soviet system. Muggeridge not only laid bare the horrors of the government-induced famine in the Soviet Union that **devastated** the countryside and caused the death of upwards of six million people, but the **complicity** of Western news media in **censoring** news of it. He reported that there were literally millions of **indigent** people, including children, wandering the countryside, desperate for food, and dying in the streets, a situation that should have inspired **indignation** on the part of the western press. Ironically, the people of the Ukraine had already been **subjugated** by the Stalinist **regime**. Their deaths were almost entirely **gratuitous**.

"Or take Gregor Maximoff's book *The Guillotine at Work: Twenty Years of Terror in Soviet Russia*, which was published in 1940. It systematically exposed the realities of Marxism-Leninism in practice, principally what he called the 'slaveholding democracy' ruled by Communist Party **patricians** in Soviet Russia. All of these works were widely available in the West.

"Tragically, many Western intellectuals consciously **abetted** the **genocide** and were **complicit** in the **deception** that attempted to cover up the horrors inside the Soviet Union. This was because many sympathized with its ultimate goals and saw these as necessary steps to achieving the **utopian** dream. Remember, it was **Lincoln Steffans**, one of the leading American **muckraking** journalists, who, after a visit to the Soviet Union, said 'I have seen the future and it works.' I call it a form of **self-delusion**, fostered by a religious **infatuation** with the Idea of the Utopia.

"But the **revolutionary** mindset goes back much farther than that. It was the architect of the bloody **French Revolution, Robespierre,** who said that 'one can't expect to make an omelet without breaking eggs.' Millions of innocent people have died since 1917, but I've yet to see them make a single omelet. They can build mighty dams and factories, but they can't fashion an environment in which freedom and the human spirit are **revered.** In reality, both the theory and the practice of Communism are **inherently** evil and need to be **eradicated** from the face of the earth."

"Have you had any contact with Russians who escaped the **Great Purge,** or from Soviet control?" Eric asked.

"A few. Most are undoubtedly arrested before they can manage to escape. I have a friend in Chicago, an engineer, who made it out alive because he was on a temporary work assignment in Turkey. He told me that the **NKVD** began arresting thousands of innocent people in 1937 – and they did it without any effort at concealment. Party members and non-Party members alike were taken right out of their offices or factories in plain view of their co-workers. The **NKVD** reached to the upper **echelons** of society as well, arresting top Party men, **commissars,** generals, even people inside the Kremlin. **Impugning** the patriotism of dedicated Party men and women cast a **pall** over all of Soviet society, paralyzing the population. People were scared stiff that they would be next, but unable to avoid their fate because they had nowhere to go and were prevented from leaving the country.

"What's particularly **aggravating** is the **complicity** of the Roosevelt administration in **sanctioning** this brutal regime, after Presidents Wilson, Harding, Coolidge and Hoover all **adamantly** refused to grant it recognition. The die was cast in 1933 when Roosevelt extended diplomatic recognition to the Soviet Union, despite its gross violations of human rights and the **genocide** it had already **perpetrated** against its own citizens. Roosevelt **rationalized** his decision by **purportedly** extracting certain **concessions** from Stalin, among them promises that the Soviet Union would refrain from attempting to subvert our government or support groups inside the United States engaging in such activities. But, these were hollow concessions that the Soviet Union had no intention of living up to. Nor did Roosevelt insist upon the **repatriation** of American citizens who had been illegally detained, or arrested, by the Soviet Union, many of whom were in slave labor camps.

"From that date forward, the Roosevelt administration has advanced the myth of American-Soviet **accord** by pretending that Soviet-directed and financed espionage does not exist. It was a **blatant** retreat from reality that **jettisoned** any **semblance** of morality or honesty. Not only is the Roosevelt administration riddled with Communists and **fellow travelers**, but the Communist Party USA, which operates with virtual impunity within our borders, is directly financed by Moscow. And things have gotten far worse now that the Soviets have become our wartime allies, and criticism of their regime is considered almost unpatriotic in official circles. Furthermore, the President and his supporters are **loath** to criticize them for fear of puncturing this **insidious** myth, and administrative officials are expected to fall in line with the grand charade. This effectively **emasculates** our country's ability to counteract Soviet espionage on multiple levels."

"Natalia told us that your brother was a **Bolshevik**. Is that true?"

"Yes, sad to say, Ellen. He was several years older than I and received a scholarship to Moscow State University in 1915. Once there, he was swept up in the **euphoria** surrounding the Bolshevik movement and soon **succumbed** to **Marxist-Leninist doctrine**. I **attribute** it to his professors there, many of whom were Marxists. The University had become a **bastion** of radical thought. Of course, much of the population was already **disgruntled** with the Tsarist regime. Many of his fellow students were similarly drawn to the **fallacious** communist ideology, believing it to be a **panacea** for all of Russia's **domestic** ills under the Tsarist government. They **manifested** a blistering **disdain** for the **monarchy, deprecated** the **aristocracy** generally, and **scapegoated** capitalists and those with even a **modicum** of property. The problem is, they failed to grasp that Russia was just emerging from a **predominately** agricultural economy whose farming methods were practically **antediluvian**, and had not yet embraced capitalism and the modern industrial economy. Since then, Communism has spread like a **corrosive blight** across the landscape and bred **fanatical adherents**. There were few **iconoclasts** around to challenge the **prevailing** political **ethos**. The peasant class had no **context** by which to contrast the more limited brutality of the czarist regime with the violence that the Bolsheviks were to systematically **mete** out after they took control.

"It was during this time that my brother began to attend these **incendiary** political rallies at which Lenin, Trotsky and other Bolsheviks delivered the most **mendacious** political **orations, exhorting** their **boisterous** followers to topple the existing capitalist system, a system that had not even taken hold in Russia. It was not an environment in which one could remain **complacent** or **retiring**. He listened as one **bombastic** speaker after another **inflamed** the populace, and was **captivated** by their **grandiloquence** and **scathing**

indictments of capitalism. And these views were reinforced by one of his professors at the University, a **zealot** who served as his political **mentor** in the field of **Marxist-Leninist doctrine**. Before long, he became totally **credulous** and began **regurgitating** the party line. What was it that **Kipling** said? 'If you can keep your head when all about you are losing theirs...' It would have taken a will stronger than mine to resist the **confluence** of pressures to which he was subject at that time, and break through his **intransigence**.

When he returned home on school holidays, I **beseeched** him in the strongest possible terms to abandon his **infatuation** with **Bolshevism**. My **dilemma** was that I lacked the knowledge and **rhetorical** skills to engage in effective **disputation** with him and **rebut** his **blatantly** false **assertions**. He **reproved** me **vehemently** for **undermining** his views and not getting on board with what he saw as the wave of the future. He exhibited a **vociferous antagonism** to the capitalist system and considered me the political equivalent of a religious **heretic**. His views were totally **antithetical** to my own, but advanced with a lot of clever **sophistry**. And, unfortunately, my father, who shared my views, lacked the education to **refute** his opinions and act as an effective **arbiter** of our differences. It was a **dichotomy** we simply could not bridge. But, I was **resolute** and would not compromise my principles.

"Even then, I could see what the **Bolsheviks** were about and knew it would end in disaster for the Russian people. Too many of the uneducated masses were attracted by an **amorphous**, yet **corrosive**, movement whose ultimate **delineations** were still **inchoate**, and subject to the **whims** of a small **coterie** of leaders. They simply failed to exercise what little critical **faculties** they possessed. Lenin was, in reality, **aloof** from the hopes and **aspirations** of the common workingman, but he had an ability to unite the **disparate** groups in the country into a working **coalition** by fanning their grievances. Employing his class warfare **rhetoric**, he **expounded** upon **alleged** capitalist **avarice** in a **cynical** effort to gain support of the **disaffected** classes. He also **fomented** a mood of **covetousness** – one of the seven deadly sins – against the **bourgeoisie** to advance his political goals.

"I think what allowed him to succeed was that people in each of these **heterogeneous** groups – peasants, industrial workers, civil servants, intellectuals – often with conflicting goals, read their hopes and aspirations into **amorphous**, but ultimately meaningless, Bolshevik slogans, like 'Forward.' Ultimately, of course, Lenin was far worse than the **despot** he replaced, and every last **vestige** of freedom was **eradicated** from the Russian landscape. And if Lenin wasn't bad enough, Stalin is evil **incarnate**.

"While I was not necessarily a supporter of **Tsar Nicholas**, I knew that he was far preferable to what replaced him. Most of the common folk, whether

impoverished peasants or **destitute** workers, were simply too **docile** to challenge the Marxist **juggernaut**, and were quite willing to **jettison** the Tsar for an uncertain future and a **dynamic** they could not **fathom**. Those **aggrieved** by the Bolsheviks were roundly **derided** for being capitalist **stooges**. The political tide was definitely moving in the wrong direction. Sadly, with each visit, my brother and I became progressively more **estranged,** and our conversations increasingly **divisive**. Our attempts to **reconcile** the political divide ultimately proved **fruitless**."

"What about the spy network in the United States? Are these mostly recent immigrants, or are any of them homegrown?" Ellen inquired.

"Eric, I must say, your daughter is **exceptionally** well informed. She exhibits an **uncanny** level of **cognitive** ability and understanding far beyond her years. And she asks the most **penetrating** questions."

"Thank you, Stan, but her mother and I can't take much credit for it. She's a **voracious** reader and has superior **analytical** powers for her age. And next to her religious faith, she reveres liberty above all."

"As to your question, Ellen, the Communists in this country are mostly recent immigrants, operating under strict instructions from their party handlers through the **Communist Party USA**. The Party is controlled and financed by the Soviet Union, as I indicated, despite its **protestations** to the contrary. But, some are homegrown, recruited from among the ranks of **academia**, labor unions, the **socialists**, and politically active members of the left-wing, but also falling under Party control. Idealistic, but **naïve**, college students are particularly **susceptible** to the **siren call** of Marxist ideology. Some of these young Americans, many of them indoctrinated by their college professors, volunteered for the **Abraham Lincoln Brigade** and fought on the so-called 'Republican' side during the **Spanish Civil War**. Many died there, victims of a **cynical manipulation**. These are the types Lenin referred to as 'useful idiots,' those willing to blindly accept the **dogmatic** party line and **quiescently** follow instructions from party leaders.

"Usually, they are recruited through **front organizations** that **magnanimously** proclaim some noble enterprise, but which are, in reality, designed to **ensnare** the **unwary** to the Communist cause. You would be amazed at the **facile** manner in which these groups manipulate idealistic young minds to eventually accept Marxist dogma, or socialist ideas. The **irony** is that the so-called **popular front**, which was a cleverly disguised effort to generate **enmity** towards Nazi Germany, masked Stalin's **accommodation** with Hitler whom he regarded as a **formidable adversary**.

"For those who are here temporarily from the Soviet Union, the failure to carry out party dictates will earn a swift reassignment home, and either imprisonment, or death. Failure to **adhere** to party directives and **exalt** the leader may also lead to assassination, or an accident – if you know what I mean. The party **hierarchy** tolerates neither **insubordination** nor political **apostasy**. It's next to impossible to simply walk away. Just look at what happened to Walter Krivitsky, Leon Trotsky, or my brother."

"What troubles me is how the Communists use our political system's freedoms to undermine it," Eric observed.

"Exactly! But, the fact that they exploit the constitutional liberties provided by **bourgeois** democratic societies in order to destroy them is a basic component of Marxist **dialectics**.

"So, tell me, Ellen, what do you know about the theft of the Emerson art collection? Natalia tells me that Konstantin Ivanov may be **implicated**."

"Yes. That's correct. Do you know him, Mr. Boroskova?"

"Yes. We've long suspected him of being a **fence** for property stolen by Communist operatives to fund their activities. He's been in Gary since 1928 or '29, and has been in business since 1934, I believe. He's sympathetic to the Soviet government, although I'm not sure if he's actually a Communist Party member. Most Communists aren't public about their **affiliation** with the party, anyway. And, as a businessman, he would certainly not want such an affiliation to be known, for fear of harming his business."

"We tracked him to his home in Aetna," Natalia interjected.

"Yes, we know that house. It was the office of the **Aetna Power Company**, until it closed in 1919. He acquired it about three years ago. It's certainly more **secluded** than his store, which is on a congested business block," Stan continued. "I know that his home has been used as a gathering place for Communist Party members on a number of occasions. Paul Baukus shadowed a couple of party members there last month."

"I wonder if Paul might have some idea where they might have taken the art collection?" Veronika interjected.

"That's a thought. Why don't I phone him right now and see if he can shed some light on the situation. I'd love for you to meet him, anyway."

Stan picked up the telephone from the end table next to his chair and dialed.

"Hello. Family Hotel? I'd like to speak with Paul Baukus. Would you see if he's in his room?" A minute later, he came to the phone.

"Paul? Yes, this is Stan Boroskova ... Fine, and you? ... Say, are you free this afternoon? ... You are? Good! Would you mind coming over to our house in a few minutes? I want you to meet the niece I told you about and her friends from Connecticut. ... O.K. See you soon.

"Paul has a room in the Family Hotel at 13th and Adams, and is a member of St. Casimir's. He was one of the first Lithuanians to settle in Gary, arriving shortly after the city was founded. He's an **exemplary** Lithuanian patriot and despises the Bolsheviks, particularly after they occupied Lithuania in 1940. He's also been a member of our group since its inception in 1928."

Fifteen minutes later, there was knock at the front door.

Chapter 19

A Lithuanian Pays a Visit

"Come in, Paul! Come in!"

Paul Baukus was an **amiable** looking man, short in stature, of medium build, with a dark complexion, blue eyes, and thinning gray hair. He appeared to be in his early sixties. He was dressed in blue gabardine trousers and a blue work shirt. A gold tooth was visible when he smiled. Ellen immediately took a liking to his easygoing, **avuncular** manner and calm **disposition**. He was completely **unpretentious** and spoke with a decidedly foreign accent.

"Paul, I want you to meet my niece, and her friends from Connecticut. This is Natalia, my brother Vlad's only daughter I spoke to you about. After her parents were killed, she lived with relatives outside of Moscow. A few months ago, she managed to escape to the West by way of Sweden. She just arrived in Gary on Monday. And this is Eric Anderson and his daughter, Ellen, from Stratford, Connecticut. They were instrumental in helping Natalia **elude** some Soviet agents on the train from New York. We are deeply grateful to them."

"I'm pleased to meet you all," Paul replied.

"Have a seat, Paul. Can we offer you some lemonade and pastries?"

"Why, yes, thank you, Veronika."

"So, tell me, Natalia, how did you manage to **elude** the Soviet authorities? I thought the borders were locked down pretty tight," Paul inquired.

"Well, the fact that the war was raging along the **Eastern Front** presented both **perils** and opportunities. I was willing to risk running the **gauntlet** between the Russian and German lines to make my way to the Baltic coast. I escaped through German-occupied Lithuania and boarded a fishing trawler to Sweden. It was a **harrowing** experience, and one that I'll never be able to forget."

"Lithuania, you say. I haven't been home since 1902. I'm sure it's changed a great deal since then. So, what did you do for a passport? I assume the Soviets confiscated yours after your parents were killed?"

"I didn't have one until I got to Kaunas. That's where I was introduced to a remarkable woman by the name of **Madeleine Avietenaite**, the former head of the Lithuanian Red Cross and, later, the Lithuanian Information Service. She was running a **clandestine** publishing operation, cleverly **juxtaposed** above an **infirmary**. It was a brilliant **artifice**. She and **Father Stasys Yla,** a courageous Roman Catholic priest, were publishing **samizdat** newspapers there, right under the noses of the Nazis. They succeeded in securing forged documents for me and a group of Lithuanian Jews who, after suffering from virulent **anti-Semitism**, were desperately trying to escape before being arrested by the **Gestapo**. Of course, passports would have meant nothing to the Soviets because they wouldn't have allowed me to leave anyway. But, they were useful with officials in Sweden and England, through which I had to pass."

"**Madeleine Avietenaite**? I know that name. She was the Commissioner-General of the **Lithuanian Pavilion** at the **New York World's Fair** in

1939 – an extraordinary woman by any measure. I read about her in *Draugas*, the Lithuanian newspaper. And what about you, Eric? What brings you to Gary?"

"I'm here on business for a few weeks. I'm doing some tool design for Gary Armor Plate, off Dunes Highway. I brought Ellen along because her mother had to stay home to care for Ellen's grandmother. We're living on the East Side, near Emerson School."

"Emerson? Say, I read all about the theft of its art collection in Friday's paper. In fact, they published a list of all the missing paintings in this morning's edition – thirty-three in all, I believe. The Emerson community must be all up in arms. I hope they catch the thieves and put 'em behind bars."

"That's what we'd like to talk to you about, Mr. Baukus," Ellen explained. "We believe that Konstantin Ivanov may be **culpable** in some way in the theft and thought you might be able to shed some light on him."

"Knowing Konstantin, I'm not at all surprised. But, what leads you to believe he may be involved, Ellen?"

"Because we found a fragment of a business card for Crimean Imports in the Emerson basement, near the coal delivery door through which they probably removed the paintings. It was a stupid lapse on someone's part. Imagine leaving your calling card at the scene of a crime. Of course, it was just a scrap of evidence, but there was sufficient information on it to **deduce** that it was from Crimean Imports." Ellen purposefully **refrained** from telling Paul about the painting the girls had seen hanging in Ivanov's home so as not to reveal to her father that they had broken in.

"You don't say? Well, it's very possible your suspicions are correct. As far as I'm concerned, Konstantin Ivanov is a **disreputable scoundrel**, as well as a **shrewd** businessman. His **cupidity** knows no bounds. He's been in Gary for... oh, about fifteen years. I did some carpentry work for him when he first opened his store on Washington Street. Later, he had me do some furniture repair when he acquired damaged items at estate sales – at least he said they were estate sales. I used to think that he was just a **shrewd** businessman, but now I'm convinced that many of his **acquisitions** are stolen property which he **doctors** up to disguise their origins. He seems to have an unnatural **predilection** for dealing in **purloined** items. I also came to know the types of **unscrupulous** characters he associates with."

"So, you think some of them may have been criminals or, perhaps, Communists?" Ellen continued.

"Or, a little bit of both," Paul added.

"Crimean Imports? Interesting name. Where do you think he got it?" Ellen inquired.

"**Sevastopol**."

"Sevastopol?"

"Yes. Ivanov was born in Sevastopol, on the **Crimean Peninsula**."

"So, what makes you think some of his friends are Communists?"

"Because I know some of them. One of them attends St. Casimir's, but he's no believer. For him, it's a Lithuanian social club, and his attendance is **perfunctory** at best. It's simply a place where he can **espouse** his ideology and speak Lithuanian. Not that he's **irreverent** by any means, but he doesn't have the religious **fervor** or sincerity of a true believer. It beats me how he can **reconcile** religious faith with an **atheistic** political **philosophy**."

"What's his name?" Natalia inquired.

"Juozas Adomaitis. That's 'Joseph' in English."

"What else do you know about him?"

"He's a Communist party member, or, at the very least, a **fellow traveler**. Whenever I speak with him, he never misses an opportunity to **extol** the virtues of Stalin and the Soviet Union, and **rail** against capitalists. He thinks I must have warmed up to the regime since they became our wartime allies. But, I try not to **contradict** him. Better to let him hang himself, **rhetorically** speaking that is. But, while he's a sympathizer, he's not an activist."

"Do you also know a Boris Sokolov?"

"Sure. He's part of the same bunch. Lives over on Tyler Street, near the park. I understand he's got a stepdaughter named Tanya who attends Froebel School. Perhaps you girls can **insinuate** yourself into her confidence and learn something about what her father's up to?"

"Isn't Boris Sokolov on our list, Ellen?" Natalia asked.

"Yes, he's at 1176 Tyler."

"I'm sure Ellen and I can devise some strategy for meeting her. In fact, we met some girls from Froebel High School at the beach on Friday and started **discreetly** asking questions."

"My brother-in-law, Jacob Zvingilas, plays cards with some Lithuanians and Russians at Norton Park. Boris Sokolov and another Russian, Mike Ivanski, are among them. I've asked Jacob to keep his ears open."

"Mike Ivanski? Do you mean Mikhail Ivanski?"

"Yes, that's the same man, only with the Russian spelling."

"I tried looking him up in the city directories at the library, but couldn't find him. He was supposed to be living at 1209 Johnson Street."

"Yes, he's still there, just as on the documents Natalia brought from London," Stan observed.

"That's good. I'll mark that in my notes," Ellen replied.

"So, Paul, Stan tells us you've been in Gary a long time," Eric inquired.

"That's right. Almost from the beginning. It'll be thirty-five years next month. I arrived in September 1907, from Saginaw, Michigan, where I worked in a coal mine. I followed my cousin, Anthony Baukus, from Michigan. He was a building contractor. Tony and I were the first Lithuanians in Gary. I helped him build many of the houses in the Central District, Baukus Hall, and St. Hedwig's, the Polish Church on the east side of Broadway."

"Where in Lithuania do you come from?" Eric inquired.

"A tiny place nobody's ever heard of called Paezerai – Lakeside Village, in English. It's in the **Suwalki** province near the Polish border. My father, who I **venerated**, was a poor peasant who **augmented** his **meager** earnings by fishing in the local lakes and streams and selling his catch to the Jewish fish merchants. It wasn't terribly **lucrative,** but we got by. I lived a somewhat **nomadic** existence in my youth. Lithuanians were **stigmatized** in those days. We were under the control of the Czar politically, and the Polish aristocracy **economically**, particularly in the eastern sector of the country near the Polish border. With my father's help, I **emigrated** at the age of sixteen to avoid **conscription** into the Russian army. I made my way to **Glasgow,** where I found an apartment in the Gorbals, a **notorious** working class district. You see, it was a lot cheaper to travel to Scotland than to New York. I spent four years working at the Glengarnock Steel Works outside of Glasgow, and saving enough money to come to America. I still remember when **King Edward VII** visited Glasgow in 1903, two years after his **coronation**. We were given the day off from work to witness the procession. But, **monarchy** never held much appeal to me, having left that behind in Russia. After sailing to New York, I traveled to Michigan, and then to Gary.

"My sister, Aggie, followed me to Glasgow, where she met my brother-in-law,

Jacob Zvingilas. They were married in 1903. Two years later, they also left for New York, with their infant daughter, Annie. They lived in **Waterbury, Connecticut** for three years, and had two more children there before leaving for Gary. I helped them build their first house at 1712 Adams Street in 1912, next to the **Neighborhood House**. Ten years later, they bought a three-flat apartment house on Jackson Street next to the Greek Orthodox Church. She and her husband now have seven children, all of them grown. My nephew, Vincent, joined the **Marians**, a Catholic re-

ligious order, and took on the **vocation** of printer and typesetter for **Draugas**, the Lithuanian Catholic newspaper in Chicago that I mentioned earlier. I have another nephew, Frank Zvingilas, who's a crane operator in the Slab Conditioning Department of the Sheet and Tin Mill. He works with Stan. My nephew, Sam, works in the grocery business for Bill Schwimmer, and Algirdus is a welder at U.S. Steel. Another nephew – Edward – just graduated from

Purdue University in May with a degree in Chemical Engineering and was hired by Sinclair Oil. He's the first college graduate in the family. We're very proud of him. I also have two nieces: Anne Petrauskas, who works at Western Electric in Cicero, Illinois, and Estelle, who's a legal secretary for Leon Grinnell, a lawyer on Broadway. She married Charles Dobrowolsky, another Purdue graduate.

"That's all the family I've got in Gary. I've always been a bachelor. And it's why I have no **compunctions** about being involved in this effort to **confound** the Soviet's efforts to undermine this country. I had always feared that Lithuania's hold on independence was **tenuous** at best, what with the Soviet Union on her doorstep. I anticipated that the incidents that the Soviet Union routinely provoked along the border would be a **harbinger** of things to come.

No matter how **vigilant** she might be, she could never hope to overcome the size and strength of Soviet military might, not to mention their **treachery.** I pray that she will regain her independence one day. That's what **motivates** me."

"How are the Lithuanians holding out right now, Paul?" Eric inquired.

"Terribly, I'm afraid. Shortly after war broke out in 1939, the Red Army captured **Vilnius,** which had been under Polish control since 1920. But, while the Soviets transferred the city to nominal Lithuanian control, its army asserted control over the whole country in 1940 and forced the formation of a pro-Soviet government. They also **nationalized** all land to gain support from the poorer peasants, and substantially raised taxes to **bankrupt** farmers. Thousands of people whom the Soviets considered a potential threat to their rule were killed or arrested, including teachers, priests, government officials, military officers, policemen, members of the **intelligentsia** – anyone with influence. Many were sent to **Siberia,** and many died there, or on the forced journey.

"Not surprisingly, the Lithuanians initially welcomed the Germans in 1941 when **Operation Barbarossa** promised to drive the Soviets out. It took the Germans only a week to occupy the country, but not before the Red Army brutally massacred several thousand Lithuanians during their retreat. The German army has been only marginally better in its treatment of the Lithuanian people, and that's where we are now. It's painful to **contemplate** how much my countrymen have suffered at the hands of these two evil empires."

"And to think the Soviets are supposed to be our allies," Ellen replied. "It's sickening."

"Where do you work now, Paul?" Eric inquired.

"I'm working at Radigan Brothers furniture, on Broadway, doing minor repairs and uncrating new shipments. It pays my bills."

"How would you suggest we put Konstantin Ivanov under surveillance, Mr. Baukus?" Ellen inquired. "We think it's possible that he's hiding some of those paintings in the backroom of his store on Washington Street. If not, he may be using his delivery truck to transport them out of Gary. If he has any sense, he'd fence them in the Chicago area where they'd be more difficult to trace, or in some other major **metropolitan** area. After all, the titles and descriptions of all of the paintings have been published in the *Gary Post-Tribune,* as you mentioned."

"Perhaps we can find someone on Adams Street whose alleyway looks across to the back of his establishment. That way, you could stake out the back of his store and monitor its activities without his getting wise," Paul suggested.

"That's it!" Natalia shouted. "We know just such a business. Don't you remember, Ellen? We saw it yesterday, when we investigated the alley behind Crimean Imports. It's the Balkan Bakery that fronts on Adams Street. Uncle

Stan and Aunt Veronika are customers of the bakery. In fact, we're eating their pastries at this very moment. What do you think, Uncle Stan?"

"That's a great idea. I'm sure Alex Christoff would be glad to help us. If you'd like, we can drive over there and speak with him this week."

"Why, that's just a half block from the hotel where I room," Paul interjected.

"In the meantime," Ellen suggested, "I'd like to visit the police station tomorrow morning to get a look at the plaster impressions they made of the tire tracks found behind Emerson and see if they match the rubbings I made on Saturday. That would confirm his involvement. After that, we'll check with you about doing some surveillance in the back of the Balkan Bakery."

"Ellen, we forgot to tell Paul about Dimitri Poliakov," Natalia suggested.

"That's right, Mr. Baukus. With the help of the local mailman we traced another one of the names on our list – Dimitri Poliakov – to the University of Chicago campus. Prior to that, he was living with his brother at 1522 Van Buren."

"Yes, Stan told me about him. I don't know him, but I believe this is significant because it may give us a linkage to their Chicago operations. Perhaps he's part of a cell in the **Hyde Park** neighborhood that may be monitoring the secret work going on at the University of Chicago. He bears **scrutiny**. When the time is right, we'll have to take a trip to Chicago and shadow him."

"Well, it's getting to be our dinner time," Ellen's father suggested. "I want to thank you for your hospitality, and for the refreshments, Veronika. This has been a most enlightening afternoon. I've learned a great deal."

"We both have," Ellen added.

"Oh, think nothing of it. We enjoyed your company very much. We love sharing stories and **anecdotes** about our homeland. It's a form of **therapy** for us, somewhat **analogous** to a **psychiatrist's** couch, and a lot cheaper," said Stan.

"Let me drive you back to the East Side," Stan suggested. "I don't want you walking all the way back, or waiting an hour for the next streetcar."

As they drove back over to the East Side, Ellen reminded Natalia and her uncle that she would be back soon to visit the **Balkan Bakery**.

By the time Ellen and her father entered the back door of their Carolina Street apartment, it was almost six o'clock. When she heard them, Mrs. Matheus poked her head into the back stairway and invited them to join her for supper.

"Thank you, Eleanor, but you don't have to do that," Eric replied.

"It's no bother, really. I could use the company. It's been rather lonely here since Ernest left to join the **Seabees**."

Ellen and her father could sense that she was lonely with her son in the service. She invited them to sit in her front parlor while she prepared ham and beans.

"So where have you two been today?" Eleanor called out from the kitchen, while she stirred the beans. "Church can't have lasted that long, unless the preacher was especially long-winded."

"Well, after going to the First Methodist Church and having brunch at Hotel Gary, we walked to Natalia Boroskova's uncle's home on Lincoln Street," Eric explained. "Natalia's uncle was far more **loquacious** than the preacher we heard this morning, but we enjoyed every minute of it."

"You walked all that way? My word, you've got more energy than I have."

"I didn't mind it at all. I enjoyed the exercise. And Ellen's got boundless energy. Once there, we both got an education about life in the Soviet Union."

"I can only imagine what it's like there," Mrs. Matheus replied. "My goodness! I've been reading about the Battle of Stalingrad in the *Post Tribune*."

As they sat down to eat, the conversation turned to Sweden and the reasons why Mrs. Matheus left home.

"After graduating from high school in Sweden, I wanted to study nursing, but my parents couldn't afford it. So, I thought, I might as well seek my fortune in America. I left Gothenburg in September 1909 and sailed to Hull, England. From there, I took a train to Liverpool, where I boarded the **Mauretania**. My, what a beautiful ship that was – and fast! I arrived in New York on

September 25, 1909. I remember the date so **vividly**. The Statue of Liberty made a lasting impression on me, after which I spent half a day on **Ellis Island**, moving from one line to the next, and answering a lot of questions, like who was going to vouch for me in America, how much money did I have, and was I an **anarchist** – can you imagine? Me, an **anarchist**?

After a brief **sojourn** in New Jersey with my brother, Fred, I took the Pennsylvania Special to Chicago. My good friend, Alma Anderson, from **Svanskog**, had already settled there and invited me to share an apartment with her. I was only twenty-two when I arrived, and lonely. I met Ivar Carlson in 1913 and gave birth to a little girl in April of the following year – Alvida

Linnea. Ivar and I never married and, soon, he drifted out of my life. I earned my living by keeping house and cooking for wealthy people in Chicago. I married Ben Matheus in 1917 and had three more children, two girls and a boy. We moved to Gary in 1922. Ernest – the one in the **Seabees** – is my youngest.

My three girls are all married now. Two are in Gary and one lives in Milwaukee. Alvida lives on Jackson Street, near the Greek Church, and Helen lives on Idaho Street in Aetna, above her in-laws. She married Russell Siler, whose father has a plumbing business. But, he's serving in the **Seabees** right now, just like my Ernest. They have a little boy now – Glennie – who was born in March. Here's a photograph of my daughters, Alvida Linnea and Helen, taken last Easter. That's Alvida on the left and Helen on the right. My daughter, Alice, married Ray Hanaway and settled down in Milwaukee. They have two children: Don, who'll be three in December, and Janice, who's a year old. This photo was taken of them a couple of years ago when they were in Gary. Ray's a wonderful son-in-law.

"You see, when Mr. Matheus moved to Milwaukee in 1930 to look for work, he took Helen and Alice with him. Alvida and Ernest stayed home with me. It was our way of coping with the Depression. I had to fend for myself by running a boarding house for steelworkers, mostly Swedish, and cooking for wealthy people. They liked my cooking. Times were tough during the Depression, but **austerity** was the common lot of most of the people in Gary, so we learned to accept it. I've been cooking for Dr. Bills for about five years now. I rented this house last year. So, far, it's worked

out all right. Helen came back to Gary after graduating from high school in

Milwaukee. She's the smart one in the family – a real bookworm. Both she and Alice were married in 1938. Since then, it's been just me and Ernest. That's why I was sorry to see him enlist in the Navy, though I tried my best to

dissuade him – after all, he was only seventeen. He's at **Great Lakes Naval Training Station** right now. He's a good boy and sends me most of his pay. I just hope this war doesn't last too long and he'll return home safely."

"As do we, Mrs. Matheus," Eric replied.

"Now, can I interest you in some pumpkin pie and coffee?"

"You don't have to twist our arms when it comes to pumpkin pie, or any kind of pie for that matter," Ellen replied, smiling.

Conversation came to a virtual halt while they consumed their pie.

"My, that was good, Eleanor. May I call you Eleanor?"

"Certainly, Eric. I want us to be on a first name basis. Incidentally, I make the pie with Carnation Evaporated Milk. It gives it that rich taste."

"I'll have to remind Edna about that. Say, may we help you with the dishes?"

"No, thank you very much, but I wouldn't think of putting my guests to work. I'll just do them up while I listen to the radio."

"Radio! I almost forgot, Dad, *Inner Sanctum*'s on tonight!"

"Well, then I think we'd better call it a night, Eleanor. Ellen wouldn't think of missing *Inner Sanctum*. She missed it last Sunday when we were on the Twentieth Century Limited, and I never heard the end of it. Thanks, again, for dinner."

Before retiring to their apartment, Ellen took the opportunity to telephone Mrs. Mildred Wirt and arrange a Tuesday afternoon appointment with the late school superintendent's widow who headed up Auditorium programs for the Gary Public Schools.

By the time they got upstairs, it was seven o'clock and just in time to tune in to *Edgar Bergen and Charlie McCarthy*. Ellen and her father always got a kick out of the wisecracking Charlie's **witticisms**:

Edgar: "When I see a pretty girl, it makes me want to get married."
Charlie: "Aren't you buying a saddle after the horse is in the glue factory?"

Edgar: "Charlie, I hope you've been doing your homework."

Charlie: "I can't take this schoolwork anymore – it's driving me nuts."

Edgar: "Well, Charlie, I'm sorry, but hard work never killed anyone."

Charlie: "Still, there's no use taking chances."

At seven thirty, the **whimsical** wise-cracks of Charlie McCarthy were **super-seded** by the sound of the creaking door that heralded the opening of Ellen's favorite program, *Inner Sanctum*, with host Raymond Edward Johnson:

Good evening friends of the creaking door. This is your host, inviting you into the Inner Sanctum, once again. Come in. You're early tonight. The **coroner** *hasn't arrived yet, but it's all right. The corpse is here. Yes, that's him over there in the corner, the slightly* **decapitated** *gentleman sitting with his head in his hands... ha, ha, ha ...*

Ellen enhanced the mood by switching off the floor lamp so she and her father could listen in darkness to "Dead Man's Magic." Then, it was off to bed.

Chapter 20

Gathering Evidence

Ellen awoke to a **torrential** rainstorm on Monday morning, with sizable raindrops glancing off her bedroom window. It was nine thirty and her father had already left for work. After finishing a bowl of Post Toasties and a glass of grapefruit juice, she heard Mrs. Matheus calling her from the back stairwell.

"Ellen... telephone for you..."

"I'll be right down, Mrs. Matheus."

Ellen put on her bathrobe and slippers and scurried down the stairs into her landlady's front parlor.

"Thank you, Mrs. Matheus... Hello, this is Ellen."

"Ellen? It's Natalia. I got a call this morning from Helen Feczko, you know, the Froebel student we met at the beach on Friday."

"Yes, I remember her. The one who lives on Van Buren Street."

"That's right. She's been doing a little investigating for us and found out that Stasha Poliakov should be attending the dance on Tuesday evening at the Miramar Ballroom. Here's our chance to talk to her. It's a 'back to school' dance, and we're going!"

"Who's playing?"

"Somebody named **Tommy Dorsey**."

"Tommy Dorsey! Are you kidding? That's fabulous! Will **Frank Sinatra** be with him?"

"I think that's what she said. And a group called the Pied Pipers."

"Wow! I can't believe it. What time should I meet you?"

"The doors open at seven thirty, but Helen advises us to arrive early to make sure we get in. She says there's bound to be a big crowd. Uncle Stan and I can pick you up at seven. Perhaps Melanie would like to join us?"

"I'm sure she'd love to come. It's not often that one gets the chance to hear Tommy Dorsey and Frank Sinatra. I'll ask her as soon as we get off the phone."

"Aunt Veronika has offered to take me to Gordon's this afternoon to help me pick out a new dress. She's taken charge of my wardrobe, such as it is. She says I don't have anything suitable for dancing. She also says my **underpinnings** need **refurbishment** – whatever that means. She also knows where to get nylons on the black market since they stopped making them. She says that the manufacturers have shifted their operations to the production of parachutes and other war-related products. Either that, or she says I'll have to paint black

BRINGS BEAUTY
TO BARE LEGS

Goes on so Easily

Lasts so long

Only 40c at
Drug and
Department
Stores...

"Stocking Stick"

LEG MAKE-UP

The Armand Co., Des Moines 6, Iowa

seam lines on the back of my legs to **simulate** stockings. I'm putting myself in her hands. **Sartorial** elegance was a luxury we couldn't afford back in the Soviet Union. Everything I wore was so **utilitarian**."

"I'm sure you're going to be the belle of the ball. By the way, I've arranged an interview with Mrs. Mildred Wirt, the widow of the late school superintendent, for Tuesday afternoon at one o'clock. I'd like you to meet me in front of the Ambassador Apartments at 6th and Monroe Street a few minutes before one. We'll have plenty of time to get ready for the dance after our meeting."

"Sure thing, Ellen. I'll be there."

Though the heavy downpour was not **abating**, Ellen was not about to let the day go to waste. She had planned to have Melanie accompany her to the police station on Monday morning, but discovered that she was out running errands for her mother. She turned on the radio and learned that thunderstorms were expected to last until late afternoon. After dressing, and borrowing an umbrella from Mrs. Matheus, she dashed off down 7th Avenue in the direction of the Gary Municipal Building on Massachusetts Street, which housed the police and fire departments. With an air of confidence, she approached a large oak desk in the lobby. A **morose** looking officer looked up from a copy of *Police Gazette*.

"Excuse me, sergeant, but I'd like to examine the evidence collected at Emerson School on Friday."

"And who would you be, if I may ask?"

"Ellen Anderson. I'm an Emerson student, and I may have some information about the theft of the art collection."

"You don't say. And how is that?"

"Because I believe I saw a truck pulling out of the driveway early Friday morning," Ellen replied, **embellishing** the truth a bit.

Ellen could **discern** that the sergeant had serious **misgivings** about dealing with someone as young as she. Under the circumstances, she tried her best to **ingratiate** herself. It was not the first time she had dealt with **obtuse** and **pompous** police officers who were quick to dismiss the suggestions of a **perspicacious** young person. She realized that it was a problem she would have to address **tactfully**. **Mollifying** such individuals with a dose of **flattery** was a technique that had worked for her before.

"Have you been with the police department long?" she asked.

"Sixteen years, come Saturday."

"Boy, I'll bet you've worked on a lot of interesting cases?"

"You bet. I've had my share of excitement, particularly after I joined the force in '26. Things were pretty exciting in Gary during **Prohibition**. Some of the Chicago bootleggers ran wild here, mostly in the Central District. Shootings were a regular occurrence – **turf wars**, if you get my drift. Things settled down after they repealed the **Volstead Act** and legalized the sale of alcohol again."

"Did you ever think of writing a book about your experiences? If you did, I'd love to read it."

"My wife's been harping on me for years to write a book. I may do it once I've retired from the force, but not now, while I'm still working. You can never tell whose feathers you might ruffle. I have been keeping a diary, though, of all the cases I've worked on. They've involved murder, assault, **breaking and entering**, **embezzlement**, **grand larceny**, **bootlegging**, gambling, **hit and run**, **blackmail** – you name it. I've seen it all. So, what's a sweet young thing like you getting mixed up in criminal investigations? Are you sure you haven't been listening to too many detective shows on the radio? *Gangbusters*, perhaps?"

"Natural curiosity, I guess. Admittedly, I'm just a **novice** at this, but I live just a half block from Emerson and I thought I could be of some help, even if it's just keeping my eyes open. After all, it's my duty as a citizen. And, like I said, I might have seen a truck leaving the back of Emerson the night of the robbery."

"You don't say! Well, I suppose it can't hurt for you to have a look around. Come with me."

The overly **officious** sergeant **resignedly** led Ellen to an office on the second floor and introduced her to the officer in charge of the evidence room.

"George, this is Ellen Anderson, an Emerson student. She'd like to have a look at the evidence we collected at the school on Friday."

"Sure thing, Sarge."

"Well, I've gotta be getting back to my desk, missy. I hope you find what you're lookin' for."

"Thank you, sergeant."

"Well, this is our evidence room. And what would you be looking for?"

"I'm particularly interested in the plaster casts the officers made of the tire tracks behind the school."

"If you'd like to have a seat, I'll bring them out."

Ellen pulled up a chair at a large oak table in the center of the room. The officer, who was reasonably **accommodating**, opened a storeroom and brought out two plaster casts, placing them on the table in front of her. The tags attached to each read: "Emerson School – Rear Yard – Firestone All Nylon

500 – Aug. 28, 1942."

"For the life of me, I can't imagine what you hope to find," he said, **incredulously**. "Just let me know when you've finished. You know where my office is. Just leave the casts on the table here. I'll put them away."

After he left, closing the door behind him, Ellen reached in her purse and pulled out the paper rubbing she had made on Saturday in the Washington Street alleyway. She held it next to the cast. It didn't take much mental **acuity** to **discern** that one was an exact match, down to the wear marks on the outside of the tread. She had no intention of revealing her findings to the police just yet, but did plan to return to the Washington Street alleyway and confirm the make and model of the tires on the delivery truck to confirm that they corresponded to the identification on the evidence tag. Satisfied that she had learned what she came for, Ellen poked her head in the adjacent office and informed the officer that she was finished.

"Find what you were looking for, young lady?"

"No, I'm afraid it wasn't much help."

"I'm not surprised," he replied, with an air of **condescension**.

As Ellen left his office, she could hear him muttering something **dismissive** under his breath. He didn't press her for details about what she had seen, presumably because he did not take her seriously in the first place. This suited her just fine. She preferred to maintain her **anonymity** in the face of his **incompetence,** and hold her cards close to her vest.

Having **ascertained** what model tires had been identified by the police, Ellen was anxious to determine if they matched those on the Crimean Imports delivery truck. Exiting the police station, she raised her umbrella against the persistent drizzle, drew the smell of the damp morning air into her nostrils, and headed off in the direction of Broadway. Pausing briefly at the Palace Theater to examine the stills of the current offering – *The Pride of the Yankees*, with Gary Cooper – she crossed to the west side of the street and ambled

 down Broadway, crossing the Wabash Railroad tracks on her way to 11th Avenue. The west side of Broadway was filled with taverns and small businesses, including Jack's Department Store, House of Muscat Furniture, Buffalo Lunch, the Broadway Hardware & Supply, Saratoga Billiards, and, at the corner of

11th Avenue, Union Drugs. When she got to Washington Street, she was re-minded of the fascinating mix of ethnic establishments that filled the street, and the **preponderance** of taverns, cafes, restaurants and coffee houses that it harbored, each, presumably, with its own unique ethnic or working class **clientele**. Based on the **wizened countenances** of some of the pedestrians she saw on the street, however, some of whom had trouble walking a straight line, it was not an area through which she would normally have chosen to walk alone and, certainly, not at night. Under the circumstances, she wished that Melanie had joined her.

The district **exuded** a **seediness** reflecting its working class character and the lower **socio-economic status** of its residents, a number of whom were probably **transients**. It was a district to which she would normally have felt a decided **aversion**. Under the circumstances, she avoided making anything more than **nominal** eye contact with those she passed, for fear that some **un-savory** and **slovenly** old **codger** might engage her in conversation, or solicit a coin for a drink. **Suppressing** her **reticence** for the moment, she walked briskly. At the Oriental Café, at the corner of 13th and Washington, she made a beeline for the alley, quickening her pace lest she encounter a **vagrant** or other **disreputable** character in her path. **Fortuitously**, the truck she sought was still where it had been parked on Saturday morning. In the time it took her to kneel down and examine the markings on one of the sidewalls, she quickly **ascertained** that they were, in fact, Firestone All Nylon 500s, just as the evidence tag on the plaster casts indicated. With nothing more to keep her in the alley, she broke into a sprint until emerging, safely, at 13th Avenue. A minute later, she was back on Broadway and heading for home.

Chapter 21

An Appointment with Mrs. Wirt

On Tuesday afternoon, Ellen and Natalia met at the **Ambassador Apartments** for an appointment with **Mildred Harter Wirt**, the widow of the late school superintendent. Located at 6th and Monroe, across the street from the First Presbyterian Church and Jefferson Park, the Ambassador Apartments were among Gary's most fashionable. The English basement and first floor exterior were surfaced in white limestone block, the upper floors in red brick. Some of the windows, including those on the top floor, were accented with decorative design elements. The building's recessed **façade** was laid out behind an elegant, flowered courtyard. When the girls entered the lobby, they scanned the mailboxes for that of Mrs. Wirt. She was in Apartment 203. Ellen also noted the mailboxes of **Gladys Pierce** and **Henrietta Newton**, two members of the Emerson faculty whose classes she had selected on her first day in Gary. They rang Mrs. Wirt's bell.

"Yes, may I help you?" came a voice over the intercom.

"Mrs. Wirt?"

"Yes."

"This is Ellen Anderson. Natalia Boroskova and I are here for our one o'clock appointment."

"Oh, yes, Ellen, just a moment. I'll buzz you in."

Once inside the door, Ellen and Natalia walked up a single flight of stairs and found Mrs. Wirt's apartment to the right, at the far end of the corridor. They knocked. An attractive woman who appeared to be in her early forties opened the door and welcomed them. She wore a brown dress accented with a gold scarf, and large buttons down one side. Her short brown hair was parted on the left.

"We're so pleased to meet you, Mrs. Wirt. I'm Ellen Anderson and this is my friend, Natalia Boroskova."

"Russian, I presume?"

"Yes, that's right," Natalia replied.

"Please come in and make yourselves comfortable. Can I get you something to drink? Coffee? Tea? Root Beer? Squirt?"

"I'll have a Squirt, thank you," said Ellen.

"I guess I'll have the same,". Natalia replied, not

knowing what it was.

"What is Squirt, Ellen?"

"It's a citrus-flavored carbonated beverage. You'll like it."

A minute later, Mrs. Wirt returned from the kitchen with two bottles and two glasses on a small tray, and placed it on the glass-covered coffee table in front of the two **Queen Anne** wing chairs the girls occupied.

"There you are. You know, I had a number of Russian children when I taught at Froebel, as well as those from the Baltic countries, mostly Lithuanians. I also had some Russian students when I taught at Gary College. Gary has such a fascinating mix of nationalities, don't you think? It's part of its special charm. Do you girls go to school in Gary?"

"Not yet. But, we've enrolled. As a matter of fact, we're both new arrivals. I'm here temporarily with my father who is doing some war-related work at Gary Armor Plate, and Natalia arrived on the same day to live with her aunt and uncle, after escaping from the Soviet Union."

"You escaped from the Soviet Union? In wartime? How did you manage that?"

"It's a long story, Mrs. Wirt, but the short version is that my parents were killed by the Stalinist government during the purge and I was able to escape to Sweden by way of Lithuania. Frankly, I'm lucky to be alive."

"What a sad story! If the memories are not too **traumatic** for you, perhaps I could persuade you to tell it to some of our school auditorium classes. We regularly schedule guest speakers. They need to hear about the realities of life inside the Soviet Union. I'm the supervisor of auditorium programs in the Gary Public Schools, and could easily arrange it for you."

"I'd like that very much, but not right now, since I will be in school myself this year. And, besides, I'm still trying to keep a low profile, for reasons we will explain."

"Of course. I certainly understand your **reticence**. Perhaps at some future time of your choosing. Now, what is it you wanted to see me about?"

"We've heard about you and your late husband from Natalia's uncle Stan, including his testimony before the **Bulwinkle Committee**," Ellen explained, "and we'd like to learn more about it. You see, Natalia's father was a Soviet diplomat, stationed in London. He had access to secret government documents and the names of Soviet agents and supporters operating in the United States, and around the world. For some reason, however, he fell out of favor with Stalin and was liquidated. The same fate befell Natalia's mother after she tried to question the authorities about his fate. Before he died, he arranged to deliver evidence of Soviet espionage operations into Natalia's hands, and she brought it with her to the United States. It implicates Soviet **operatives** inside the federal government, and **fifth columnists** in both Chicago and Gary, among other cities. So, we know that when your husband testified before Congress, he was telling the truth about the extent of Communist subversion."

"This is startling information, particularly hearing it from young people like yourselves. I truly appreciate your interest in Dr. Wirt's case. I am convinced that the emotional stress of his brave actions ultimately led to his untimely **demise.** It's just a tragedy that not enough people were willing to listen to him. Would that more people were as politically **astute** as you are. Even now, the federal government is unwilling to confront the security threats within its own **bureaucracy.** Had they listened to Dr. Wirt back in 1934, our security would not be so heavily **compromised** today. But, I believe that his case was **symptomatic** of a deeper problem that **pervaded** the **New Deal.**"

"How so, Mrs. Wirt?"

"Well, for one thing, there was widespread sympathy for the Soviet experiment within the ranks of **New Dealers**, including those in President Roosevelt's Brain Trust. Many intellectuals, writers, academics, artists, actors, and journalists developed a **romantic** attraction to communism as an ideology. Most were hopelessly naïve and easy prey for the propaganda of the Communist Party and its front groups. They had no idea what was actually happening inside the Soviet Union and, had they been presented with the evidence, probably would not have believed it.

"It was in this political environment that many were able to **insinuate** themselves into sensitive government positions where they could do our country considerable harm. If you want to delve more deeply into these matters, I would highly recommend two books by Eugene Lyons: *Assignment in Utopia* and *The Red Decade.* Lyons spent six years in Moscow as a correspondent for the United Press and was **privy** to many horrors of the Stalin regime. He explains how Stalin was able to control the press reports leaving the Soviet Union. Basically, if you wanted to stay in the good graces of the regime, and avoid being expelled, you had to tailor your **dispatches** to suit the **censors.** As a consequence, the stories reaching the West were carefully screened to omit references unflattering to the Soviet Union. Virtually nothing of the famine, the persecution of the **Kulaks**, the slave labor camps, the **show trials**, religious persecution, the internal passport system, or the torturing of the people for their gold, silver or western currencies could pass the **scrutiny** of the **censors**.

"Many American newspapers and periodicals of opinion – the *New Republic*, *The Nation*, *The New Masses* – during this time were simply mouthpieces for Soviet propaganda. In this environment, it was fairly easy for Communists to gain employment with the federal government, or work their way around the federal bureaucracy to best serve the demands of their Soviet controllers. After the Soviet Union was invaded in June 1941, and they became our ally, criticism of the regime was actively discouraged by the administration. Those with the **effrontery** to criticize the Soviet Union are susceptible to being labeled '*red-baiters*' by the Communists in our midst and their fellow travelers in the press."

"That's incredible, Mrs. Wirt – that Stalin could kill millions of his own people and yet successfully pressure the Western press to keep it under wraps. It doesn't say much for journalistic **integrity**."

"Well, the word is out now, thanks to Mr. Lyons, and others. But, many in the liberal camp still won't accept the truth because it conflicts with their **utopian** ideals, and everything they had previously heard or read. Lyons even recounts the story of a man whose wife – a naïve liberal – had a nervous breakdown after attending one of Lyons' lectures in New York City. It appears that his tales of horror shattered her **romantic illusions** about life in the Soviet Union. The husband came to Lyons' home and begged him to visit her in the hospital and explain that what he had said wasn't true. Can you imagine? It just goes to show the depth of the human capacity for **self-delusion**."

"What were the names of those books, again? I simply must read them," Ellen replied.

"The first is *Assignment in Utopia*, published in 1938, which is the story of Lyons' six years as a United Press correspondent in the Soviet Union. *The Red Decade*, which came out last year, is his in-depth **exposé** of the Communist penetration of American life in the 1930s and early 40s. After reading *Assignment in Utopia*, and grasping the full import of the **atrocities** committed by Stalin, you will fully comprehend how naïve and gullible many Americans have been for Soviet propaganda."

"Now, I remember. That's the book your Uncle Stan recommended to my father and me on Sunday."

"That's right, and I'm sure he will let you borrow it."

"If not, I would be happy to let you borrow mine," Mrs. Wirt suggested.

"That's awfully kind of you."

"But you were asking about Dr. Wirt when we got sidetracked."

"Yes, we thought it would be valuable if you could enlighten us about what you know of Dr. Wirt's experiences in Washington, when he encountered the

Communists and what you may have learned since then."

"Unfortunately, while I accompanied Dr. Wirt to Washington on that occasion, I did not attend the dinner at Miss Barrows' home, so I can't tell you much more than what came out at the **Bulwinkle hearings** and what Dr. Wirt told me of his experiences."

"That's all right, Mrs. Wirt. We haven't had a chance to read the **transcript** of the Committee hearings as yet, so your **recapitulation** of the events would be particularly valuable to us."

"Well, the event that **precipitated** the whole affair was held in the home of **Alice Barrows,** a woman who lived in McLean, Virginia, just outside of Washington, DC. We learned afterwards that she had been a member of the Communist Party since 1919, the same year she went to work for the U.S. Office of Education in the Interior Department. She finally left that position earlier this year to become executive secretary of the **National Council of Soviet-American Friendship,** a Communist front group designed to advance the cause of world Communist domination.

"Miss Barrows had worked with Dr. Wirt more than twenty-five years ago when the New York City schools were attempting to implement the **Gary Plan**, and was strongly supportive of his work. Shortly after that, she took a job with the U.S. Office of Education and served as editor of the *Platoon School* magazine. There was a certain **irony** in their close **collaboration**, however, what with her **covert** Communist sympathies and Dr. Wirt's decidedly conservative and free market views. It was an **incongruous** association, to say the least. I guess you could say that Dr. Wirt represented the conservative side of the progressive education movement, and Miss Barrows, the **radical** side. Ironically, I think she **naively** assumed that Dr. Wirt shared her political views and those of her guests. When you run in Communist circles, it's easy to believe that others share the same world view.

"It was that dinner party that brought their political differences to a head. While they had worked together **amicably** for many years in the interests of shared educational goals, the economic Depression finally drove a wedge between them.

"What Dr. Wirt heard from those in attendance was shocking, to say the least, and it aroused his **ire**. And Miss Barrows wasn't the only Communist in the group. **Hildegarde Kneeland**, an economist in the Agriculture Department, was also a Communist Party member. I later learned that she was an informant connected with the Perlo Group, a part of the underground Communist apparatus. **Laurence Todd**, a correspondent for the Soviet propaganda agency **TASS,** was also there. Several of these attendees at the dinner party expressed the view that **thwarting** the economic recovery and **prolonging** the country's **destitution** could force a **fundamental** transformation of the economic order and help **precipitate** a government takeover of business and industry. They viewed President Roosevelt as the **Kerensky** of that revolution, in other words, as a **transitional** figure who would eventually be replaced by a dictator, like Stalin, or, at least, an autocratic government. In my view, Miss Barrows' guests let down their guard because they assumed that Dr. Wirt was among friends, or, should I say, 'comrades.'

"Despite the denials of Miss Barrows and her associates, it was clear that Dr. Wirt had touched a raw nerve and the Communists didn't appreciate the exposure. Despite the truth of his **allegations**, he became the object of **vilification** because his charges had the potential to undermine President Roosevelt and his **New Deal** agenda. The Communist **vipers** and their **fellow travelers** in the media did their best to **discredit** him. Not surprisingly, Roosevelt's defenders saw the whole matter through **partisan** lenses and, naturally, refused to acknowledge the level of Communist **infiltration** because it would have embarrassed the administration. They tried to dismiss his charges as **spurious** and unworthy of investigation. Dr. Wirt tried to remain **stoic** in the face of the **strident vilification** and **ridicule** directed at him, but I know it took its toll. What he didn't comprehend is that the Soviets have a well-oiled apparatus in this country to advance their interests and vilify their opponents. **Character assassination** is just one of their tools.

"That reminds me, I want to share a letter with you that I have shown to only my closest friends. It's in the desk here." Mrs. Wirt opened the right drawer of a beautiful mahogany desk and located the letter. She returned to the **davenport** opposite the girls.

"This letter is dated May 16, 1940, which is just about six years after Dr. Wirt's testimony before the **Bulwinkle Committee**. It's an apology, really, from John O'Connor, a former Democratic Congressman who served on that committee. Let me read it to you:

Dear Mrs. Wirt,

I write this letter with a heavy heart. They say that confession is good for the soul, but that doesn't make my task any less difficult.

*I was one of the Democrats on the **Bulwinkle Committee** that heard your late husband's testimony regarding Communist **infiltration** into the Roosevelt administration.*

I am ashamed to admit that the three Democrat members on that five-man committee conspired to prevent the committee's Republicans from converting the hearings into an honest investigation of your husband's **allegations**. *Under a procedural motion, which I introduced, the hearings were limited to an examination of Dr. Wirt under oath. Over the protest of the minority members, cross-examination of the other persons involved was **precluded**. Dr. Wirt was, thus, denied the opportunity to have his **counsel cross-examine** the other persons involved in the incident, or to **rebut** their well-staged denials. We know that the six of them met and rehearsed those denials of what they told Dr. Wirt at the dinner at Miss Barrows' home, including the statement by one that President Roosevelt was the Kerensky of the coming American Revolution.*

*I personally have no doubt of the truth of Dr. Wirt's allegations. My subsequent investigation of the backgrounds of those who attended the dinner, including Miss Barrows, reveals that all were Communists or Communist sympathizers whose allegiance was to the Soviet Union. One, in fact, was a Soviet official, as you are no doubt aware. Their well-rehearsed denials were simply a reflection of the fact that Communists have no **compunctions** about lying to advance their cause or spare it from embarrassment. Once Miss Barrows' guests met to plan their denials, they marshaled the aid of their friends in the Communist apparatus and the media to tar the reputation of your husband. It is a pattern I have witnessed many times before, where the criminals turn the tables on their accusers. Dr. Wirt was the victim of just such a campaign of **vilification** that I fear may have been responsible for his untimely **demise**.*

*Politics is a dirty business. I myself was a victim of the President's **purge** against me for failing to fall in **lockstep** behind his New Deal programs, losing my seat in Congress in 1938. I regret not taking a principled stand earlier against his Executive overreach. But, you must understand that we were all caught up in the **euphoria** of the New Deal in its early years, and Dr. Wirt threatened to undermine the President's agenda. Simply put, domestic political considerations outweighed concerns about national security. As a consequence, the Democrat Party became **complicit** in the **character assassination** of a good man by the Communist Party and its supporters. Instead of being hailed as a patriot, Dr. Wirt was successfully labeled a 'red-baiter' by this country's enemies. Having succeeded in **vilifying** Dr. Wirt, the Communists have been able to further **insinuate** their way into the federal bureaucracy and operate with virtual **impunity**. Had the government listened to Dr. Wirt in 1934, we might have been more vigilant in resisting this wholesale*

*assault on American security interests. This situation has been **exacerbated** by the American-Soviet wartime alliance.*

*I have tried, in my own small way, to make **restitution** for my
sins by coming out publicly against the ill-treatment **accorded** your
late husband.*

*He was, in truth, a **Jeremiah** crying in the wilderness, and a patriot to his country. I pray that his lesson will not be lost on a grateful nation, including this now **chastened** public servant, once they
learn the truth of his **allegations.***

Wishing you all the best in the coming years, I am

Sincerely yours,

John J. O'Connor (D-NY)

"He sent along this clipping from the *Utica Observer-Dispatch* explaining
his confession."

**O'Connor Admits Helping
To Discredit Dr. Wirt**

Washington—Former Representative John O'Connor (D.-N.Y.), "confessed" in a statement today that he had helped prevent a thorough investigation in 1934 of charges by the late Dr. William A. Writ that a group of New Dealers were plotting a new American revolution.

O'Connor, who was defeated for renomination in President Roosevelt's 1938 "purge," said he was sorry for "turning the thumbscrews" on Wirt and expressed belief that most of the latter's charges had come true.

"That's an incredible confession, Mrs. Wirt.
It's a rare politician who will publicly admit
his mistakes, particularly on a matter of such
critical importance."

"You're quite right, Ellen. You will also be
interested to know that, since Dr. Wirt's death,
I have been informed that Alice Barrows had
been an informant for the Soviet secret police, and assigned
the cover name 'Young Woman.' In the period before the
United States granted diplomatic recognition to the Soviet
Union – that was in 1933 – she had an affair with a man
named Boris Skvirsky, an **Amtorg** employee who was acting as the USSR's unofficial representative in the United
States. **Amtorg,** by the way, is a company organized on
behalf of the Soviet Union to promote trade with the United
States, but also serves as a front for Soviet espionage, both
military and industrial. Later, she even had a **liaison** with
Soviet Ambassador **Alexander Troyanovsky**. Apparently,
her **romantic liaisons** with known Communists convinced
Moscow to sever their ties with her, although she continues
to defend the Soviet Union in her role as executive secretary
of the **National Council of Soviet-American Friendship.**
"Now that the United States is allied with the Soviet Union

against Nazi Germany, it is generally considered ill-mannered to criticize the Soviet Union. This **complacency** has made it even easier for Communists to **insinuate** themselves into sensitive government positions. This **cavalier** attitude toward national security has its origins in the highest **echelons** of the American government, including the White House. In fact, Roosevelt was quoted as saying that he didn't consider the Communists as any present or future threat to the country. Can you imagine? He was **adamant** when he told **Congressman Martin Dies** of the **House Committee on Un-American Activities** to confine his investigations to the Nazis and Fascists, instead of the Communists. Even now, there are Communists in the Departments of State, Treasury, Agriculture, the Army Signal Corps, the Office of War Information, and other government agencies where they are not only in a position to pass sensitive government secrets on to their Soviet handlers, but to influence foreign policy as well. The ones I've learned about are **Harry Dexter White**, **Lauchlin Currie**, **Charles Kramer,** Lawrence Duggan, **Nathan Silvermaster**, a man named **Hiss** – whose first name I can't recall right now – and others too numerous to mention. You could almost characterize it as a Soviet occupation of the American government."

"I find it hard to believe that educated people would be attracted to communism as an ideology or an economic system. Even apart from the bloody purges, and the **willful** starvation of millions of innocent Soviet citizens, communism is the **antithesis** of the natural human **instinct** for freedom and dignity," Ellen suggested.

"Intellectuals are people who have built their careers on the creation and **dissemination** of ideas," Mrs. Wirt observed. "Those ideas can have an **inordinate** influence far beyond the size of the intellectual class. On balance, the political and economic ideas generated in the 19th and 20th centuries by some intellectuals have made the world a far worse and more dangerous place, particularly the **pernicious doctrines** advanced by Karl Marx and his supporters. Lenin, Stalin, and Hitler were all influenced by Marx. In fact, Hitler viewed German Communists as potential recruits because they had already accepted the view that an all-powerful state was necessary to realize the **utopian** vision. The Soviet Union and its supporters in the West also viewed the Fascists sympathetically because they saw them as the **vanguard** that would undermine the Western democracies, making it easier for the Soviet Union to take control afterwards. They only differed as to the particulars of that vision. The similarities between **National Socialism** and Soviet Communism vastly outweigh the differences, despite the wartime urge to **blur** them.

"Intellectuals are no different than most people, and are **susceptible** to falling for the most absurd ideas, particularly when they venture outside their particular field of **expertise**. As teachers and writers, however, they often feel powerless to affect real political change. They have big ideas, but little or no power to **effectuate** their **implementation**. Following the Bolshevik Revolution in 1917, many intellectuals in the West became **proponents** of Marxist ideas, whether **Marxism-Leninism, Trotskyism,** or, as in England, **Fabian socialism**. These ideas offered an **illusory** hope for a better world, and, most significantly, a world in which the intellectual class would play a dominant role. Naturally, this mentality stroked the **egos** of intellectuals who saw themselves at the **vanguard** of world revolution, and addressed the **ennui** with which many of them were **afflicted**.

"What intellectuals want more than anything is to be taken seriously. And they are deathly afraid of being intellectually or socially **ostracized**. This can make them **unwitting** captives of the **dominant** political **ethos**, as it did in both in the Soviet Union and Nazi Germany. Similarly, once Marxist ideas gained currency in the West, including the United States, many intellectuals jumped on the bandwagon because it enhanced their intellectual **bona fides** within their intellectual **milieu,** or within their narrow political culture. Of course, one defining characteristic of Communists is their endless quest for ideological purity and their tiresome **semantical** arguments on fine points of political theory. Put five Communists in a room and they'll soon be divided into five splinter factions based on **subtle nuances** of opinion. Little did these Western intellectuals realize that Stalin was exterminating them as a class in the Soviet Union. While the influence of Stalinism in the United States has waned somewhat with revelations about the **purges**, mass starvation, and the reaction to the **Molotov-Ribbentrop Pact**, it still remains a powerful force within **leftist** circles. They haven't abandoned the Communist ideology, but have resorted to the argument that it requires better implementation.

"Even though Trotsky was murdered in 1940, his reputation is resurrected **posthumously** as a means by which Stalin and his **minions** can **vilify** their political rivals in the Communist camp. **Trotskyites** view themselves as representatives of genuine Marxism, not only because of their belief in permanent worldwide revolution, but because of their opposition to the unaccountable Stalinist **police state** into which Bolshevism has **degenerated**. Consequently, they are **anathema** to the Stalinists.

"I should **qualify** my view of intellectuals by saying that not all are Communists – far from it. But, Communists exert a dominant influence in many **realms** of American intellectual and cultural life, or certainly did before the **Molotov-Ribbentrop Pact** caused many of them to fall away. Ironically, the Soviets viewed their Western supporters with contempt for their **naïveté** and innocence. Why, they even dubbed the various Communist front groups

'**Innocents Clubs**' because of their ability to draw these **unsophisticated** political **naifs** into their fold.

"But we must **concede** that some of the same characteristics that apply to the Communist **fellow travelers** apply to the behavior and attitudes of the Progressives and **statist** Liberals as a class. For example, some so-called 'progressive' ideas were widely accepted in the field of education despite the lack of **empirical** evidence to justify their **implementation**. The educational testing movement, for example, was **spawned** by the testing of recruits for World War I. It subsequently had a **pernicious** effect on several generations of students who were wrongfully classified as **uneducable** and denied the benefits of a **liberal education** on the premise that they lacked the **mental capacity** for **analytical** or higher order thinking. It was believed that some students were incapable of doing anything more than **repetitive** jobs in industry. Many of these students were simply new arrivals without a command of the English language. There was nothing **deficient** about their **mental capacities**. I observed that closely in my work in the Auditorium Department at Froebel, and encouraged many recent immigrants to go to college.

"Yet, that movement found general acceptance at the Teachers College of Columbia University, and was spread throughout the country by teachers and future professors who were educated there. In fact, one of the reasons why many New York parents had an **antipathy** to the Gary plan, otherwise known as 'Work-Study-Play,' was that they **erroneously** assumed that it was designed to train future factory workers. Not surprisingly, they wanted more for their children.

"Dr. Wirt was in the conservative camp of progressive educators. He believed in the value of a well-rounded education in which work, study and play all had a role. He realized

WORK   STUDY   PLAY

that most young men and women graduating from our high schools would find jobs in industry or business, but he most **emphatically** believed that they deserved the benefits of a **liberal education** to prepare them for both a meaningful life and active citizenship. When he helped establish Gary College, it was a reflection of his belief in providing opportunities for higher education for all. What he accomplished in Gary was **unprecedented** for its time."

"My mother has a similar view of intellectuals. She says they have their feet planted firmly in the air," Ellen replied. "Intellectuals are just as susceptible as the general population to behaving like lemmings. I have often thought that once a mind is consumed by ideology, it's a simple enough matter to select supporting sources to provide a **scholarly veneer** – in other words, **ideology** with **footnotes**."

"That's very clever, Ellen, and very perceptive. And what do think about all this, Natalia?"

"I am in total agreement with you both. From my perspective, I cannot **fathom** why anyone in the West would be attracted to Communist ideology, or would allow government to gain **inordinate** power, even for **purportedly benign** purposes. You can never anticipate to what uses such power will be put in the future by **unscrupulous** and power-hungry politicians. If the American people had the opportunity to witness the untold misery that communism has brought to my homeland, they would be **repulsed** by it and **repudiate** it **categorically**. And I experienced it first hand. Just ask any refugee from the Soviet Union who has been able to escape."

"I'm convinced that the greatest threat to liberty is government," Ellen added. "That's why the Founding Fathers took such pains to prevent its overreach through the Constitution. You know, like **federalism, checks and balances, separation of powers**, the **Bill of Rights**, and the assignment of strictly **enumerated** law-making powers to Congress. President Roosevelt's New Deal has already run **roughshod** over the Constitution, and he was prepared to pack the Supreme Court after it ruled some of his legislation **unconstitutional**. Fortunately, there were members of Congress from his own party who wouldn't **countenance** his eagerness to govern like an **autocrat**.

"One of my favorite quotes is that of **Frederic Bastiat**, a brilliant 19th century French economist and legislator, who said 'government is the great fiction through which everybody endeavors to live at the expense of everybody else.' That's what President Roosevelt is doing – furthering this great fiction, that somehow the burden of big government will not fall **inevitably** on the people at large, with a **concomitant** loss of freedom. Bastiat recognized more than a hundred years ago what President Roosevelt and the Democrats are trying to accomplish today."

"So, you've read Bastiat's *The Law?*"

"Yes, Mrs. Wirt, it's my economic bible."

"Well, you'll be pleased to know that it was one of Dr. Wirt's favorite books as well. It certainly informed his economic thinking and his **hostility** to communism and other **totalitarian** movements, as well as misguided government planning. He was also **enamored** of the writings of **Ludwig von Mises**, particularly his book *Socialism*, which proved twenty years ago that socialism and communism are totally unworkable economic systems, and doomed to fail."

"That's reassuring to know. Well… you may find this hard to believe, Mrs. Wirt, but we believe that a Communist cell in Gary is responsible for the theft of the Emerson art collection last week. In fact, Natalia and I tracked at least one of the paintings to the home of a Central District furniture dealer who lives in Aetna."

"That's incredible news! Are you sure about this? Like most people, I was led to believe that it was simply the result of some **run-of-the-mill** burglary," replied Mrs. Wirt. "Do you have any idea where the rest of paintings are now?"

"We have a strong suspicion, but nothing to take to the authorities, yet," Ellen replied. "That will require further investigation. We can tell you that we believe the theft is part of a bigger plot to steal sensitive government secrets, and our aim is to get to the bottom of it. That's why we have to be **circumspect** and don't want to make any **precipitous** moves that might **imperil** our exposing the greater danger to the country."

"That's certainly understandable. Your secrets are certainly safe with me. I would like nothing more than to **vindicate** my late husband's charges and his **reputation**."

"I just thought of something," Ellen replied. "Natalia brought a cache of secret documents with her from London that her father had **surreptitiously** removed from the Russia embassy. Among them are the names of over 700 Soviet agents operating in the United States, more than 400 of whom are now working for the federal government. Perhaps, you will recognize some of those names, Mrs. Wirt."

"That's a distinct possibility. Our **ill-fated** association with Alice Barrows brought us into contact with a number of people we later learned to be Communists, both inside the United States government and out. I'm sure many of them are still active. And since going public with his charges, Dr. Wirt received confidential communications from many other people informing him of other Communists in sensitive government positions. These informants continue to communicate with me as well. I would love to have a chance to examine your list and compare it with what I have collected."

"That's wonderful. We can't thank you enough for this enlightening conversation and for **corroborating** what we had heard about your husband from Natalia's Uncle Stan. It's obvious that we have a big job ahead of us. Natalia's uncle, who fought in the White Russian army, has been mentoring us about the Soviet threat, and guiding our investigation. I don't know what we would do without him. Well, we won't take up any more of your time. We would definitely like to call upon you again. Your insights have proven invaluable."

"Please do. I would love to have you visit me anytime. It's a pleasure speaking with such intelligent young people."

With that, the girls were escorted to the front door, and made their way to their respective homes.

Chapter 22

Dancing at the Miramar

By the time Ellen arrived home after her meeting with Mrs. Wirt, she had just a few hours to prepare for the dance that evening. Before her father came home from work, she took a leisurely bubble bath in the claw foot tub, donned her best set of pink rayon **lingerie**, her only pair of pre-war nylon stockings, and the orchid rose dress she had worn to the **Ozzie Nelson** dance at the Ritz Ballroom in Bridgeport back in April. Slipping into her black patent leather shoes, and dabbing some **eau de Cologne** behind her ears, she was just in time to hear her father coming up the back stairs.

"Well, aren't you **beguiling**," he exclaimed as he entered the kitchen. "I'm sure you're going to turn a few heads."

"Oh, Dad, I just hope I get asked to dance a few times. I'm mostly going for the music, and to do a little investigation. I've never heard **Tommy Dorsey** in person before, or **Frank Sinatra**. And, besides, Ken is the only boy I'm interested in. Why don't you have a seat. I just have to warm up our dinner."

Natalia's Uncle Stan was prompt, as usual, arriving a few minutes after Ellen summoned Melanie and found her all dressed and ready to go. Melanie was particularly **alluring** in a lovely dark blue swing dress with white polka dots that **accentuated** her curly red hair. When they climbed into Stan's blue Packard sedan, they were **awestruck** by the transformation Aunt Veronika had affected with her niece. Natalia's new dress was done in a **stunning** floral print of roses on a clotted cream background, **adorned** with delicate lace accents on the collar and hem. Nylon hose and red leather shoes to match the roses completed the outfit.

"You look stunning, Natalia. That dress is simply gorgeous. You've got great taste," Ellen exclaimed.

"I can't take too much credit. Aunt Veronika has a **discerning** fashion sense. It was she who found the dress at Gordon's, but I immediately fell in love with it. She also helped me select my petticoat and some adorable bras and step-ins. She got the nylons from one of her friends with black market contacts. I plan to take her along whenever I go shopping for clothes."

The sidewalk outside the Miramar Ballroom was already crowded with young people when their car pulled up to the curb across the street, alongside Froebel School. The doors were scheduled to open at seven-thirty.

"Are you sure you girls have enough money?" Uncle Stan inquired.

"Yes, we're prepared. But, I have a feeling that the boys won't let us pay for anything once we get inside," Melanie suggested.

Waving 'goodbye' to Uncle Stan, the girls crossed the street just as the outer doors were opened, and made their way up the stairway to the second floor ballroom. A **queue** of eager teenagers and adults had formed, leading to a ticket counter manned by two older women, both of whom were dressed in dark blue satin gowns.

"That'll be seventy-five cents, please," said one, as Ellen approached the counter.

The ballroom was **resplendent** in a 'Back to School' theme, and **festooned** with streamers, **buntings**, balloons, and banners of Gary's high schools hanging from the vaulted ceiling, these representing Emerson, Froebel, Horace Mann, Lew Wallace, Roosevelt, Tolleston, Wirt, and Edison. On stage, band members were adjusting their music stands, getting their music organized and loosening up their lips and fingers. A violinist was tuning his instrument. Ellen recognized Tommy Dorsey emerging from back stage and speaking with several band members. By eight o'clock, the band was set, the lights were dimmed, and a spotlight brought Tommy Dorsey to center stage. An announcer stepped up to the ribbon microphone, raised his hands to quiet the audience, and introduced the celebrated bandleader:

"Ladies and gentleman, it is my pleasure to welcome you to the Miramar Ballroom this evening for a very special treat. Direct from Chicago where they just played an exclusive engagement at the famous **Trianon Ballroom**, I give you the Sentimental Gentleman of Swing himself, Tommy Dorsey, and his orchestra."

With a swift downbeat, and the **elation** of the crowd, Tommy Dorsey opened

the evening with *Kiss the Boys Goodbye*, from the movie of the same name. It was a song Ellen had heard many times on the radio and that reminded her of the boys now in the armed forces. She loved the band's sweet sound, highlighted by Tommy Dorsey's smooth trombone and the **mellifluent resonance** of his band's saxophone, clarinet and string sections. She barely had time to applaud the bandleader's introduction when a dark-haired boy in a blue suit approached and asked her to dance. A few seconds later, she was in the middle of the expansive dance floor, surrounded by dozens of **swaying** young couples. Natalia and Melanie were standing on the

periphery of the dance floor when they, too, were approached and **whisked** onto the **parquet** by eager young men. For Ellen, one dance followed another – *Marie, Stardust, There Are Such Things* – each with a new partner. After the fourth dance, her partner asked if she'd like a glass of punch.

"Yes, that would be nice. I am feeling a little **parched**."

"I haven't seen you before. Do you live around here?"

"No, afraid not. I'm from Connecticut," Ellen replied, putting the punch glass to her lips. "I'm only here for a few weeks. Then, it's back to high school in Stratford."

"Stratford? Isn't that near Bridgeport? I have an aunt in Bridgeport."

"You don't say? That's where my grandfather has his tool and die business, and where my father works."

"I should have introduced myself. My name's Bob Bazin. What's yours?"

"Ellen Anderson."

"Swedish?"

"That's right. What about you?"

"Hungarian."

"That's interesting. We met a Hungarian gentleman when we arrived last week – our cab driver. His name was Victor Toth."

"Oh, sure, I know Vic. He goes to my church. We live behind the church on Van Buren Street. He lives on Jackson, next to the Files."

"You must mean the Hungarian Reformed Church at 13th and Jackson?"

"Say, you're pretty well informed for someone who's only been here a week."

"Just a good memory, I guess. Victor drove us past the church on our way to my friend's uncle's home. Say, may I ask you a question?"

"Sure. Go right ahead."

"Do you know someone by the name of Stasha Poliakov?"

"Sure. She's in my class at Froebel. Last year, we were in the same freshman English class."

"Do you see her here this evening?"

"I haven't seen her yet, but I'll let you know if I do."

"Thanks. I'd appreciate that."

At that moment, a fair-haired boy no taller than Ellen approached **apprehensively**, smiled shyly, and asked her to dance.

"Of course. I'd love to." The boy's eyes lit up.

Ellen soon realized that she wasn't going to get any **respite** from dancing – not that she objected. She loved the attention, even if it wasn't Ken who was holding her. The boys seemed to hover around her like bees around a hive. She hoped Melanie and Natalia were having similar success.

"And now, I'd like to bring out the Pied Pipers and Frank Sinatra to sing their No. 1 hit song *I'll Never Smile Again*."

The reaction when Frank Sinatra stepped out on the stage was **unnerving**. The girls in the crowd rushed the stage. They screamed, shouted and applaud-

ed. The boys showed greater restraint, but applauded enthusiastically. Overall, the **acclaim** was so deafening that Ellen was forced to cover her ears. She'd never heard anything like it. Finally, as the Pied Pipers stepped up to the microphone, the **commotion subsided** enough for the orchestra and singers to begin:

I'll never smile again, until I smile at you...

Ellen found herself **enthralled** by Frank Sinatra's warm baritone voice, particularly with the opportunity of standing in the front row. Despite her enthusiasm, however, she thought she'd leave the **swooning** to the **bobby-soxers**.

"Excuse me, Ellen, but I've found Stasha Poliakov for you," said Bob Bazin.

"She's over in the corner near the refreshment table, in the light blue dress. I can introduce you, if you'd like?"

"That would be swell, Bob."

"Stasha. I'd like you to meet Ellen Anderson, a friend of mine from Stratford, Connecticut. Ellen, this is Stasha Poliakov."

"I'm pleased to meet you, Ellen."

Stasha, who wore a belted, knee-length maroon dress, stood about an inch taller than Ellen. Slender and attractive, her shoulder-length black hair was complemented by blue eyes, a turned-up nose, soft chin, and engaging smile. She wore an amethyst pendant necklace with earrings to match.

"Likewise. I heard about you from Helen Feczko who lives on your street. We met at the beach on Friday. If you don't mind, there's something very important I'd like to ask you. Perhaps, we could step outside where we can hear each other talk. And, if you don't mind, I'd like to have my friend, Natalia, join us."

"Sounds mysterious, but why not. I'm **intrigued**. Lead the way."

Miramar Ballroom
Tuesday, Sept. 1

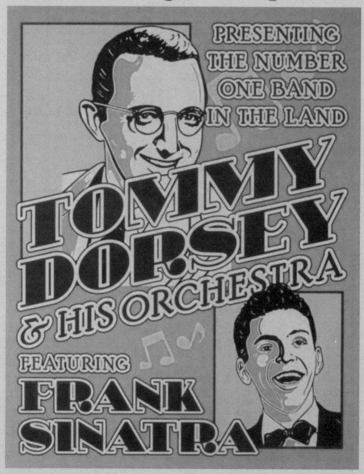

PRESENTING THE NUMBER ONE BAND IN THE LAND

TOMMY DORSEY & HIS ORCHESTRA

FEATURING FRANK SINATRA

Chapter 23

Illuminating Revelations

When the girls stepped out onto the Madison Street sidewalk, the last **remnants** of daylight were bathing the **adjacent** Froebel School athletic field in an **iridescent** glow.

"Stasha, I'd like you to meet my friend, Natalia Boroskova."

"I'm pleased to meet you. So, what's this all about?"

"We'd like to ask you about your uncle, Dimitri."

"Sure, go right ahead."

"Are you aware of his political leanings?"

"Funny you should ask. He and my father are always fighting about politics. Dad's a Republican, but my uncle's a Communist. Uncle Dimitri used to live in the flat above us, but, frankly, he became so **argumentative** that Dad finally had to ask him to leave."

"Where did he move?"

"Somewhere on the South Side of Chicago, as far as I know, near the University of Chicago. He's only been back once, and that was to pack up some of his belongings. My father visited him once in Chicago on family business having to do with my grandfather's estate. If it hadn't been for that, I doubt if he would have had any further contact with him. I heard him mention that Uncle Dimitri lived within walking distance of the Hyde Park train station. Frankly, I think he's up to no good. Where he gets the money to live I don't know. He quit the job he had at the Screw & Bolt Works."

"I should explain that Natalia is a refugee from the Soviet Union and is now living in Gary. Her parents were both liquidated by the Communists."

"Oh, how awful. I'm so sorry, Natalia." She gave her a warm hug. "So, how did you get away?"

"It's a long story, but I escaped by boat with some Jewish refugees and made my way to Sweden before coming to the United States."

"What else can you tell us about your uncle?" Did he have any friends in Gary?"

"A few. He's been **ostracized** by most of those in the Russian-American community. Most of them want nothing to do with Stalin or communism. We discussed Stalin last year in American history. Miss Jones told us all about the purges. Why, even the top military men were **liquidated**. And look what he did to the **Kulaks**. My grandfather had a small farm in Russia before he left in 1912. Had he stayed, our family might be in **Siberia** now, or worse."

"So, what did your father and uncle argue about?" Natalia asked.

"Mostly about **communist ideology**. Uncle Dimitri is a true believer in the communist **dogma**. You know, all that stuff about the **proletariat** and the **bourgeoisie, dialectical materialism,** the **class struggle,** and other **abstruse** points of doctrine. He's convinced that communism is the wave of the future and that my father should get on board before it's too late. My father will hear none of it. He is so happy to be in this country, with all its freedom and **abundance**, and away from all the economic **adversity** and **absurd** political infighting in Europe. He knows that communism can do nothing to **alleviate** human suffering and is the cause of a great **genocidal holocaust**. Ultimately, my father realized that arguing with him was **futile**, and asked him to leave."

"What does your father do for a living?" Ellen inquired.

"He has a small tailor shop and cleaners at 11th and Jackson. It's called Dutch Cleaners. Funny, isn't it, us being Russian? I help him out after school."

"Do you also know a girl named Tanya Sokolov?" Ellen continued.

"Sure. She was in the American history class I told you about. She lives on Tyler Street, near 13th Avenue. I'm not sure of the exact address. Her step-father's a Communist, too, but she's not proud of it. She admitted as much in class one day. That's an awful burden for a young person to bear, but we know it's not her fault."

"Are there any other local Communists of whom you are aware," Ellen continued.

"There is one who used to come around when my uncle was living with us, a woman named Galina Borovsky. She's a mean looking woman, built like a fullback, with **broad** shoulders and big hands, and face that could stop a speeding freight train. And I know where she lives, too, because I saw her there one day after church. She lives in the 1500 block of Fillmore Street, near St. Mary's Russian Orthodox Church. I don't have the exact address, but I could identify the house. It's just a couple of doors north of Reverend Kedrovsky's home."

"Interesting. I looked for her in the city directory, but found no listing," Ellen replied. "Perhaps she's trying to maintain a low profile."

"Could you point her out on sight?" Natalia asked.

"Sure. I could never forget that face. Like I said, it could stop a speeding freight train."

"I think it's time that we told you why we've been asking all these questions. Natalia and I have reason to believe that this band of Communists in **implicated** in the theft of the art collection from Emerson High School last week."

"No kidding? I never would have guessed that. Not that I would put it past any of them."

"We also think they've been involved in some of the burglaries on the West Side, perhaps as a way of funding their **illicit** activities. You could be a big help to us. If you observe anything, or come across any evidence, would you please let us know? Perhaps your uncle left something **incriminating** behind in his apartment," Ellen suggested.

"I'd be happy to help you."

"Thanks, Stasha. I wonder if you could also arrange for us to meet Tanya Sokolov. She may be able to give us some clues."

"That shouldn't be too difficult. She and her mother go to my church. Her father won't have anything to do with religion. Communists are **atheists**, or at least **agnostics**, as you know. Their **opiate** is an all-powerful government."

"That's good, Stasha. Marx called religion the '*opiate of the masses*,' and you've turned the tables on him. Well, thank you so much. You will be doing your country a real service, and the Emerson community as well, if you can help us get our art collection back," Ellen suggested. "Oh, and please don't say anything about the Emerson art theft to anyone, including your parents. It might compromise our investigation."

"You have my word, Ellen."

"I've written my name, address and phone on the back of this card in case you need to get in contact with us," said Natalia. "I live on Lincoln Street, across from the Lithuanian Church."

"Well, I think we'd better be getting back to the dance," Ellen added. "Our friend, Melanie, is probably wondering what's become of us. And the boys, too..."

When they returned to the ballroom, Melanie was still dancing, apparently **oblivious** to their brief absence. The band was just wrapping up *I'm Getting Sentimental Over You*. Bob Bazin asked Ellen to dance, again, just as the band **segued** to *The Song of India*. Like Ellen, Natalia and Melanie had no difficulty attracting dance partners. Then, suddenly, the tempo quickened, with Tommy Dorsey's arrangement of *Boogie Woogie,* eliciting a dazzling display of energetic **choreography** and athletic **prowess** from the more skilled and **ostentatious** dancers who **cavorted** across the dance floor. One of the band members then stepped forward to perform *Der Fuehrer's Face,* Spike Jones' **satirical lampoon** of Adolf Hitler, which elicited **uproarious guffaws** from the crowd. This was followed by Glenn Miller's *In the Mood* and *Chattanooga Choo Choo*; Benny Goodman's *Sing, Sing, Sing* and *Let's Dance*; *Drum Boogie,* with Gene Krupa on drums; and concluding with a **medley** of Jerome Kern favorites, including *Smoke Gets in Your Eyes.*

After a brief intermission, Tommy Dorsey brought back the Pied Pipers and Frank Sinatra for *Oh, Look at Me Now* and *Just As Though You Were Here*. The band played until eleven o'clock, but even that wasn't enough for the **enraptured** members of the audience who hoped the music would go on forever. Closing out the evening was Frank Sinatra singing *The Song Is You*. The audience demanded an **encore**. Dancing stopped, the audience crowded the stage, and the girls mouthed the **lyrics** from the crooner's lips. As the sound waves from the band's final chord **reverberated** through the hall, terminating in an **eerie** silence, the crowd broke into a sustained round of applause. In fact, it took more than a minute before the **accolades** subsided. Sadly, the evening had come to an end. The visit of Tommy Dorsey and Frank Sinatra to Gary's Miramar Ballroom would become just a wonderful memory to be **savored**.

As the **revels** concluded, and the crowd poured out of the hall, the girls waved 'goodbye' to many of their dance partners, and to Stasha Poliakov.

"I told Uncle Stan to meet us at eleven fifteen at the same place where he dropped us off. Tomorrow, he's promised to drive us over to the Balkan Bakery and introduce us to Alex Christoff."

The girls didn't have to wait long. Uncle Stan was right on time.

FAMILY

LOAF

SLICED

BALKAN BAKERY, GARY, IND.

FAMILY LOAF

Chapter 24

Stakeout at the Bakery

On Thursday morning, Ellen awoke early to make scrambled eggs and bacon for her father and herself before he left to catch the Fifth Avenue bus to Gary Armor Plate.

"Dad, I'll be staying at Natalia's place for a couple days, if you don't mind. You'll have to get dinner for yourself. She's invited me to spend the next two nights at her house."

"Well, I suppose I can eat at Walgreens or one of the other restaurants on Broadway for a couple of days, or heat up a can of pork and beans. You take care of yourself now." He kissed her on the forehead and was out the door.

Ellen arrived at the Boroskova home a few minutes before noon. Natalia was waiting eagerly for her.

"Uncle Stan will be ready in a minute, then he'll drive us over to the Balkan Bakery and introduce us to Alex Christoff," she explained.

Uncle Stan emerged from the kitchen, and reached for his hat in the front closet.

"Ready to go, girls?"

A few minutes later, he pulled his car up in front of the Balkan Bakery, a small family-run establishment in a two-story brick building at 1337 Adams Street. A bell rang as the three entered the store. The brightly lit space contained glass cases in an L-shaped configuration, and a counter with cash register at one end. In each case, three shelves displayed a mouth watering assortment of breads and pastries, including white, wheat, and pumpernickel breads, muffins, glazed and cake donuts, croissants, cream puffs, chocolate éclairs, as well some Macedonian Tulumbi and other ethnic delicacies. Behind the counter, stood a coffee machine and another for producing hot water for tea and hot chocolate, and a cooler with a variety of Nehi and Waverly soft drinks. Two round tables with chairs also occupied the area out front. A photo of the Christoff children, George, Steve and Helen, and one of the bakers, taken in 1930 with a goat cart in front of the bakery, and with Alex observing through the store window, hung prominently on a side wall. A jovial-looking middle-aged man in a stained white apron approached the counter.

"I didn't know you kept a pet goat, Alex?"

"No, Stan, that's not my goat. It was owned by the **itinerant** photographer who took the photo. It cost me fifty cents. You don't know how many people comment on that photograph. So, who are these two lovely young ladies?"

"I'd like to introduce my niece, Natalia, who came to live with us last week. And this is her friend, Ellen Anderson, from Connecticut."

"I'm pleased to meet you both. What can I get you? Some nice chocolate éclairs? A fresh loaf of bread?"

"No, thank you, Alex. The smells are very **enticing**, but we're not shopping today. I have something more important to ask you."

"Sure, what would you like to know?"

"It's a favor, really – something out of the ordinary. I assume you've heard about the robbery at Emerson High School last week?"

"Of course. Everyone's been talking about it. I can only imagine how the people of this neighborhood would feel if someone had done something like that at Froebel School. We have a small collection of original art at Froebel, but nothing like that at Emerson."

"Well, we have a strong suspicion that the owner of the furniture store be-

hind you – Crimean Imports – may have had something to do with it."

"You don't say? What makes you think so?"

"Well, Ellen and Natalia discovered a fragment of his business card in the basement of Emerson on Friday afternoon, near the rear exit."

"Yes, and I just confirmed that the tires on Mr. Ivanov's delivery truck match the plaster impressions taken by the Gary Police in the Emerson schoolyard," Ellen added. "I was at police headquarters on Monday and compared them to the rubbing I made of the tires on Saturday. There's no mistake. They're an exact match, even down to the wear marks." Alex's wife, Susie, and daughter, Helen, who had emerged from the back room, listened intently.

"That's **astounding**! You know, I've never met this Mr. Ivanov, except to wave when we're both putting out the trash. In fact, I didn't even know his name. So, how can we help you?"

"Natalia and I would like to put the rear of his store under surveillance from your back room, provided there's a place where we can observe his comings and goings without being detected?"

"Certainly. These Communists have been a thorn in my side as well. Some of them organized the American Slav Congress with the intention of supporting the Russian war effort and endorsing a **Balkan Federation,** with **Macedonia** as one of the 'republics,' so-called. Their intention is to **conflate** the desire for an independent Macedonia with communist ideology. I'm a member of the Macedonian Political Organization that is **endeavoring** to support independence for the people of Macedonia, but wants nothing to do with communism, or Soviet influence. It's bad enough that the Communists want to gain control over Macedonia and the rest of the Balkans, but then they bring their **contentious** ideological battles to this country. The tension has resulted in heated **acrimony** and several physical **altercations** in Gary over the past several years. Our **caucus** is taking steps to **neutralize** their influence."

"I hear you. The story to which you have **alluded** is one I hear from members of other ethnic groups in Gary that are struggling with the influence of communist and socialist ideas imported from Europe," Stan added. "So, can you show us where the girls can set up their stakeout?"

"Sure! If you follow me, there are a couple of windows at the back of my store that look out on the alley. The glass is frosted, but if we crank them open a bit, you can observe what's going on out back. And if we keep the lights off back there, it's highly unlikely you'd be detected. I can give you a couple of chairs to make you comfortable."

Alex Christoff led them around the counter and to the rear of the store. His eight-year-old son, Chris, who had been listening in on the conversation, accompanied them.

"We do our baking in this room. Here are the ovens. The rear of the store is used mostly for storage and to accept deliveries." The rich aroma of baked bread and other culinary delicacies permeated the space which was otherwise occupied by three flour-covered tables.

Alex cranked the window open just enough for the girls to peek out without being observed by anyone in the alley. He brought them a couple of wooden chairs.

"This is perfect, Mr. Christoff. We can't thank you enough."

"Think nothing of it. I'm happy to be of help. By the way, how long do you intend to keep his store under surveillance?"

"We really can't say. Perhaps, two or three days. Naturally, it all depends on the **odd** chance that some activity will **manifest** itself. We suspect that he may have the paintings stored in his back room. If there is any activity, we expect it will be after dark, so we're prepared to stay late. Uncle Stan can pick us up, so we don't have to walk home from here after dark."

"That's wise. This isn't the safest neighborhood at night. You'll just need to turn the lock on the front door before you leave, so the place is secure. But, if you have any problems, we live right upstairs. When do you want to start?"

"Right now, if that's all right?"

"Sure thing! When you get hungry, there's a lunchroom next door – the European Coffee House – where you can **procure** sandwiches and drinks. And, if it's closed, you can just help yourself to a loaf of bread or a pastry here. There's butter and milk and a little sandwich meat in the refrigerator."

"You are very kind, Mr. Christoff."

"I am pleased to help you any way I can. Just think of it as my contribution to the effort. I just hope you can catch the criminals and put them behind bars. Oh, and girls, our telephone is in the front, behind the counter. Feel free to use it when you need to call your uncle. You'll also find back issues of the *Gary Post-Tribune* there on the floor. You may get a little bored sitting back here for hours without something to read."

"Thank you very much."

As Alex Christoff and Uncle Stan left them, the girls positioned their chairs next to the partially opened window and settled in for the day. To pass the time, they began reading from the stack of *Gary Post-Tribunes* that had **accumulated** near the back door.

"Natalia, listen to this. The Germans have stepped up **aerial** bombing of

the island of Malta. Just how much can they take? The residents describe the **cacophony** from the explosions as **horrific**. According to this article, the American tanker Ohio made it into Grand Harbor with **vital** oil supplies. Fortunately, they've received enough food to **ameliorate** the famine. Otherwise, they might have been forced to surrender. The article also says that the Allied naval **batteries** have been able to sink so much Axis shipping that **Rommel** will have trouble continuing his campaign in North Africa."

"That's very good news. I've been reading this article about **Marshal Zhukov** being appointed to command the defense of Stalingrad," Natalia explained. "It says the **Luftwaffe** has been **wreaking havoc**, practically reducing the city to rubble. The German 6th Army is now mounting an offensive to take over the city, leaving **wanton** destruction in its path.

I think Stalin's too proud and **wily** to allow such a thing to happen, even to the point of sacrificing thousands of his own people in order to avoid **capitulation**. It would be a major **debacle** and **humiliation** to have the city named after him captured by the Germans. I can't think of a more effective means of **tarnishing** his **reputation**. Hitler has really thrown down the **gauntlet** by taking on Stalingrad. It could turn out to be a **watershed** in the war, and **precursor** to Germany's ultimate defeat. I think Hitler's **hubris** has finally gotten the better of him."

By late afternoon, the girls had read, or scanned, practically every issue of the *Post-Tribune* the backroom had to offer.

"Tomorrow, we'll need to bring some books with us to pass the time," Ellen suggested.

"No problem," replied Natalia. "Uncle Stan's got a large library of books on twentieth century Russian politics and history, as you've discovered. I'm starting with Sergey Melgounov's book, *The Red Terror in Russia* – the book he mentioned the other day. I'm determined to become an expert on Russian and Soviet history and the horrors **perpetrated** by the Communist regime. My ambition is to eventually earn a **doctorate** in Russian history."

"That sounds like a **laudable** goal. When I've finished Walter Krivitsky's book, I'll ask your Uncle Stan for a recommendation, too," Ellen added. "But, I'll think I'll start with the books by **Eugene Lyons** that Mrs. Wirt and your uncle both recommended."

As afternoon drifted into evening, the backroom was bathed in darkness and the girls had to be content with quiet conversation, it being inadvisable to turn on the lights. Sitting in the darkness of the backroom, they began to share their life experiences and future plans.

"Do you have a boyfriend, Ellen? Somebody back home?"

"Yes, his name is Ken Swenson, and we are very fond of each other. But, he intends to enlist in the Navy at the end of the coming school year, so any plans we might have made will have to be **forestalled** at least for the duration of the war. Besides, both of us plan to go to college. He works in a Stratford bookstore and is a **bibliophile**, like I am. What about you? Did you have a boyfriend back in the Soviet Union?"

"There was one boy I liked very much. His name is Tomas Yovanovich. I met him while I was living with my cousin. He was a handsome boy, with dark eyes and sandy brown hair. While he's not a **virtuoso**, he played the violin beautifully – even better than I do. We attended several concerts in Moscow together and also a performance of **Boris Godunov** with the **Bolshoi Opera Company**."

"So you like opera? You know what they say? If it's Godunov for Boris, it's good enough for me."

"That's very funny, Ellen – operatic **levity**. I will have to remember that one. Anyway, as I was saying, our **ardor** was very sincere. He even kissed me once on the Moscow Metro, but it never got more **amorous** than that. He was always the soul of **rectitude** around me. He was only sixteen when we were ordered to dig tank traps outside of Moscow. And he was the one who carried me back home when I suffered frostbite. He also visited me during the **ensuing** weeks as I regained the feeling in my toes. Just before I escaped, he was **conscripted** into the Soviet Army and sent to fight in the south. For all I know, he may be in Stalingrad right now. I fear I'll never see him again."

"What a **horrendous** time in which to grow up," Ellen lamented. "Just when our whole lives lie before us, we find ourselves thrust into **cataclysmic** events not of our own making. Such is the result of this ideological **obsession** with power that grips most of the world."

"And I fear that it won't stop with the war's end," Natalia observed. "The Soviet Union is committed to world domination. I envision Eastern Europe falling into its grasp once Germany is defeated."

"How can you be so sure?"

"Well, it's largely a consequence of Hitler's overreach. He can't sustain a war on two fronts. I predict that **Operation Barbarossa** will become a **futile quagmire** for the German army. His **Wehrmacht** will suffer the same fate as Napoleon's army, consumed by Stalin's **inexhaustible** source of **cannon fodder**, and the **brutality** of the Russian winter. And, when the Russian Army drives it back into Germany, it will fill the political **vacuum** with its own **political puppets** and gain **hegemony** over the Eastern European nations. Once Germany **capitulates**, the United States and its democratic allies will simply not be in a position **logistically** to stop the Soviet advance. That's my prediction."

"That's a scary thought, but makes perfect sense."

Both girls lapsed into silence. The rest of the evening was relatively un-eventful. The only activity which broke the alley's stillness was an occasional visit to the trash cans from the businesses on Washington or Adams Streets. Save for the delivery of a chest of drawers, the Crimean Imports delivery truck sat idle.

Ellen removed a flashlight from her purse and began studying a map.

"You know, Natalia, I've been studying this map of Chicago. I thought it would be helpful if we familiarized ourselves with the area where Dimitri Poliakov moved – 5468 S. Woodlawn Avenue. Did you know that his apart-ment is just a few blocks from **Stagg Field,** where your uncle Stan believes those secret experiments are being conducted? And wouldn't it make sense for them to move the paintings to Chicago where they can be disposed of more **surreptitiously**? The University of Chicago campus starts here, at 54th Street, and extends as far south as 60th Street. Here's South Woodlawn Avenue, which runs through the campus, and near the Rockefeller Chapel and the **Oriental Institute**. That should give us a few guideposts if we ever wind up in that area."

The girls maintained their vigil until past midnight, then called Natalia's uncle to pick them up.

The following morning, they returned to the bakery with some books to occupy their time, while they continued to observe the back of the furniture store. Alex Christoff, his wife Susan, and son, Chris, periodically came back to check on them, or bring them a cup of coffee, bread and butter, or a piece of pastry. Chris, in particular, appeared to be innocently taken by the two lovely young ladies who were temporarily **ensconced** in the back of his family's bakery. At noon, Ellen brought back some ham sandwiches from the European Coffee House next door.

"Any activity, yet?" Alex inquired, poking his head into the back room.

"No, it's been relatively quiet, Mr. Christoff. Perhaps, later this evening," Ellen replied. She was **engrossed** in Walter Krivitsky's book *In Stalin's Secret Service* while keeping one eye open for signs of suspicious activity.

"Natalia, I'm reading something here that appears to explain why your father was arrested. Listen to what Krivitsky has to say:"

> *It was no news to me that the **OGPU** watches every step taken by Soviet officials, however high their rank, and especially when they go abroad. Every Soviet ambassador, minister, or trade **envoy** is subject to such surveillance. When an official like **Tukhachevsky** went out of Russia on a government commission to attend the funeral of **George V**, when an official like Marshal Yegorov was sent on a goodwill trip to the **Baltic countries**, when an officer like General Putna was assigned to the post of military attaché in London, all their comings and goings, and their conversations, were subject of a deluge of reports by **OGPU** agents.*

"That just about says it all. It's just as my Uncle Stan told you. They keep close watch on both public officials and secret agents to ensure their loyalty. Most diplomatic officials, as well as members of the **NKVD**, are trained in **spy-craft** and **cryptology**. My father must have been under constant surveillance while he was in London. I know it must be hard for Americans to imagine the extent of the Soviet's worldwide reach. But, you have only to look at my own experience to see that it's true. Had I not secured your aid on the train from New York, I might have fallen into their hands as well."

The girls continued their reading, but now with the aid of flashlights. Then, several hours after the Christoffs had closed the shop for the evening, the girls heard some noise **emanating** from the rear of the furniture store. Ellen glanced at her watch. It was just shy of ten thirty. It started when they heard someone leave the store and climb into the cab of a delivery truck, larger than the one they had seen before. A moment later, the overhead garage door was raised, revealing an interior loading dock. The girls could hear the muffled sound of voices coming from inside, but the words were **unintelligible**. A half dozen wooden crates rested against the loading dock's railing.

"I'm sure they're speaking in Russian. Perhaps, I can make out what they're saying," Natalia whispered. Standing at the side of the window, she positioned her ear to the opening and listened intently...

"Ellen," Natalia whispered. "It's just as we suspected. Those crates contain paintings. I heard Mr. Ivanov tell one of his assistants that they're to be delivered to a warehouse on the South Side of Chicago. It seems like they crated each painting, and they're about to be loaded into the truck."

"We need to find out where that warehouse is located. Wait... I have an idea. Did you notice that the truck has only a **canvas** covering in the back? What if we were to climb in the back of the truck when they're not looking and hide behind the crates? Then, before the truck gets to its destination, we can jump out."

"But that assumes that they'll leave the truck unattended long enough for us to climb aboard. And how will we get back home?"

"Easy. We simply walk to the Illinois Central tracks and catch the South Shore."

"I'm **skeptical**," Natalia replied. "That sounds pretty dangerous. What if we're **abducted**? There's no telling what they might do to us. And who would know?"

"I'm willing to take that chance. And, as a precaution, we'll leave a note for the Christoffs. If it comes to that, they'll bring in the Gary police and force Mr. Ivanov to tell them where they've taken us. We'll leave our purses on top of this shelf so there's nothing to identify us. And we'll take just enough money for train fare home. If the truck leaves with the evidence, there's no telling how long it will take us to locate the warehouse and the art collection."

"Why don't we just call in the police, now," Natalia suggested.

"We could do that, but then we'd miss a golden opportunity to expose the Communist cell in Chicago and its espionage activities. They're sure to go into hiding if the police move in. We need to be patient."

"You're right, of course. I hadn't thought of that," Natalia replied.

"Those paintings can, perhaps, lead us to the real **masterminds** and their **ulterior** motives. Here, I'll leave the note sticking out of my purse. I've got enough money in the pocket of my slacks to get us back home," Ellen explained.

Ellen and Natalia counted as three men dragged at least thirty wooden crates into the truck from the loading dock. Then, one of them climbed into the cab, pulled the truck into the alley, and closed the store's delivery door, while another secured the canvas that covered the back of the truck. They watched as both men returned to the store, presumably for final instructions.

"Here's the chance we've been waiting for. Quick! Be sure to lock the door as we leave."

The concrete alleyway was illuminated by a full moon and random light bulbs that marked the rear entrances to some of the business establishments on Washington and Adams Streets. Ellen and Natalia moved with **alacrity,** but no little **trepidation** through the darkness to the rear of the truck. Climbing onto the rear gate, they squeezed their **agile** bodies through the narrow opening at the edge of the canvas tarp that covered the back of the truck. Once inside, they wormed themselves into a hiding place behind a succession of wooden crates. A few minutes later, they heard the two men climb into the cab and start the engine. Soon, the truck was pulling out of the alley, presumably on its way to Chicago, they hoped. In the darkness, Natalia squeezed Ellen's hand.

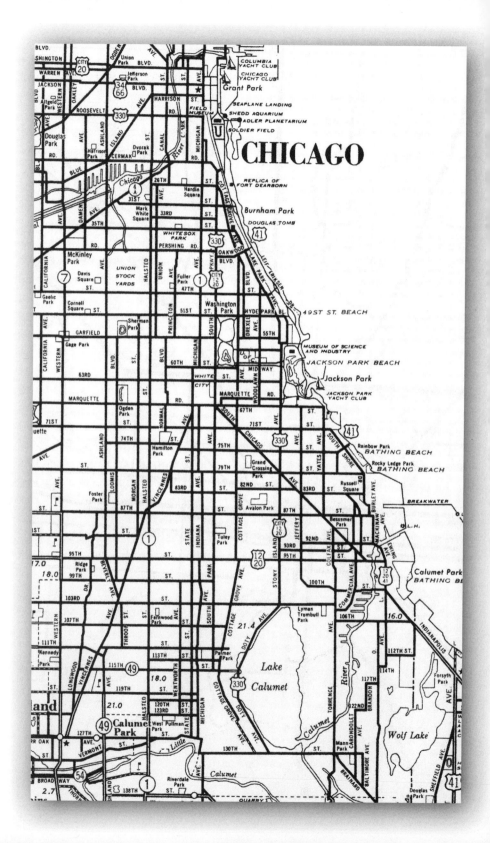

Chapter 25

Taken for a Ride

Lying in the pitch black darkness of the delivery truck, the girls reflected on the **audaciousness** of their **hasty** action. Ellen, in particular, began to entertain **misgivings** that her decision may have been overly **capricious** and **foolhardy**. Realizing that she was **flouting** her father's instructions about staying out of trouble, she just hoped that her **fortitude** would hold out until they had completed their mission.

Not surprisingly, the girls found it difficult to **gauge** where they were going. Apart from the **claustrophobia** induced by the tight **confinement**, the truck's route was so **tortuous**, and the stops and turns so frequent, that it was next to impossible to **ascertain** the direction in which they were traveling. And, as newcomers to the area, they had little knowledge of the highway system to **surmise** the route the truck might have taken. On several occasions, it was obvious that the truck was stopping at railroad crossings, as evidenced by the warning bells, crossing gates, and passing railroad cars. On one occasion, the truck stopped for what seemed like more than five minutes for one of the lengthy freight trains that typically travel through Northwest Indiana and South Chicago.

"I just hope we'll have an opportunity to jump out of the truck before the drivers open the canvas," Ellen whispered.

"Me, too," Natalie responded. "Don't you think it would be best if we could jump out at a stop light or stop sign when we think the truck is getting close to its destination? That'll lessen our risk of being detected and, perhaps, **apprehended** by the drivers."

"That's an excellent idea. But, the question is: when is the most **opportune** time? If we jump out too early, we may lose them altogether and this will all have been in **vain**," Ellen observed. "Why don't we play it by ear and wait for a **propitious** opportunity to make our escape based on the **recurrence** of stops. According to my watch, we left about ten forty. Chicago is about thirty miles from Gary. I would estimate that the trip would take about an hour to an hour-and-a-half, depending on traffic lights, stop signs, and railroad crossings. I suggest we start paying especially close attention at about eleven forty-five."

The girls were increasingly **wary** of the clues provided by the truck's movements. At eleven forty-five, they began to move **stealthily** to the rear of the truck, thankful that they had worn slacks and tennis shoes. They squatted on opposite sides of the cargo space and braced their feet against the crates to avoid being tossed about and alerting the drivers, but near enough to the canvas covering to afford an opportunity of viewing the outside world. As Ellen had suspected, they were somewhere on Chicago's South Side. When the truck pulled up to a traffic light, Ellen peeked out and read the nearby street sign. It was 73rd and Stony Island Avenue. She knew from her study of the Chicago map that Stony Island was one of Chicago's north-south avenues. She also remembered that the University of Chicago campus began at about 60th Street. From her observations at a succession of stops signs, she was able to discern street signs at 67^{th,} 63rd and 57th Streets. One block north, presumably at 56th Street, the truck turned left, passed under a railroad **viaduct**, and continued west to South Ellis. It was at that point that the truck turned right and headed north on South Ellis.

"I think we should jump out now," whispered Natalia. "They must be getting close to their destination."

"Not yet," countered Ellen. "Let's count about four more blocks, then we'll both jump out. When we do, follow me and run like mad. We'll find a place to hide until we're certain they didn't see us. Then, we'll follow the truck on foot."

The truck didn't travel four blocks. At 53rd Street, it made a left turn. Ellen could discern that they had come to a 'T.'

"O.K.," she whispered. "At the next stop sign, squeeze through the canvas, grab the handle on the side of truck and let yourself down gently to the ground. I'll do the same. And try to jump toward the middle of the truck so it's less likely we'll be observed in the rearview mirrors."

As the truck slowed in anticipation of the next stop sign, the girls each squeezed through the narrow opening at their edge of the canvas, grabbed the handles, and let themselves easily down to the ground. The roar of the diesel engine drowned out whatever noise their landing might have caused. A **privet hedge** in front of a nearby brick townhouse provided a convenient temporary cover, and they quickly ducked behind it. Once they were convinced that their presence had gone undetected, they set out on foot in pursuit of the truck. Keeping themselves at a comfortable distance, they observed the truck proceed one more block west on 53rd, then turn right. At that point, they lost sight of it. When they approached what turned out to be South Drexel Avenue, they, too, continued north, hoping that the truck had not **eluded** them. They were not disappointed. They approached 52nd Street just in time to see the truck being admitted to a seven-story brick warehouse located a block west. Halfway up the building were painted, in large letters, the words 'Hyde Park Moving & Storage.' The girls watched cautiously from a safe distance until after the door was closed. At that point, they felt confident enough to approach the building and take note of its address – 815 E. 52nd Street.

"Come with me," whispered Ellen. "I want to get a look inside."

The girls moved **surreptitiously** to a **vantage point** on the west side of the warehouse and, in the darkness, positioned themselves behind a small wooden storage shed in the neighboring yard. From there, they crept to one of the warehouse windows whose shade had, **fortuitously**, not been pulled all the way down. Kneeling on the ground near several rusted oil drums, their eyes level with the brick window ledge, they commanded an unobstructed view of the interior space. When the driver and his associate emerged from the truck, three men in blue coveralls approached them. After shaking hands, and conversing briefly, the driver jumped up on the rear gate, pulled back the canvas covering from the back of the truck, and climbed inside. His sidekick soon joined him. Then, one by one, they passed the wooden crates to the men waiting below. Ellen counted thirty-two crates in all, a number which approximated the thirty-three paintings that the *Gary Post-Tribune* had reported stolen. Then, she remembered the painting that Mr. Ivanov had foolishly kept for himself, hanging in the bedroom of his Aetna home. That made thirty-three.

"There's nothing more we can do tonight," whispered Ellen. "I suggest we get out of here and hustle ourselves over to the Illinois Central station. I just hope we haven't missed the last train."

Retracing the route the truck had taken, the girls followed S. Ellis Avenue south to 57th Street, passing Stagg Field on their way.

The girls felt a unique sense of **exhilaration** as they walked eight blocks east on 57th Street to the station that served both the Illinois Central and the South Shore railroads. It was twelve twenty-five a.m. The schedule posted on the platform indicated that they had arrived in time to catch the twelve forty-five train to Gary, the last one of the evening. Physically and emotionally drained, they sat down on one of the station benches and took a deep breath of cool night air. Ellen couldn't help but feel a sense of **smug** satisfaction that she and Natalia had emerged **unscathed** from their ordeal and outwitted the thieves.

Chapter 26

Making Friends at Froebel School

By the time the South Shore crept into Gary Station, it was one thirty in the morning, and the city was enveloped in darkness. Only the flames of the blast furnaces of U.S. Steel and the glow of an occasional street lamp or automobile headlight provided them with illumination. A Safeway cab took Ellen to Carolina Street first, then drove on to Lincoln Street, where Natalia's Uncle Stan and Aunt Veronika were sitting at the kitchen table, nervously sipping black coffee as she entered.

"So, where have you been **gallivanting** this evening? We were scared half to death thinking that something had happened to you girls. When you didn't call from the bakery for me to pick you up, we thought something **appalling** might have happened to you," Aunt Veronika exclaimed, her voice laced with **anxiety.**

"We were never in any real danger, but we did take a risk that you never would have approved of. About ten thirty, we observed men in the alley behind the bakery loading Mr. Ivanov's delivery truck. It was the paintings all right. I could **discern** it from their conversation in Russian. Ellen saw an opportunity after the men finished loading the truck to climb aboard and hide behind the crates. We guessed, correctly, that they were headed for Chicago. When the truck got to the vicinity of the University of Chicago, we were able to jump out when the truck slowed for a stop sign. We followed the truck on foot for two more blocks where we saw it pull into a large brick warehouse – Hyde Park Moving & Storage. It was just a few blocks from where Dimitri Poliakov moved after leaving his brother's house in Gary. They never saw us jump out of the truck. After we followed them on foot to the warehouse, and watched them unload the crates, we hurried over to the South Shore station. Once back in Gary, we took a cab home, and here I am."

"Well, what we can say? That was a pretty **audacious** move. I would have advised against it, but I'm pleased with what you have been able to accomplish. This is a significant breakthrough. Ellen's father called earlier in the evening. I covered for you by telling him that you went to the movies and were both spending the night here. If anything had happened to you, however, I would have blamed myself. Can we assume Ellen is safely back home now?"

"Yes, the cabdriver dropped her off first. She's probably asleep by now."

"Well, you'd better get some sleep as well. You must be exhausted."

"Actually, I'm wide awake after our experience. There's nothing like riding in the back of a truck driven by art thieves to heighten the senses. But, I do need to wind down. We can talk more in the morning."

By the time Ellen was dropped off at 750 Carolina Street, and crept up the backstairs, her father was already sound asleep. After undressing and brushing her teeth, she slid into bed and was soon fast asleep herself.

The next morning, Uncle Stan and Aunt Veronika let Natalia sleep undisturbed. When she finally awoke about ten thirty, she was offered a full breakfast of scrambled eggs, bacon, toast, and coffee. Stan and Veronika joined her at the kitchen table.

"You got a call this morning, but we didn't want to wake you. It was Stasha Poliakov. She's arranged for you and Ellen to meet Tanya Sokolov today at one o'clock on the front steps of Froebel School. She said you would know what it's all about. I assume you do?"

"Sure! Tanya Sokolov is the stepdaughter of that Communist Party member who lives on Tyler Street, the one on our list. His first name is Boris. This may be another big break. In the meantime, it's clear that we face a real **conundrum**. We now know where the paintings are located, but to move in **prematurely** would compromise our efforts to expose their ultimate plans. I think the only thing we can do for the present is to wait and hope that the paintings are not **dispersed** before we alert the police and arrest the whole lot of them. We need to be patient until then."

"I totally agree," Stan replied.

~~~~~~~~~~~

When Ellen met Natalia at the Boroskova home later that morning, Natalia handed her an eight by ten glossy black-and-white photograph. In it were pictured a half dozen men and one women sitting, or standing, at a picnic bench in a park. Two of them were playing chess, two were playing checkers. The others were standing around and talking.

"What's this?"

"Take a guess."

"Members of the Communist cell in **Norton Park**."

"Correct! You're amazing!"

"You're putting me on? Is it really?"

"No, I'm not kidding. Paul Baukus brought it over this morning. His brother-in-law, Jacob Zvingilas, who owns one of those miniaturized cameras, snapped it last week. He and Paul were playing checkers at a neighboring table. It was the first time the two of them found the entire bunch together at the same time. That's the Norton Park Pavilion in the background, from which they borrow the chess sets. And what's even better, Paul has identified the whole lot of them. The man on the left with the mustache playing chess is Yevgeny – Gene – Alexandrov, the one who lives on Adams Street over the European Coffee House. His partner on the right is Alexei Kropotkin. At the other end of the table, playing checkers, are Dimitri Poliakov on the left and Mike Ivanski on the right. That's Boris Sokolov hovering over the chess players. Galina Borovsky should be obvious. She's the one built like a fullback."

"Imagine that – Communists using chess sets provided by the Park Department paid for by American taxpayers. Under the circumstances, you'd think they could at least spring for their own entertainment. Methinks there's something rotten in the State of Indiana, or the City of Gary," Ellen exclaimed. "Talk about **irony**."

"But wasn't there one more Communist on the list? I thought there were seven in all?"

"You're talking about Iggy Eisenberg. Paul said he was there, too, but left before Jacob could snap the picture. He's written down all the names on the back of the photo. Uncle Stan's friend in Tolleston developed this and several more photos taken the same day, but this one's the best.

"But I have even bigger news," Natalia continued. "Stasha Poliakov has arranged for us to meet Tanya Sokolov, Boris' stepdaughter, today at one o'clock in front of Froebel School. If you recall, Tanya was in Stasha's American history class at Froebel. Apparently, she's deeply embarrassed by her stepfather's political views."

"You realize what this could mean, Natalia?"

"I know, but let's not get our hopes up yet, until something positive **materializes**. In the meantime, Stasha has offered to show us around Froebel before our meeting today, and after I register for classes. Are you interested?"

"Of course! I'd love to see it."

As Ellen and Natalia **gamboled** down the front steps of the Lincoln Street bungalow, they were promptly assaulted by the heat of midday. The air was fresh and warm, but laced with the smells of **sulphur** and **coke** that gave Gary its own distinctive industrial aroma. They ambled down 13th Avenue, under the shade of the elm trees that sheltered the **verdant expanse** of Norton Park. As the girls crossed Harrison Boulevard north of the park pavilion, they heard the unmistakable sounds of a band playing in the distance. It wasn't a radio, but a real live band. The music swelled in their ears and the **cadence** quickened their steps, putting them in a **euphoric** mood. They soon found themselves marching in time with the music.

"I know that march. It's *The Thunderer*, by John Philip Sousa," Ellen exclaimed. "The Stratford High band plays it, too. Sousa was America's most famous composer of marches. In fact, they called him 'The March King.'"

At the corner of 13th and Jackson Street, the girls were **transfixed** as the Froebel Marching Band approached – more than a hundred young people in red and blue uniforms – playing instruments of every sort. Two rows of baton twirlers and a corps of flag twirlers preceded other students playing clarinet and saxophone, flute and piccolo, trumpet, French horn, trombone, baritone horn, xylophone, drums and Sousaphone. A tall drum major wielding a baton led the way. Bold letters painted on the side of two bass drums read 'Froebel High School, Gary, Indiana.' Ellen was **astounded** by the quality of sound coming out of these high school musicians in the middle of a gritty industrial city. Their director, Kenneth Resur, also in uniform, marched alongside, barking commands, a baton tucked under his right arm. His wife, Anne, walked in **sync** with the baton and flag twirlers.

"Straighten those lines people. This is a marching band, not a mob. Precision! Precision! Be aware of your position at all times!"

The girls froze in place in front of the Hungarian Reformed Church to watch the band pass by, then turn south at Jackson Street. A fair-haired little boy, whom Ellen recognized as the four-year-old 'Corky,' marched on the sidewalk alongside the Greek Orthodox Church. She had to smile. He appeared to be blowing into a gramophone horn as if it were a miniature Sousaphone, while marching in **rhythmic** time with the band. Band members waved to Corky as they passed, before turning south on Jackson on the way back to their band room. Mr. Resur patted Corky on the head as he passed by.

Froebel's towering brick smokestack loomed over the open fields in the heat

of the late morning sun. Baseball diamonds, a quarter-mile cinder running track, tennis courts, and playground equipment filled the extensive grounds. The football team was going through its morning drills: some players scrimmaging, others throwing or kicking footballs across the field. As the band played in the distance, the girls passed beneath more elms trees on their way to Froebel's **magnificent** front entrance. Stasha Poliakov sat quietly beneath the **frieze** of **cherubic** faces that graced the school's imposing **façade**.

"I hope we're not late? We had to stop and listen to the band. How thrilling!" Natalia remarked.

"You can thank Mr. Resur for that. He's one of the best band directors in the country. And you'd never guess that he was a violinist. We're so lucky to have him. And did you notice their new uniforms? They just spent the past year fundraising to buy them. They gave them their first test run today."

"Amazing! Has he been here long?" Ellen inquired.

"Since 1929. Two years later, he married one of his students – Anne Yovich, the orchestra's **concertmistress**. The other girls never forgave her. They all had their eyes on him. That was Anne – uh, Mrs. Resur – directing the baton and flag twirlers. I suppose you could say that they're Gary's first musical couple. They also perform violin duets at the Central Baptist Church, and all over Gary."

"What a great story," Ellen observed. "Music is certainly a great way of bringing people together."

"So, Natalia, I understand you'd like to register for classes? Why don't we take care of that first. Then, I'll be happy show you around."

"I'd appreciate that very much."

Stasha led the girls through the front door and up a wide flight of marble stairs to the second floor office on the left, where they found the staff busily

organizing student records for the opening of school. Anne Nikolich, one of Mr. Coons' secretaries, approached the counter.

"Hello girls. May I help you?"

"Yes, Miss Nikolich, I'd like to introduce Natalia Boroskova. She's new to Gary and would like to register for classes this fall."

"I'm pleased to meet you, Natalia. Where did you attend school before coming to Gary? Have you arranged for the transfer of your records?"

"I'm pleased to meet you, too, Miss Nikolich. I don't think that will be possible. I doubt they would honor my request. You see, I'm a refugee from the Soviet Union.

I did attend the St. Christopher's School in London for seven years, while my father was in the diplomatic service, but my high school years were spent in Moscow. I already have the equivalent of a high school diploma in the Soviet Union. My intention is to supplement my education with some courses that will prepare me for life in America. Will that present a problem?"

"Well, your situation is a bit unusual, but we're certainly not going to let that stand in the way of your enrollment. May I ask how you escaped?"

"It was after my parents were killed by Stalin's regime."

"Oh, my word! I am so sorry! Are you staying with relatives?"

"Yes. I'm now living with my aunt and uncle in the Froebel district."

"I'm so sorry to hear about the loss of your parents. Don't worry about your records. Why don't you just fill out this registration card, and list the courses you've already taken, as best you can remember them, on a separate sheet of paper. Then, I'll have you look over this list of course offerings."

After she had completed the registration card and listed the courses she had already taken, Natalia studied the list of course offerings. She selected second-year Latin with Georgia Bopp, English with Frances Uncapher, American History with Anna Jones, Government with Bert Sweigart, Auditorium with Adele Bohling Lee, and Orchestra with Kenneth Resur. She brought the list to Miss Nikolich.

"I think you have chosen wisely, Natalia. You've selected some of our best teachers."

"Thank you. My intention was to select courses that would familiarize me with American history and political institutions, and also language. I had a little Latin in England, but would like to be able to read it fluently. Latin can be of such value in understanding the **etymology** of words. I've also heard so much about your Auditorium program, and, of course, about Mr. Resur. I've played the violin since I was six."

"Your English is flawless. Now, I know why. Seven years in English schools certainly did wonders. Why, you have hardly a trace of an accent."

"Thank you," Natalia replied.

"Miss Nikolich, would it be all right if I showed Natalia and her friend, Ellen, around the school?"

"Of course. You girls go right ahead."

"Why don't we start on the first floor and work our way up, just like the students do," Stasha suggested, as she led them down to the first floor. "Froebel is what we call a 'unit school.' That means it has all grades, from kindergarten through high school, in one building. The arrangement is a bit of an **anachronism** that reflects William A. Wirt's original philosophy of education. When Froebel opened in 1912, you have to understand, scarcely more than five percent of students were graduating from high school, except, perhaps, in the wealthiest communities. It was Dr. Wirt's hope that the presence of high school students in the building would inspire the younger ones to stay in school and graduate. Most of our parents typically went only as far as the eighth grade, if that. Our grandparents, most of whom were born in Europe and had little formal education, were eager for them to go to work and help the family with expenses. Many of them came from such **grim** poverty in Europe that they were anxious to save their money and acquire property. Their children were often instrumental in helping them reach their financial goals and give them a sense of economic security that they didn't enjoy in the old country. However, with each passing year, more and more students stayed in school, and eventually graduated. The numbers of graduates grew substantially during the Depression years, mainly because there were so few jobs to be had."

"It sounds like there were a lot of immigrants in this neighborhood," Ellen observed.

"You bet! And still are. When Froebel opened in 1912, almost eighty per cent of the students were either immigrants or the children of immigrants," Stasha explained. "Even now, many of the students have parents who were born in southern and eastern Europe.

"These rooms in the southwest corner are for kindergarten," she continued. "That room in the corner is where I had kindergarten, with Mrs. Reising. She's a sweet lady, and is still here. I can still hear her playing the *Rustic Dance* on the piano while we skipped around the room, and I can remember the smell of clay and fingerpaints. The rest of the rooms on the first floor are for the elementary grades, home economics, elementary science, the cafeteria, and the little auditorium, which has its own stage. The wings at each side of the school were not part of the original structure, but were added in the 1920s. They're used chiefly for industrial arts, and band and orchestra. Now, follow me to the second floor.

"Here, on the second floor, we have academic classrooms, the office, the nurse's office, science labs, and the main auditorium. Here, have a look inside. The auditorium seats over twelve hundred, including the balcony. The stage is actually big enough for basketball games, although we use it for band and orchestra concerts, plays, student assemblies, and regular auditorium classes. You'll have Mrs. Adele Bohling Lee for auditorium. The class is run according to **Robert's Rules of Order**. We sing, have presentations, practice public speaking, and listen to classical music. Mrs. Lee is a wealth of information on the great composers. She seems to relish the role of instilling an appreciation of the classics in the younger generations. This may be a steel town, but you won't graduate from Froebel without knowing who **Felix Mendelsohn** and

Johannes Brahms are and being able to identify their music. If you follow me backstage, I'll show you the drama classrooms." She led the girls up a half dozen stairs and through a doorway at the side of the stage. "This is where the teachers work with smaller groups and on our **elocution** and play preparation. There are two rooms backstage and two more up that stairway.

"Now, if you follow me, I'll show you the band and orchestra room. It's located on the second floor of the west wing, which isolates the sound from the rest of the building. Mr. Resur is famous for running a tight ship – no talking, gum chewing or other **tomfoolery**. He is passionate about the **intrinsic** value of music and expects his musicians to share his enthusiasm. He came here in 1929 and, within a year, built the orchestra up from 37 to 108 members. In 1933, he led the orchestra to a first place finish at Chicago's **Century of Progress** competition. My sister, Nicole, played viola in that orchestra. It was the proudest moment of her life when the orchestra was presented with the first-place trophy.

"Mr. Resur took over the band program in 1937. Since that time, the Froebel Marching Band has won numerous competitions, including the annual Midwest Band Tournament at Riverview Park in Chicago. When the competition is over, each band member gets a free book of tickets to the rides. It's great that you got to hear the band in action. They're practicing for the fall football season. They practice two or three times per week during the summer to prepare for various competitions. Usually, they use the football field out back, but move over to the Armory Field if the football team is using it. They also march in all the Gary parades and other special events. Mr. Resur's wife, Anne, organized the majorette corps and took charge of all the baton twirlers, and the flag and cape swingers.

"The first floor of this wing contains the classes for woodworking, metal shop, machine shop, and drafting. My older brother learned his carpentry skills there, and now works as a carpenter in the mills. Mr. Aurit, who teaches mechanical drawing, was his mentor for industrial arts. The girls' gymnasium is down the hall here. As you can see, it has a basketball court, with a balcony around the perimeter for spectators, as well as our gym lockers. We use it for basketball, volleyball, badminton, dodge ball, and other team sports, as well as for regular physical education classes. The gym on the floor below is smaller, but has handball courts. Of course, if the weather is good, we're usually outside playing softball, field hockey, tennis, and speedball. My favorite sport is field hockey. The boys' gymnasiums on the other side of the building are a mirror image of the girls' facilities. We've had some great athletic teams at Froebel in football and basketball, and the track team has won multiple state

championships. Last year, Marce Gonzales set the state record for the 220-yard dash. If you follow me, I'll show you our swimming pool. It's below the second floor gym." The girls descended several flights of concrete stairs.

"Well, here it is. Unlike Emerson, we don't have to share our pool with the boys. We each have our own. Each one is regulation size – 22 feet by 60 feet – and has a depth of from four to sixteen feet. Both the boys and girls also have swimming teams. Unfortunately, you'll discover that the Negro students only get to use the pools on Fridays, before they're cleaned. I think it's outrageous and racially insensitive. They have just as much right to use it as the rest of the students, but they're treated like second-class citizens here. My friend, Mildred Willis – she's a Negro – wanted to join the swim team, but they wouldn't let her because it would have broken the unwritten **taboo**. I spoke to Mr. Coons, our principal, about it, but he wouldn't **relent**. Now, I know why. He was planning to retire and wanted to avoid controversy in his last year. But, we're going to have a new principal this fall – Mr. Nuzum. He's been our assistant principal. I won't quit until I get him to change this **prejudicial** policy. You'll learn that there's a lot of **racism** in Gary, including the schools. However, Froebel is the only **integrated** high school in the city because the Negro population is concentrated here, in the Central District. But, even here, a lot of the activities are segregated, even the PTAs. Roosevelt High School on 25th Avenue is an all-Negro school that was built to relieve the overcrowding at Froebel. The rest of the high schools are all White. I wish it was in my power to address the racial **bias**, but I'm only one person. Such racial **intolerance** is totally unacceptable. Maybe I'll try to get appointed to the school board after I graduate. Now, let's go up to the third floor...

"The third floor contains mostly academic classrooms, the auditorium balcony, and the school library. Mrs. Cooper is our school librarian. If you can't find what you want in the school library, there's the Bailey Branch of the Gary Public Library right across the street, or the main library downtown. Well, I guess that just about covers it. If you have any questions, I'll try my best to answer them."

"How many students go to Froebel?" Ellen inquired.

"About 2,400 in all, from K to 12, but about 800 in the high school. There were 134 in the last graduating class, including my good friend, Mary Pavlik, who was **valedictorian**. We hear that they're talking about building a new elementary school in Norton Park to relieve overcrowding at the elementary level."

"What about extracurricular activities?" Natalia asked.

"Well, apart from sports, and the band and orchestra, there are lots of clubs and organizations at Froebel. Mrs. Liggett, our other assistant principal, has been the sponsor of the Froebel Booster Club since it was organized in 1923. Its goals are to boost school spirit, promote a friendly spirit of **camaraderie** among high school girls, and promote good character. Each girl is required to bring a quotation to each meeting and recite it for the group. Then, they're collected into a booklet at the end of the school year. One of the Club's activities is an annual tea for the teachers at the end of Courtesy Week. For students of foreign-born parents, the tea represents an opportunity to appreciate the more formal and **decorous** types of activity they might not experience at home. The girls also make a study of fifty famous women of outstanding character whose examples they try to **emulate**. There's even a Graduate Froebel Booster Club to keep  the spirit alive among the alumni, and promote **philanthropic** activities in the community.

"The boys have Tri-K, which provides a venue where they can discuss the intimate problems they confront in everyday life. We also have the Froebel Press Club that writes articles about the school for the *Gary Post-Tribune*, the

Steel Dust, which is our school yearbook, a Latin Club called the 'Pompeians,' French Club, Spanish Club, Drama Club, Honor Society, Commercial Club, Safety Council, the Euclidian Circle for math students, and many more. And I almost forgot to mention our school motto, which is: 'For Life, Not for School We Learn.'"

"What about a zoo? Do you have a zoo, like Emerson?"

"We did, but it was closed a few years ago. It was one of William Wirt's goals to **incorporate** a bit of rural life into the city. With his death, a lot of his great ideas are being abandoned, including some aspects of the Work-Study-Play system."

"Well, it's almost one o'clock," Natalia said. "Time for our **rendezvous** with Tanya."

Chapter 27

Stepdaughter of a Red

By the time the girls had returned to the school's main entrance, they found Tanya Sokolov sitting quietly on the brick ledge, to the right of the double doorways. Though **diminutive** in stature, she was a **comely** girl, with blue eyes, and jet black hair tied back in a ponytail. She wore a knee-length blue print dress, white bobby sox, and dark blue tennis shoes.

"Hi, Tanya. I'd like you to meet my friends. This is Ellen Anderson and Natalia Boroskova. Tanya was in my American history class last year with Miss Jones."

"We're very pleased to meet you, Tanya," replied Ellen and Natalia, each reaching out to shake hands.

"I'm pleased to meet you, too," Tanya replied.

"Tanya, the reason we wanted to talk with you is because of something you said in Miss Jones' class last year. I'll just cut to the chase. You said that your father was a Communist, and that you were ashamed to admit it. We can only imagine what you must be going through. But, can you tell us more?"

"Actually, Boris is my stepfather, as if that's any **consolation**. My mother married him when I was twelve, about a year after my real father died in an automobile accident. She couldn't bear being alone, nor did she want me to grow up without a father. But, to be **frank**, she acted too **hastily** and has come to regret her decision. Now, if she even suggests leaving him, he beats her mercilessly, and threatens her with worse if she goes to the police. She's absolutely terrified of him because of his violent temper. He **denigrates** her constantly and orders her about as if she were his servant. If I attempt to come to her defense, he threatens me too, although he has yet to strike me."

"That's awful, Tanya. I can only imagine what you're going through," Sasha replied. "My uncle, Dimitri, is also a party member. He used to live with us until my father told him to pack his things and get out. He just couldn't **abide** my uncle's political views. Natalia, here, recently escaped from the Soviet Union and knows all about the evils of communism first-hand. The Communists killed both her parents during the purges. It's a miracle she's even here. As you probably know, few people escape from the Soviet Union."

"That's right, Tanya. Ellen and her father helped me escape from some Communist agents who followed me onto the **Twentieth Century Limited** when I left New York City. With their help, we were able to lose them in

Chicago. Since our arrival, however, we've learned that a Communist cell is active in Gary and is undoubtedly responsible for the theft of the Emerson art collection. It's like my nightmare has followed me to America."

"That's terrible! But, how did you find out that they stole the art collection?"

"We tracked the paintings to a furniture store on Washington Street owned by a Russian-American **fellow traveler**," Natalia explained.

"You don't mean Crimean Imports?"

"Why, yes, that's the one. Do you know it?"

"Actually, I've never been inside the store, but I know the owner – Konstantin Ivanov. My father drives for him occasionally. In fact, he drove Mr. Ivanov's truck to Chicago last night."

"Isn't that a **coincidence**. But, what you probably don't realize is that the truck he was driving contained the Emerson art collection."

"No! That's incredible! I knew my stepfather had Communist sympathies, but I had no idea that he was involved in criminal activity."

"That's how they raise money to fund the espionage work they perform for the Soviet Union and to finance their propaganda operations," Natalia explained. "Although the **Communist Party USA** receives substantial funding from the Soviet Union, its members are also expected to raise their own funds. We also believe they're responsible for some of the burglaries on the West Side."

"I feel so ashamed that my stepfather is involved in all this, but not surprised based on the way he **derides** my mother and is so cold to me most of the time. His behavior has caused us a great deal of **anguish**. He doesn't even try to be **conciliatory** after his **tirades**. Let's be honest. He's more than a criminal. He's a traitor to this country, that's what he is. I avoid talking politics around him. There's no point. He's very strong willed and **petulant,** and apt to get **belligerent** when challenged. His behavior is also very **erratic**. I've seen him turn on my mother – even strike her – on more than one occasion when she said something in support of President Roosevelt, or critical of Stalin. So, I just keep quiet. Nor have I ever seen him being **contrite** or **remorseful** after acting that way. If he only knew what I learned in Miss Jones' American history class last year, he'd probably throw me out of the house. I mean, I grew up in this country and appreciate everything that it stands for. And now I learn that my own stepfather is involved in the theft of the art collection from Emerson School. The Emerson community must be totally **distraught** over it. Believe me, I'd like to do whatever I can to help you recover it."

"We really appreciate that, Tanya. First, we should warn you that this will probably not turn out well for your stepfather," Ellen cautioned. "With or without your help, he will probably wind up in federal prison on **espionage** charges, not to mention criminal charges for being an **accomplice** in the burglary itself."

"I'm prepared for that. After all, he will only be getting what he deserves. I couldn't live with myself if I didn't help bring the lot of them to justice. And, besides, this may be the only way mother can **sever** her ties to him."

"That's what we hoped you'd say, Tanya," Natalia explained. "What we need for you to do is to keep us **apprised** of his activities and the people with whom he associates, both in Gary and, if possible, Chicago. Just keep your eyes and ears open, and record any names and locations you hear. And, if they're planning any meetings, we want to know about it."

"I already know some of these people. Mike Ivanski was the other man in the truck on Thursday evening. He's the quiet type, and **submissive** to the dictates of the party leaders. He lives over on Johnson Street near the Car-patho-Russian Church. He does **odd** jobs, construction mostly. I believe he acts as a courier to the Chicago cell. And then there's Galina Borovsky. She's one tough cookie, a real hard-liner, and not very friendly by nature. She has a **haughty** manner, and can fly off the handle when challenged. She doesn't hesitate to **reprimand** those who fail to toe the party line, and in the harsh-est language, or criticize them for their failings. I can't imagine any one of the group standing up to her, what with the kind of **venom** she dishes out. I recently discovered that she works as a matron at the city jail. She probably got her job by **insinuating** herself into the confidence of local Democrat pol-iticians. Plus, she's got the build for a police matron. She lives on Fillmore Street, near the Russian Orthodox Church. Based on her **obnoxious** manner and **tirades**, I certainly wouldn't want to tangle with her. Both she and Mike Ivanski have been in our house many times.

"Oh, and then there's Iggy Eisenberg. He's an **eccentric,** intellectual type, fond of **theoretical** arguments. He reads books on an **eclectic** range of topics and has **unorthodox** views on diet and exercise. I suppose you might call him **idiosyncratic**. He cornered me once in my home and proceeded to lecture me on a number of **esoteric** subjects, including the existence of space aliens and **vegetarianism**. You'd never guess from his appearance that he's an **enforcer** with the local electricians' union. He lives on Jefferson Street, near 11th Avenue, above the Athenian Coffee House. I know there are others, but those are the only ones I'm familiar with."

"That's a big help, Tanya. Do they have any regular meeting place?"

"No, the meetings are **convened** in members' homes, about every two weeks. They met in our basement a couple of months ago. Their last meeting was at Konstantin Ivanov's home in Aetna. In fact, they're probably overdue to meet at our house."

"What about the Chicago cell? What can you tell us about that?"

"Not much. I believe it operates somewhere in Hyde Park, near the University of Chicago. I overheard my stepfather once saying something to Iggy Eisenberg about some research going on at the University of Chicago, but I have no idea what it's about."

"That confirms our suspicions," Ellen explained. "We have reason to believe they are trying to steal the secrets of the experiments on nuclear fission called the **Manhattan Project**."

"Nuclear fission? What's that?"

"Nuclear fission is the splitting of the atom. Scientists are working on splitting the atom with the goal of producing a powerful new weapon. Imagine what a **calamity** it would be if that technology got into the wrong hands? Think about the military advantage of being the first country in the world to produce an atomic weapon? If the Germans develop such a weapon first, it could change the course of the war. And if the Soviet Union produces an atomic weapon first, it's **plausible** that it would change the direction of the post-war world. That's why we think the Communists are trying to **infiltrate** the Manhattan Project in Chicago," Ellen explained. "Ironically, nuclear fission offers many peaceful **derivatives**, including atomic energy, that could benefit mankind, but that's not what they're interested in."

"That sounds pretty **ominous**. Do you think my father could be involved in this?"

"It's very possible," Natalia suggested. "Not on the technical side, of course, but perhaps as a courier. If they've succeeded in infiltrating the work at the University of Chicago, they'll need **confederates** to transport the plans out of the country, either through diplomatic **channels** or onboard some Soviet vessel. The University of Chicago is not the only place where experiments are being conducted, of course, but, according to my Uncle Stan, it's one of the most important. And whoever's working there will probably be **privy** to the results of experiments being conducted in other sites around the country. Few people on the outside know anything about this, but Uncle Stan became **privy** to the nature of the work through one of his contacts."

"So, Tanya told us you're going to be a sophomore. What are your plans after high school?" Natalia continued.

"I'm studying typing and shorthand and hope to get a job in a law office, or something like that. I've always been interested in the law."

"Have you thought about going to law school? Just because you're a woman is no reason why you can't **aspire** to a professional career in the law," Ellen added.

"That would be wonderful, but we could never afford it. Even college would be out of the question, unless I can go part-time to **Gary College**. Besides, my stepfather is so **stingy** with his money, and so **obstinate**, that I would never presume to ask him for any financial help. As it was, he **berated** my mother for buying me a used typewriter – and this with her own money. She works part-time at the Paradise Food Store on 11th Avenue and saved for two months in order to buy it for me. Normally, he expects her to turn over all her earnings to him after paying the household bills and buying groceries, like she was a child. Under the circumstances, I figure my best course is to learn what I can in high school and then get a good job. I can already type seventy words a minute, with minimal errors, and that's after only one year of typing. Miss Gohdes, my typing teacher, says that, if I keep up the good work, she'll help me find a part-time job in an office next year."

"Well, it sounds like you have a definite plan formulated. We certainly wish you the best of luck," Natalia replied.

"Say, how about we all go to the beach tomorrow? It will probably be our last opportunity this season now that school's starting," Ellen suggested.

"Sure, I'd love it," Tanya replied.

"Me, too," Stasha added.

"That's a wonderful idea," Natalila replied. "Uncle Stan and Aunt Veronika were already talking about it. But, if we pick up Tanya and Stasha we won't have room for you and your father in our car."

"That's O.K. We can take the bus or, perhaps get a ride with Melanie's father or one of her friends. Why don't we just plan on meeting there at eleven o'clock?"

"Sure thing," Natalia replied.

The girls parted on Jackson Street, near the side entrance to Froebel. Stasha headed home to 15th and Van Buren. Natalia and Tanya headed west on 13th Avenue, while Ellen continued north on Jackson Street.

"**Do svidaniya**, Ellen!" Natalia shouted. "See you soon."

Chapter 28

Labor Day Weekend at the Beach

Ellen waited in the shade of the two-story brick building at the corner of 11th and Jackson that housed Joe Plemich's neighborhood grocery store, Central Florists, and Dutch Cleaners, among other business establishments. With no streetcar immediately in sight, she ran into the grocery store, where a decal of the Old Dutch Cleanser girl greeted her at the door. She was greeted by the proprietor, an affable man in a white butcher's apron who stood behind the meat counter. She ordered a couple of pork chops, and bought a loaf of Richter's pumpernickel bread, a half dozen peaches, a box of Wheaties, a large bag of Peerless potato chips, and threw in a small box of Cheez-Its for good measure. A few minutes later, as she stood on the sidewalk with her shopping bag, the Tolleston streetcar pulled up in front of the store. But, an older gentleman was at the controls, not her friend, Tom Smelko, as she had hoped.

Ellen got off at 7th and Broadway in front of the W.T. Grant store. Broadway was jammed with shoppers on Friday afternoon, most of them mothers with children in tow, doubtless buying school supplies and clothes in anticipation of the start of classes on Tuesday. 'Back to School' sales messages were painted prominently across store windows. Melanie McGuire was standing in her front yard talking with Virginia Kelley when Ellen arrived at Carolina Street with her shopping bag full of provisions.

"Check your mailbox, Ellen. Your class schedule should have arrived. We just got ours."

"Thanks. Say, Melanie, how would you like to join us at the beach tomorrow? I promised my Dad I would spend some time with him before school started and you're welcome to join us. Natalia and couple of Froebel girls are coming, too. We plan to meet them at eleven o'clock."

"Sure thing. I'll ask the girls. Since it's Saturday, I'll bet we can get Virginia's father to give us a ride. My father's working overtime this weekend and needs the car. If not, we can just take the bus."

"I just left Natalia. She registered for classes at Froebel today, and one of our friends gave us a tour of the school. It's very much like Emerson in many respects, only somewhat bigger, and has two swimming pools."

Ellen put down her groceries on the front steps for a moment and retrieved her mail from the mailbox. An envelope from Emerson High School was on top. She hurriedly tore it open and scanned the schedule:

PROGRAM CARD FOR FIRST SEMESTER

Name Ellen Anderson .... Date Sept. 8 ....19.42....

Parent or Guardian Eric Anderson ..... Gr. 12 ......Room .204....

Address 750 Carolina St. ....Phone none..... Cl..........

Total Credits ..7......Age .17....Reg. No. ....Locker No...316..

Period	ROOM	SUBJECT	TEACHER
8:15	310	English	Mrs. Pierce
9:15	209	Physics	Mr. Flinn
10:15	302	Trigonometry	Miss Talbot
11:15		Lunch	
12:15	112	A Cappella	Miss Sayers
1:15	Aud.	Auditorium	Mrs. Palmer & staff
2:15	305	Civics	Miss Newton
3:15	Gym	Physical Education	Miss Reynolds

A note was tucked inside her schedule that read: "See Miss Sayers at 12:00 noon in room 112 to audition for A Cappella."

"Let's see your schedule, Ellen," Melanie urged, taking it from her hands.

"I see we both have English at 8:15, Auditorium at 1:15, Civics at 2:15, and Physical Education at 3:15. You're going to love your teachers. I've already had Miss Talbot for Algebra, Miss Newton for American history, Gertrude Palmer for Auditorium, and, of course, Miss Reynolds for physical education. I had Miss File last year, but she enlisted in the **WAVES**."

"Well, I've got some **epistolary** responsibilities to perform before dinner, so I'll say 'goodbye' for now," Ellen exclaimed.

"You lost me. **Epistolary** responsibilities?"

"Letter writing."

"Then, why didn't you just say 'letter writing?'"

"That's what my mother always says. It's because I'm trying to improve my vocabulary and the only way to do that is to use new words in **context**. I hope you don't mind."

"No, not as long as you define them for me."

"O.K. And I'll try not to be too **verbose**."

"There you go again. You're a **veritable** fountain of big words."

"Sorry. I'll try to keep my **multisyllabic utterances** to a minimum."

"I give up. You win."

Ellen went upstairs and spent the rest of the day in the front parlor, writing letters to her mother, Ken, Betsy, Linnea, and Christine, leaving them in the mailbox for the postman. The morning *Post-Tribune* was still resting on the kitchen table and Ellen began to **peruse** the headlines. One of the front-page stories reported on the continued German advance on the city of Stalingrad. Another reported German attempts to liquidate the Jewish **ghetto** in Lakhva, Poland, sparking the first documented Jewish uprising of the war. And, in the Pacific, Japanese marines attacked the Allied airfields at Milne Bay in Papua New Guinea, but were **repulsed** by Australian troops. The action marked Japan's first defeat by Allied land forces.

After they had **devoured** their dinner, Ellen informed her father that the Boroskovas and some of the girls would be joining them at the beach on Saturday – "no excuses!"

"I'm looking forward to it, sweetie. I've had my nose at the grindstone so long that I haven't had a chance to see what Lake Michigan looks like. It's nice of you to allow me to join you and your friends. Are you sure your 'old man' won't be in the way?"

"Of course not, Dad. You're always welcome. By the way, we're going to meet the Boroskovas there. They've already got a full car."

As they finished their dessert of sliced peaches and ice cream, Ellen told her father about Froebel School and the Froebel Marching Band.

~~~~~~~~~~~

Saturday was already shaping up to be an unseasonably warm day as Ellen, her father, Melanie McGuire, and several of her Carolina Street friends piled into Virginia Kelley's blue 1938 Oldsmobile sedan, with Virginia's father at

the wheel. The beach was far more crowded than it was on Ellen's first visit, this being the last Saturday of summer vacation. A few wispy **cirrus** clouds were scattered across an otherwise **tranquil** blue sky.

No sooner had Ellen and her **entourage** staked out a patch of sand for themselves than Natalia, her aunt and uncle, and Tanya and Stasha arrived. None bothered to use the bathhouse as they had all worn their swimsuits under their street clothes. They spread out their blankets and shielded themselves from the sun's warm rays beneath three rented beach umbrellas.

"Eric, it's good to see you. How's work?" Stan inquired.

"Fine, thanks. They're a great bunch of people to work with. The only pressure we're feeling is from the **War Production Board**. They expect us to go into production by the end of September – and that may take some doing. How about you?"

"We're feeling the same kind of pressures in slab conditioning. The demand for steel has never been greater. The work is kind of **tedious**, but the pay is good, and we have the satisfaction of knowing that we're contributing to the war effort. Besides, my life doesn't revolve around my work. I get my chief satisfaction from reading and keeping up-to-date on the current political situation. Speaking of Communists, I'm reading a fascinating article here by the Austrian economist **Ludwig Von Mises** on socialist economic planning. Did you know that Von Mises predicted in 1920 that socialism would never work? That's right – in 1920. He argued that socialist **central planning** is **untenable**, because without a system of free markets, and the signals provided by a mechanism of free exchange, nobody knows what anything costs to produce and, therefore, nobody knows what anything is worth. This causes a fundamental breakdown in the entire system of production and distribution, and the misallocation of resources. Sadly, many voters don't appreciate the free market system and the wealth it uniquely provides. This leads to calls for state intervention that distort the free market economy. Then, these **distortions** lead to public complaints by voters that the economy is not working properly.

"The problem is compounded by politicians who employ the most extreme forms of **hyperbole** to mislead voters. The voters then pressure the government to fix it, so the government passes another law. Law by law, distortion by distortion, the economy **deteriorates**. The society does not start out on a path to socialism, but the interventions into the free market **espoused** by ignorant and **demagogic** politicians expand the state's power, so the result is ultimately the establishment of a socialist economy. Here's what Von Mises says: 'The middle-of-the-road policy is not an economic system that can last. It is a method for the realization of socialism by installments.' Von Mises also points out that socialism is not an economic system at all, but a system of **wealth redistribution**. That's the **inherent** flaw in contemporary liberalism, Progressivism, or other forms of **statism**. They lack a limiting principle. Their **adherents** will continue to buy votes with taxpayer dollars until they run out of other people's money and the economy collapses from debt and fiscal mismanagement."

"How true," Eric replied. "After all, politicians are always willing to tinker with the economy to pander to uninformed voters. I mean, when did you ever hear a politician say 'we're going this far and no farther?' They always have new electoral hurdles to cross and new groups of voters to which to **pander**. And the same dynamic is repeated by successive generations of politicians who have their own **panaceas** for fixing the economy that they **foist** on new generations of naïve voters. They simply can't resist tinkering with the system and causing new distortions. Voters are no better because, ultimately, they're the ones making the demands on the politicians and buying into their **nostrums**. The only solution is limited government and keeping government from interfering in matters best left to the free market and a free people.

"The Roosevelt administration has been an absolute disaster on that score," Eric continued. "Had he refrained from intervening in the economy on such a scale, the Depression might have been over in a year or two, like it was in 1920-21. Unlike Roosevelt, President Harding resisted demands for a **fiscal stimulus**. He cut the government's budget nearly in half between 1921 and 1922, slashed tax rates for all income groups, and reduced the national debt by a third. I wish that politicians would **reaffirm** our founding principles, instead of **venturing** off into the uncharted waters of government **interventionism**."

"One can only hope. Unfortunately, this country is on a middle-of-the-road path of socialism on the installment plan that will produce the same disaster that Lenin and Stalin accomplished in my native land with the use of brute force. My fear is that there's only so much one man, or dedicated band of men, can do to stop this **juggernaut** when the broad societal forces are conspiring against them. At this **juncture**, I only wish the people of the United States could see this as clearly as we do. Most people have only the most **cursory** understanding of what is happening inside the Soviet Union, and **exert** very little effort to educate themselves on the issues.

"Take the **siren song** of the Communists in this country. They pretend to be sympathetic to the plight of the worker, the unfortunate, the poor, of the **Negro** who is suffering from **discrimination**. They **cynically** call it 'social justice.' If only their victims knew the true nature of Soviet justice. The people in the Soviet Union live in **abject** poverty and in constant fear of arrest by the secret police. 'Justice' is most likely to be **meted** out with a bullet to the back of the head, or a long sentence in the **gulag**, where workers labor for years in frigid and **inhumane** prison camps. Workers are subject to the absolute dictates of the Party under Stalin's authoritarian control. There is no 'dictatorship of the **proletariat**' or any meaningful place for workers in the **body politic**.

"I vividly recall the early years of the Depression when the Soviet **propa-**

ganda organs, like the *Daily Worker*, were urging American workers to enlist in the '**Great Soviet Experiment**.' Fueled by reports of the **Five Year Plan**, thousands of unemployed Americans were lured by the promise of jobs in Soviet automobile and tractor factories. Once there, however, their passports were **confiscated** and they were trapped in the jaws of the **totalitarian regime**. Many of these unfortunate souls, and their families, were shipped off to slave labor camps scattered across the Soviet landscape. Many died on the way, including most children, the aged, and the **infirmed**. It was 'social justice' – Soviet style.

"Gary was not immune to these **cynical** appeals that drew unemployed workers to the Soviet Union. Some figured they'd be better off working full time in a Russian tractor factory than remaining on the **relief** rolls in this country. In 1932, when many of us were lucky to be working one or two days a week, one of my co-workers – a negro by the name of Arthur Washington – was lured by these promises of full employment. I urged him not to go, but he could not be **dissuaded**. I even went to his home and made the most heartfelt **entreaties** to him and his wife. I told him that the Soviet promises could not be trusted. But it was to no avail. He and his wife packed up their three children and all their belongings and sailed off to **oblivion**. His brother, Martin, who also worked in our department, received letters from the family for a time, but suddenly they stopped. A couple of years later, he finally received a letter from Kolyma, a slave labor camp in eastern Siberia, informing him that Arthur's wife and children were all dead, and that he had received a ten-year sentence at hard labor as an 'enemy of the people.' Martin's appeals to the State Department on behalf of his brother were answered with the usual **bureaucratic doubletalk**. The story of mass terror, **deportations**, and executions is one that could have been repeated thousands of times.

"And the Americans were the lucky ones. Soviet nationals or Eastern Europeans falling under the control of the **NKVD** were more likely to be shot, or perish on their way to the camps. More than a million citizens of Lithuania, Latvia and Estonia were arrested after the Soviet Union occupied the Baltic nations in June 1940. Fathers were separated from their wives and children. The communists' **modus operandi** was to arrest the educated classes – teachers, professors, political leaders, priests, business owners, journalists – anyone who might oppose their countries' **absorption** into the Soviet Union. They did the same to the Poles, nearly two million of whom were arrested when the Soviet Union invaded their country in September 1939 and were shipped to the frozen wastes of Siberia in cattle cars. I also have it on good authority that more than 20,000 Polish officers were executed in 1940 by the **NKVD**, their bodies dumped in mass graves in the Katyn Forest west of Smolensk.

These were not just members of the regular armed services, but **reservists** who were members of the educated and professional classes who might form the basis for the post-war **resurgence** of an independent Poland."

As Eric **ruminated** further on the **implications** of their discussion, Ellen appeared suddenly from across the sand.

"This conversation looks pretty heavy, you two," Ellen exclaimed, almost out of breath. "How about taking a dip in the lake, Dad? The water's great – not too cold."

Uncle Stan pulled his wife up by the hand and dragged her to the water's edge. Reluctantly, she dipped one foot in, then the other. A moment later, the two of them were fully **immersed** in the **invigorating** surf. Ellen's father did the same, and was soon swimming out to the lifeguard station, with Ellen in hot pursuit. She caught up with him just as he grabbed hold of the platform.

"I almost beat you, even with your head start," she exclaimed.

"Didn't I say that you should have gone out for the Stratford High swimming team?"

"Maybe I will, when I get back home, that is."

By the time she had returned to her blanket, Ellen noticed Natalia sitting **pensively** and looking **forlorn**, her gaze focused **wistfully** on the horizon. While her expression could not be described as **lugubrious**, it did **evince** a touch of **pathos**. There were tears in her eyes.

"Is there anything I can do, Natalia? You look terribly **distressed**."

"It's nothing, really. Lying here on this beautiful beach was **reminiscent** of the years I spent in England when we took family outings to **Brighton**. It makes me realize how fortunate I am to be in this country, away from all the death and destruction in Europe, and my homeland. But, I miss my parents terribly, and the people I've left behind, like Tomas. Sometimes, I just can't help feeling **glum**."

"Such feelings are perfectly normal. I can't imagine being in your shoes and going through what you've been through. But, I'm glad you're here with us now, and that you can now build a new life for yourself." She put her arm around Natalia's shoulder and gave her an affectionate embrace.

"I never would have thought that a random meeting on a railroad observation car would have led to such a wonderful friendship," Natalia replied, tearfully.

"Nor would I."

Chapter 29

The Bugles Blow

When Ellen awoke at seven o'clock on Tuesday morning, she rubbed the sleep from her eyes and quickly dressed for school. She chose one of the new dresses she had purchased at Howland's in Bridgeport, a red print daytime frock with princess seams, wing collar, nipped waist, and a gently flared skirt, finished off with a white bow. She paired this with navy blue ankle-strap sandals atop white ankle socks. She didn't feel much like eating, though she scrambled some eggs for herself and her father, and downed a full glass of orange juice, just to be safe. With no books to be concerned about as yet, she grabbed her purse and tucked a small spiral notebook into its side pocket.

She was the first one out the door that morning. Her father's 5th Avenue bus didn't arrive until ten minutes after eight, leaving him a little time to enjoy the morning paper and a cup of Swedish gasoline. As she left the house, and the rear screen door banged behind her, she found Melanie already standing on the sidewalk out front. She was dressed in a brown plaid skirt and white blouse, her red hair tied back in a ponytail. Students were walking up Carolina Street, both singly and in groups.

"I like your dress. It's cute," Melanie exclaimed. "Where'd you buy it?"

"At Howland's Department Store, in Bridgeport, Connecticut, just before I left for Gary. My Dad was in a generous mood. I got it on sale. It was only $1.79."

"We've got some smart dress shops on Broadway, too, but my mother thinks I'm already too preoccupied with clothes and makeup. I'm better off working on my Dad when I want a new dress, or a pair of shoes. He's a real softy."

As the girls neared 7th and Carolina, students were congregating on the steps of the school and outside of Rubin's. It was a few minutes before eight o'clock. Two members of the R.O.T.C. were standing at the flagpole, ready to hoist the Stars and Stripes. Melanie introduced Ellen to some of her classmates. Then, suddenly, from inside the school came the sound of "Assembly," and the flag was quickly hoisted up the flagpole. Students stood at attention and held their hands over their hearts, or saluted, while the bugles blew. As the last note faded away, the students streamed in on the way to their morning registers.

Ellen said 'goodbye' to Melanie for the time being and made her way to Room 204, at the west end of the second floor hall. Standing outside the door was Miss Esther Tinsman, Emerson's veteran biology teacher, who greeted the senior girls as they entered and took their seats behind the lab counters. As the girls continued to file in, Ellen's eyes gravitated to the **plethora** of stuffed animal specimens that lined the shelves and cabinets around the room. A stout woman with dark hair, Miss Tinsman appeared to Ellen to be in her mid-forties. She wore a dark blue suit and a white blouse. A white handkerchief peaked out from her breast pocket, and a decorative pin graced her lapel.

"Good morning girls."

"Good morning, Miss Tinsman."

"I trust you all had a good summer and are ready to put your shoulders to the wheel once again. Just think, one more year and, hopefully – if you work hard – we're going to let you all out on **probation**. You may chuckle, if you'd like. That was a joke. This begins our fourth year in Register. And, of course, few of you escaped from my biology class. I hope you will all make the most of your last year at Emerson. Remember, school and life are what you make of them. You won't regret the hard work you do here at Emerson. And, after you graduate, when you pick up a grasshopper, as I hope you'll do often, I hope you'll remember that it was Miss Tinsman who taught you that it belongs to the Order Orthoptera and the Suborder Caelifera, and that you can distinguish between the thorax and the mandibles. Well, enough of **entomology**. And I want to remind all of you to be punctual. If, on the other hand, you are **dilatory** and arrive late to class, you will be marked absent. I can't stress enough that success in life depends, first of all, on being on time. Now, let me take the roll. Just raise your hands as you hear your name called: Elizabeth Adams, Lorraine Alamsha, Ellen Anderson... there's a new name and face. You're new to my Register, aren't you? Nor did I have you for biology, did I, Ellen?"

"That's right, Miss Tinsman. I'm new this year. My father is in Gary on a temporary work assignment. I'm from Stratford, Connecticut."

"Why, yes, I met you in front of the school the day after the art collection was stolen. My, you're a long way from home. Well, I'm happy to welcome you to Emerson, Ellen. I know you're going to like it here, however long you stay. Now, where was I? Gloria Angotti..."

No sooner had Miss Tinsman completed the roll than the bell rang and it was time for Ellen to move on to Room 310, her first period English class, with Gladys Pierce. Unlike her register group, which was composed of about forty girls, senior English was almost evenly divided between the sexes. Mrs. Pierce, a slight woman with dark hair and an engaging smile, stood at the head of the class. Her name was already written in **cursive** on the blackboard. She wore a green plaid suit, white blouse and the kind of sensible black shoes typically favored by school teachers, probably something to do with being on their feet all day.

"Good morning, class."

"Good morning, Mrs. Pierce."

"I hope you're all looking forward to a year of reading some of the great works of English literature, and polishing your grammar." A few muffled groans could be heard from the back of the room.

"I heard that, Randall Sullivan. I wouldn't be too quick to **decry** the study of English grammar. Let's **dispel** that **misconception** right now. I want **to instill** in all of you an appreciation of the fact that proper grammar is essential to your daily life, even if you don't **acknowledge** it at this stage of your existence. Let's just say that I'll try to make it interesting for you doubters. Remember, people will judge you on the basis of your spoken and written grammar. If you intend to apply for a job in which communication is critical, a grammatical **lapse** may doom your chances. Your employer may interpret your error as **indicative** of more wide-ranging educational **deficiencies**.

"This year, we're going to be reading the **immortal bard**, William Shakespeare, as well as Charles Dickens, the English **romantic** poets, Thomas Hardy, and, if we have time, D.H. Lawrence. No, not *Lady Chatterley*, George Settle, but *Sons and Lovers*, a work of far greater **literary** merit. I hope I can instill in all of you an appreciation for the classics and the **profound** insights these writers bring to their craft.

"There's more to life than pulp fiction, you know. *The Shadow* and *Doc Savage* simply can't compare to Dickens' *David Copperfield*, or Shakespeare's *Macbeth*. Great literature is much more than a good story. It's a way of imparting great truths through the lives and experiences of their characters. You may be interested to know that Miss Benscoter is working on a shorter, **abridged** edition of *David Copperfield* for use in freshman English. She hopes to get it published in a few years. Abridged editions may be more **concise**, and they have their place, but I think they lose the literary complexity and **nuance** of the author's original **unabridged** language. You're old enough to handle that complexity now.

"As a part of our work this year, I also plan to spend some time on literary terms. I will present you with literary **vignettes** that illustrate these terms or characteristics of literary expression. For example, who can tell me what a **simile** is? Millie Zivonovich?"

"A **simile** is a figure of speech that compares two essentially different things, usually in a phrase introduced by 'like' or 'as.'"

"Can you give me an example?"

"Let me see… How about: 'the sun looked like a big yellow ball.'"

"Very good, Millie!"

"Then, how do we distinguish a **simile** from a **metaphor**? Ellen… Anderson?"

"Well, unlike a **simile**, a **metaphor** compares two unrelated objects or things without using the words 'like' or 'as.'"

"Example?"

"'All the world's a stage, and all the men and women merely players,' from Shakespeare's *Twelfth Night*."

"You know your Shakespeare, I see."

"Well, I've read some of his plays. I'm from Stratford, Connecticut, after all."

"Ellen's referring to the fact that Shakespeare came from **Stratford-upon-Avon**, in England, and that her hometown is named for it. Excellent, Ellen."

"There's one other term I'd like to leave you with today – **personification,** which is also called **anthropomorphism**. Would anyone like to have a 'go' at this one? Edward Madden?"

"Let me see. **Personification** is a literary device that gives human qualities to non-human objects like animals, **inanimate** objects, or an abstract concept."

"And can you provide us with an example, Edward?"

"Rudyard Kipling. His *Jungle Book* has talking animals. Kaa is a talking cobra. I just saw the film a few months ago with Sabu. And if you go to the **Oriental Institute** in Chicago, you can see statues of Egyptian gods in half human/half animal form. And then there are my friends who talk to their cars when they **conk out**, like they were human beings."

"Those are great examples, Edward. Thank you."

"Speaking of literary terms, I also want you to be aware of the idea of literary **allusion** in a text. Literature is full of **allusions**, whether references from the Bible, classical mythology, history, art, music, and so forth. For example, what if I said that chocolate was Ellen's **Achilles' heel**? Virginia Kelley?"

"That chocolate is her weakness. This is an **allusion** to Greek mythology. Achilles' heel was his weakness because his mother failed to dip it in the **River Styx** when he was an infant, along with the rest of his body."

"Very good, Virginia. I'm pleased that you remembered this from your study of mythology in freshman English. You will discover that to be an effective reader, you must grasp the meaning of various **allusions** sprinkled throughout literature. This is certainly true if you plan to go on to college. Writers will typically assume that their readers share a certain level of **cultural literacy,** a literacy that you gain by **accretion** through your school years. It's what we mean when we say that someone is 'well-read.'

"I also plan to review the principle parts of speech, sentence structure, the essay, and business communication this year. You will be expected to demonstrate mastery of correct grammar in a series of essays, and an ability to **fashion cogent** arguments, in support of your **thesis**. And, finally, you will all be responsible for writing a term paper, using the standard rules of **scholarly citation**. Later in the semester, I will more fully explain what this will **entail**. Whether you plan to go on to college or not, you'll need to express yourself with clarity and good grammar. You will need to know when it is appropriate to use formal forms of oral and written **discourse** and when **colloquial** forms of expression are acceptable. And don't feel offended if I point out your lapses in spoken grammar. I won't **equivocate** when I hear you say 'ain't,' or 'done' instead of 'did,' or 'good,' instead of 'well.' I also have a particular **aversion** to **trite** and **hackneyed** expressions, or **redundancies**. So, please don't tell me about some 'new and novel **innovation**.' My aim is to help you **expunge** these grammatical **faux pas** before you leave my classroom and enter the real world where the **approbation** of your peers, or supervisors, will be critical to your success. If you're going to be **credible**, you must speak with grammatical precision. One day, you will thank Mrs. Pierce for setting you on the correct grammatical path. Do I make myself clear?"

"Yes, Mrs. Pierce."

After calling the roll, and assigning seats, she called on two of the boys to distribute copies of Shakespeare's *Macbeth*, a literary **anthology**, and an English grammar book to each member of the class. Ellen found herself sitting in the row near the windows, with a birds-eye view of the Emerson zoo and the Little Building. Melanie sat two seats behind her.

"Your assignment for tomorrow will be to read Act 1, Scenes 1 and 2 of Macbeth. We're going to spend the next class **explicating** the text, line by line. Are there any questions?"

"Mrs. Pierce, is it true that you know **Hoagy Carmichael**?"

"Well, I don't know what that has to do with *Macbeth,* or literary explication, but, yes, I do know Hoagy Carmichael, or did, when I was in college. We were in the same class at Indiana University a few years ago. I won't go into how many years ago that was because then you would just do the math and figure out how old I am. And, as you should know by now, a lady never reveals her age. But, I will say that it was back in the **heyday** of the Charleston, raccoon coats and flivvers – you can look those up." She smiled **impishly**. "Yes, Hoagy started out playing the piano with a group called the Collegians at campus events, and writing his own songs. I'm sure you know many of them – *Up* *a Lazy River, Stardust, Georgia on My Mind, Two Sleepy People*, and many more. Now, he's world famous, of course, and a movie star as well. Some of you may have seen him in *Topper* with Cary Grant and Constance Bennett at the Gary Theater a couple of months ago. I have to admit that it's a thrill to go to the movies and see someone with whom you once attended English class.

But, I **digress**. Are there any more questions – about Macbeth, that is? Hearing none, class is dismissed."

With her English class **truncated** by a full ten minutes, Ellen and Melanie **hovered** in the third floor hallway, while Ellen read the inscriptions on some of the trophies in the cases that lined the wall. On both ends of the third floor, students filled four rows of desks in the study hall. Catherine Greenwald, another of Emerson's English teachers, was monitoring the east end study hall.

"I had Mrs. Greenwald for junior English," Melanie whispered. "She has an **infectious** passion for literature. I memorized a half dozen poems in her class, and I thought I wasn't good at memorization. In fact, I can still recite: *There is another sky*, by Emily Dickinson; and *Annabel Lee* by Edgar Allan Poe. She's even known to bribe students with candy bars as an added **inducement** to memorize lengthy poems. I remember her rewarding Fran Kent with a Three Musketeers for memorizing 'Shylock's lament' from *The Merchant of Venice*."

When the bell rang, the halls were again crowded with young people rushing

hither and yon. The science lab – Room 210 – was one floor down, in the southeast corner. Ellen's physics teacher, Mr. Floyd Flinn, was already inside, standing behind a black marble lab counter with a sink at one end and several stacks of books at the other. Students paraded in and took their seats. He was a man of medium height, dark wavy hair, and wore wire-rimmed spectacles. He was dressed in a dark blue, double-breasted suit and flowered tie. His calm **demeanor** projected an **aura** of efficiency and scientific **inquisitiveness**. Various scientific instruments were arranged on the counter in front of him. As students sat down, he began passing out copies of the semester's class **syllabus**.

"Good morning, students. My name is Mr. Flinn. Some of you may have already had me for chemistry, or general science, so you'll have an idea of what kind of work I'll expect from you in physics. We're going to be covering a variety of topics in the physical sciences this year, including the laws of motion, work and energy, properties of matter, mechanics, heat, **thermo-dynamics**, electricity and electrical energy, electric circuits, magnetism, **hydraulics**, measurements and calculation, light, **optics**, **momentum** and collisions, and modern electronics. We'll also consider the scientific method and the process of laboratory investigation. You'll also have an opportunity to conduct a variety of experiments illustrating the physical principles we'll be studying. The **syllabi** I'm passing out will **delineate** the **salient** points we'll be covering this semester."

After taking the roll, Mr. Flinn spent the remainder of the period discussing the role of physics and physical laws in everyday life. He asked for volunteers to distribute textbooks.

"Over the past century, we have witnessed the development of the **internal combustion engine**. Now, even as we speak, scientists are working to harness the power of the atom – something we call **nuclear fission**. Work on nuclear fission accelerated in the 1930s when scientists came to the conclusion that manipulation of the **nuclei** of atoms was possible. In 1932, **Sir John Cockcroft** and **Ernest Walton** at Cambridge University in England were the first to split the atom and cause a nuclear reaction by the use of artificially accelerated particles. This research has now taken on a **heightened** importance, particularly for its military potential. It's quite possible that the Nazis are also interested in the military potential of atomic energy. Of course, this is all **speculative** at the present time. This semester, we're going to look at the principles involved in nuclear fission. I want you to appreciate that physics is far more than an academic exercise, but is very much related to everyday life, or death."

Ellen sat **dumfounded** as Mr. Flinn explained in depth the basic scientific principles of what she was **intimately** involved in trying to expose. Only, it wasn't the Nazis who were implicated in this case, as he suggested, but agents of the Soviet Union anticipating the potential of atomic energy in the post-war world. She was almost tempted to speak up and set the record straight, but wisely held her tongue.

Her next class took her to Room 302: trigonometry with Miss Minnie Talbot. Miss Talbot, who had been teaching at Emerson since 1918, was the senior

member of the math faculty. In addition to **trigonometry**, she taught both **geometry** and **calculus**. A woman of average height and build, she wore a light blue silk dress and gold-rimmed spectacles. Her graying hair was pulled back in bun, a style much in favor among Emerson's female teachers. She appeared well organized, and had a seating chart all prepared. As she called the roll, she directed each student to take the seat she had assigned them. Ellen found herself in the front row, near the door.

"There, I think we're all accounted for. I trust you all had a good summer. I certainly did. I spent most of July and August visiting my sister in Nashville, Indiana, just outside of Bloomington, and a week with my parents in Wisconsin. The weather was delightful, with plenty of time for reading and relaxation. We attended some lovely concerts given by faculty and students of the Indiana University Music Department and did some hiking in Brown County State Park.

"We're going to start the year with a review of the principles of algebra and geometry. Before we get into trigonometry, I want to make sure you're comfortable manipulating algebraic expressions and solving equations. From your geometry, you should already know something about similar triangles and the **Pythagorean Theorem**. Trig has many practical applications in the natural and social sciences, but the chief ones are in geography, astronomy, physics, engineering, and chemistry.

"Basically, trigonometry is a branch of mathematics that deals with triangles, particularly those plane triangles in which one angle has 90 degrees. Trigonometry deals with relationships between the sides and the angles of triangles and with the trigonometric functions, which describe those relationships. It has applications in both pure mathematics and in applied mathematics."

Miss Talbot spent the remainder of the period reviewing some algebraic formulas and reviewing the principles of the **Pythagorean Theorem** and similar triangles.

"Does anyone in the class remember who **Pythagoras** was?"

"A Greek mathematician and philosopher," answered a girl in the third row.

"Correct, Betsy. Can anyone tell the class exactly when he lived?"

"About five hundred years before Christ. I know he lived before Socrates and Aristotle."

"That's right, Robin. He is one of a group we call the pre-Socratic philosophers, and lived from about 570 to 490 B.C. In other words, before Socrates."

Before the end of class, Miss Talbot **delegated** to several students the task of passing out the trigonometry textbooks.

"Your assignment for tomorrow is to read pages one through four of the first chapter and to do the problems illustrating the **Pythagorean Theorem**. We'll discuss these tomorrow."

As the bell rang for lunch, Ellen found Melanie hovering outside her classroom.

"I had study hall, while you were in there with 'Whispering Minnie.' How would you like to go to Rubin's for lunch?"

"Sounds swell. Lead the way."

Ellen felt the late summer warmth envelope her body as she and Melanie left the building and ambled down the front steps. As they crossed the street, the sidewalk outside Rubin's was already crowded with students, some drinking Waverly pop and eating hamburgers. The girls entered the confectionary and found two stools at the far end of the lunch counter. A good-looking young man wearing brown slacks and white dress shirt approached. He took particular note of Ellen.

"Who's your friend, Melanie?"

"This is Ellen Anderson, Frank. She's new this year. Ellen, this is Frank Roman."

"Pleased to meet you. So, what do you think of our school?"

"I like it a lot. The teachers I've met so far are great and the students are very friendly."

"Frank plays quarterback on our football team and he's also going to be in A Cappella with you this year, Ellen."

"Fantastic! An athlete who sings. Sounds like a winning combination. So, when does football season start?"

"This Friday, at Proviso. That's in Illinois. Our first game at Gleason Field is next week, against Tolleston," Frank explained.

"And what do you think of your chances this season?"

"Pretty good, I think. We were 6-1-1 last season and have many of our starters returning this year. Coach Rolfe thinks we stink, but he always says that. He just wants to make sure we don't get too cocky or **shirk** our responsibilities to the team. Well, it was nice meeting you, Ellen. I guess I'll be seeing you after lunch."

"So, what can I get for you girls?" asked Pop Rubin, sidling up to the counter, his **brusque** voice **belying** a kindly, **avuncular** disposition. He appeared to Ellen very much the **stereotypical** soda fountain proprietor.

"I'd like a plain hamburger and a chocolate malt," Melanie replied.

"I'll have a cheeseburger with a little ketchup, and also a chocolate malt."

"Coming right up! The **condiments** are right over there."

"You know, if we were in the school cafeteria, they'd make us eat our vegetables – even lima beans," Melanie said. "Mr. Carlberg – he teaches history

– wouldn't let us return our trays until we had
cleaned our plates of every last bean. He's our
unofficial cafeteria monitor."

"We have a teacher like that back in Stratford
– Mr. DeLeurere. He takes nutrition seriously.
You gotta love 'em. They mean well. It's a man-
ifestation of the principal of **in loco parentis**."

"In loco what? Does that have something to do
with crazy parents?"

"No, silly. **In loco parentis** is Latin for 'in
place of the parents.' Mr. Carlberg performs the
role in school that your parents play at home –
making you eat your vegetables. They believe
in a healthful **culinary regimen** and its **salutary** health benefits. I don't
feel too badly, though. I get plenty of vegetables at home. My mother sees to
that. I have to laugh when I think about the time I was just a kid and didn't
want to eat my lima beans. My mother **chided** me by telling me there were
starving people in India who would love to eat those lima beans. I told her:
'Then, why don't you send them to India?' She sent me to my room without
supper and told me I was a fresh kid." Melanie snorted into her straw and
almost spilled her malted milk.

Ellen watched as dozens of students passed in and out of the screen door,
many buying soda pop and candy bars, others hamburgers, apples, or ice cream
sandwiches. Some youngsters bought penny candy.

"See those kids. They're not even supposed to be in here," Melanie explained.
"If you're in the fourth grade and below, you're not supposed to leave the
school grounds – not that I expect eight-year-old kids to be fully **compliant**
with school regulations when an **enticing** assortment of sugary treats tempts
them. Periodically, Mr. Spaulding or Mr. Bohn have to come over and shoo
them back across the street."

Ellen spied *Doc Savage* and other pulps on the magazine rack. It made
her think about *Macbeth* and what Mrs. Pierce had said, though she doubted
that *Macbeth* would be a big seller at Rubin's. She had already observed
several boys reading *Action Comics* on the school's front lawn. As twelve
o'clock approached, students began filing out of the East Side confectionary

and slowly making their way back towards the school. Ellen's next class was A Cappella, a select choral ensemble that met in Room 112, with **Miss Grace Sayers**. Remembering that she was scheduled for a twelve o'clock audition, she promptly said 'goodbye' to Melanie and made her way to the last room in the first floor's east corridor, opposite the stairway. Miss Sayers, who was just finishing her lunch, looked up from her desk and smiled as Ellen entered the room. Miss Tinsman, who shared lunch with her, excused herself as Ellen entered. The room contained a console piano and desk upfront and was lined with wooden writing chairs instead of desks. A pretty brunette sat at the piano.

"You must be Ellen Anderson? Are you ready for your audition?"

"Yes, Miss Sayers."

"What part do you sing, Ellen?"

"First soprano."

"Excellent. We could use another first soprano. Ellen, I'd like you to meet my accompanist, Nell Warda, one of our June graduates. She's staying on to help me this year, as she has for the past three years."

"I'm pleased to meet you, Nell."

"I'm pleased to meet you, too. I hope you're going to like it here at Emerson."

"Nell has been taking piano lessons since she was eight and plays like a dream. You should hear her play Chopin. But, why don't we start with some scales? Just sing on aaahhh."

After reviewing three or four scales over two-and-a-half octaves, Miss Sayers handed Ellen the sheet music of *I Dreamt I Dwelt in Marble Halls*, from **Michael Balfe**'s **operetta**, *The Bohemian Girl*. A duplicate copy rested on the piano, in front of Nell. Ellen knew the melody, which she had heard in the 1936 Laurel and Hardy **comedic** version of *The Bohemian Girl*, but had never sung it before.

"Do you know it?"

"Well, I've never sung it, but I do know the melody, from Laurel and Hardy."

"I saw that film, too. Wasn't that a funny one? It was at the Tivoli a few years ago. I think it was their best comedy, though they **altered** the plot a bit from the operetta. Nell will play the introduction. Just come in where it says 'Arline.'"

Ellen began **tentatively**, but soon fully embraced the emotion **embedded** in the **lyrics**.

> *I dreamt that I dwelt in marble halls,*
> *With vassals and serfs at my side,*
> *And of all who assembled within those walls,*
> *That I was the hope and the pride.*
> *I had riches too great to count, could boast*
> *Of a high ancestral name;*
> *But I also dreamt, which pleased me most,*
> *That you lov'd me still the same...*
> *That you lov'd me, you lov'd me still the same,*
> *That you lov'd me, you lov'd me still the same.*

Students began filtering in as she sang, quietly taking their seats. As her **lilting** and **mellifluous** voice trailed off into a faint **pianissimo**, the students already in the room applauded enthusiastically. Ellen observed Frank Roman among them. She blushed, then smiled appreciatively.

"That was lovely, Ellen, lovely. It sounds like you've had voice training."

"Yes, I have. I studied with Patricia Brown in Stratford."

"Well, it's obvious that you have a beautiful soprano voice, and the makings of a fine soloist. I was particularly struck with the expressive manner in which you are able to **modulate** your tone in keeping with the lyrics. Needless to say, you've passed your audition. Why don't you sit here in the front row? You know, I can still remember Leota Olson singing that number so beautifully in our production of *The Bohemian Girl* back in 1930. Mladen **Sekulovich**, a Serbian boy who's now making his way on Broadway, played Devilshoof in that cast, but he changed his name to **Karl Malden**. His younger brother, Dan, was in A Cappella a few years ago."

By the time the rest of the students had arrived, the choir had swelled to about fifty singers, about thirty girls and twenty boys.

"Welcome back, singers. You know your places, I'm sure: sopranos, altos, tenors, and basses by the windows. I hope there are enough chairs for everyone.

I may move you around a bit, later, to get a better balance of parts, but you're fine for now. You will be interested to know that I have already lined up several concert appearances for the choir, the first of which will be in mid-October for the Gary Chamber of Commerce's fall banquet. And, of course, we'll be getting ready for our annual Christmas pageant and *Everyman*. Those interested in doing a skit for *Spice and Variety* may want to start thinking about what you'd like to do, or what acts you'd like to organize. If there's a musical component to your skit, I will be happy to work with you after school, and arrange for Miss Cromer, or Nell, to play for you. Now, let's warm up with some scales..."

The hour flew by as Miss Sayers passed out sheet music and the choir reviewed some familiar numbers from the previous year, including the choir's signature *May the Lord Bless You and Keep You*. Ellen detected that some choir members had been with the group for several years already, some with good, strong voices. Overall, the **consonant** voices of the **ensemble** produced a full, rich sound. She left class feeling a sense of emotional **exuberation.**

Her next class, on the second floor, was Auditorium with Gertrude Palmer and Melba Cromer. Early arrivals filed in and took seats near the stage. By the time the bell rang, nearly two hundred seats were occupied with students of every grade from the seventh to the twelfth. Ellen already knew that Auditorium was a central part of William Wirt's vision for the Gary Schools, and his Work-Study-Play system of education.

Once everyone was settled, Mrs. Palmer asked everyone to stand and sing **Emerson Loyalty**, with Miss Cromer at the keyboard:

O, Emerson Our School
O'er other schools we'll always rule.
We will link your name
With fairness, honor, and with fame.
Each one, O Emerson,
We'll stand by you till time is done.
And still with voices loud an clear,
We'll cheer for you Emerson.

"Thank you, students, for that **zealous** outpouring of school spirit! Please be seated. For those of you who don't know me, I'm **Mrs. Palmer**. Joining me this hour will be **Miss Cromer**, who played so beautifully on the piano, and who will leading our singing."

Mrs. Palmer was an attractive woman with dark hair and blue eyes. She wore a maroon silk dress with a circle pin on the collar and a decorative handkerchief pinned below her shoulder. She **projected** a confident air and appeared totally in command of her audience, seemingly able to keep even the most **obstreperous** students in line. The students appeared most **deferential** in response. She stood in the center aisle of the auditorium, and spoke in an easy, **conversational** manner, projecting her voice clearly to those on both sides of the room. Miss **Melba Cromer**, a small woman with a bright smile,

blue eyes and brown hair, and wearing a dark blue sweater over a flowered blouse, sat on the piano bench.

"So, what is Auditorium? Literally, of course – if you know your Latin – it's a place where you hear. But, it's much more than that. Our classes will consist of variety of programs presented by students, teachers and outside visitors. We will sing the Emerson School songs, the popular college fight songs, and American folk songs. We will also listen to some of the finest pieces of classical music ever written and learn about their composers. This year, you're going to have **innumerable** opportunities to practice your public speaking by addressing an audience, performing in a play or radio drama, and learning **parliamentary procedure**. Every week, we will elect a new chairman, and a secretary to keep the minutes. We have a variety of **didactic** goals in Auditorium. We will watch educational movies and **travelogues**, and the auditorium will provide a **forum** for community leaders in the fields of government, public safety, business, art, music, literature, and journalism, as well as members of the **clergy**, and local **philanthropists**. Our aim is to bring the wider world to your doorstep and to provide you with a sense of its opportunities. We also want to **cultivate** in you an appreciation for some of the finer things in life and **foster** a love of classical music, the opera, art, drama, poetry, and the cultures of other nations.

"Auditorium is also the place where our school spirit is most in evidence. And in that regard, I want to say a few words to you about the terrible tragedy that befell our school at the end of August. I refer, of course, to the theft of our beautiful art collection. Those paintings – some of them quite valuable – were donated by graduating classes since 1920. It's hard to imagine our school without them. Thus far, the police have no leads as to their whereabouts or of the **miscreants** who **absconded** with them. So, I want to ask all of you to keep your eyes and ears open. Perhaps, one of you will uncover a clue that will lead to their recovery."

As she listened intently to Mrs. Palmer's words of **lamentation**, Ellen's conscience was in **turmoil,** knowing full well where the paintings were now hidden and that the theft was possibly part of a plot far more **sinister** than anyone in the auditorium might have imagined.

"Our first item of business today is to elect our chairman for the week. In doing so, I want you to embrace the philosophy of the Auditorium, which is that every person has value and should have an opportunity to develop to his or her full potential. I expect you to behave as mature adults and not as members of **cliques**. I want you to support your classmates, particularly those who may be inclined to be shy or **diffident**, as they develop their self-confidence in public speaking and dramatic performance. After you graduate from Emerson, there's no reason why any of you should feel **inhibited** or **inarticulate** in public gatherings. Do I make myself understood?"

"Yes, Mrs. Palmer," responded the students, mostly in unison.

"Now, do I hear any **nominations** for the position of this week's class chairman?"

"I nominate Dan Barrick," shouted a girl from the back of the room.

"I nominate Steve Cajewski," shouted a girl in the front row.

"It doesn't have to be just boys. Girls are eligible to run as well," cautioned Mrs. Palmer.

"O.K. I nominate Helen Dziurdzy," cried a boy in the fourth row.

"Do I hear a motion to close the nominations?"

"So moved."

"All in favor?"

"Aye."

"Any nays? Hearing none, I declare the nominations closed. Now, for the vote by show of hands. Will you two girls serve as vote monitors?" Mrs. Palmer singled out two girls in the front row.

"All those in favor of Dan Barrick, raise your hands." The girls took a minute to count the raised hands on each side of the auditorium.

"Now, all those in favor of Steve Cajewski, raise your hands."

"Finally, all those in favor Helen Dziurdzy, raise your hands."

The girls conferred briefly, then one stepped forward and announced:

"Dan Barrick has been elected chairman with 143 votes."

"Way to go, Serb," came a good-natured shout of encouragement from the right side of the room.

"O.K., Dan. Now, I'll ask you to step forward and take over the meeting. Here is your gavel. Use it with **discretion**. And the rest of you, observe closely so you can **emulate** Dan's performance when it's your turn to chair the class."

Ellen recognized Dan as one of the tenors in A Cappella. She assumed he was Serbian, judging by the **appellation** coming from amid the crowd. His first official act was calling for nominations for the position of secretary. After a second set of nominations, Doris Nikchevich was elected secretary.

"Our daily agenda will begin with our chairman calling the meeting to order,

the reading of the previous day's minutes by our secretary, followed by announcements from the floor," explained Mrs. Palmer. "Have you got your notebook out, Doris? Dan will also have responsibility of introducing any special guests. If there are no special guests, or activities, he will then **defer** to Miss Cromer or myself to proceed with the regular class activities. There will be times when we will be assisted by Miss Harrison, or another member of the auditorium staff, such as when we break up into smaller groups to practice public speaking and **elocution**, or to rehearse our plays or dramatic readings. Our goal is to prepare you to speak both **extemporaneously** and with the benefit of a printed text in front of you, and to learn to project and clearly **articulate** your words so that even those in the rear of the auditorium can hear you clearly without the use of a microphone.

"Dr. Wirt once described the Auditorium class as being at the heart of the Work-Study-Play system. With his passing, it's a legacy he has left to each one of you. I hope you will all take advantage of it and allow it to enrich your lives. For the remainder of today's class, we're going to sing some American folk songs. Would our monitors help me pass out the song books?"

When the 2:10 bell rang, Ellen was off to Civics with **Miss Henrietta Newton** in Room 305. She met Melanie in the third floor hallway.

Room 305 was lined with maps and charts illustrating periods in world and American history, including the Colonial Era, the American Revolution, Westward Expansion, the Mexican War, the Civil War, as well as current political maps of the United States and Europe. Portraits of George Washington, Thomas Jefferson, and Abraham Lincoln were also mounted on the walls, as well as a colored charcoal portrait of Ralph Waldo Emerson, for whom the school was named. Miss Newton stood at the doorway, monitoring hallway traffic, and greeting students as they entered her classroom and took their seats. Her **demeanor** was as dignified as the **impeccably** tailored gray suit she wore. It was obvious that she knew many of the faces already from the American history class they had taken with her the year before. Miss Newton

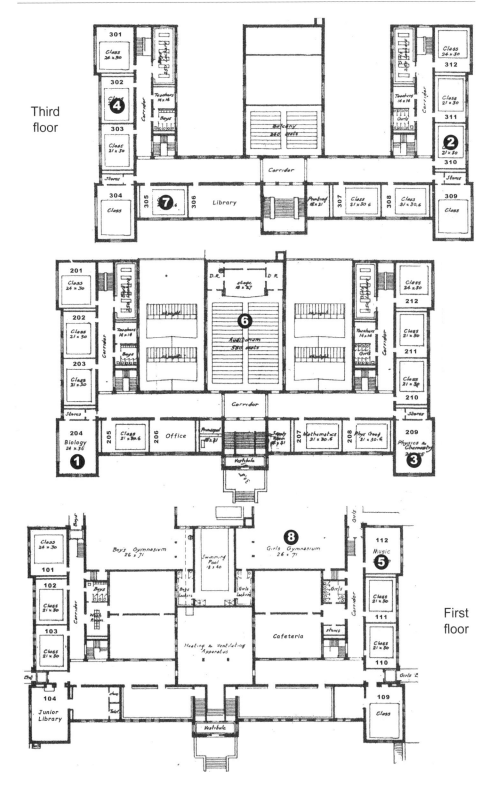

Third floor

First floor

had been teaching history and civics at Emerson since 1918 and was, by now, teaching the children of that earlier generation. And, while she acknowledged various **familial** relationships, she **tactfully** refrained from calling attention to their academic **prowess**, or lack thereof, a habit of which some teachers were **wont** to engage. She had a reputation as a tough, but **evenhanded** grader.

After all the students had taken their seats, Miss Newton called the roll, nodding as students cried "Here," or raised their hands in response. Assigning seats to conform to her seating chart was the next order of business. Ellen found herself three seats from the front in the row nearest the windows.

"There. I think that does it. Well, for those of you who may not know me, I'm Miss Newton. This begins my twenty-fifth year teaching at Emerson, so

I know many of you, or, perhaps, some members of your family. I can't emphasize enough how important Civics is, and will be, to your future lives. Soon, we'll be turning you loose in a **chaotic** world, a world **fraught** with **peril**. That peril is fueled by ignorance and dangerous political ideas – something we call **ideology**. What is 'ideology,' you may ask?" She walked to the front of the room, picked up a piece of chalk and wrote the word on the blackboard. "The root word of ideology, as you might expect, is the word 'idea.' An **ideology** is a set of conscious and unconscious ideas that reflect certain goals, expectations, and actions. That's a fancy way of saying that ideology is a **comprehensive** vision, a way of looking at the world. Ideologies are systems of abstract thought that are applied to the real world. An ideology starts out as a theory devised by philosophers, which politicians then attempt to impose on society. They do this first by destroying the existing order, followed by the imposition of what they think is a Utopia governed by an elite. Who can tell the class what the dominant ideologies are in the world today?"

"Yes, John."

"Fascism and Communism."

"Quite right. Fascism and Communism are the two leading ideologies contending for dominance in the world today. Communism has its philosophical roots in the ideas of Karl Marx. Fascism also draws from Marx, but also from various late 19th century political thinkers. In the 20th century, of course, **fascism** has been primarily influenced by **Adolf Hitler** who wrote *Mein Kampf*. Translated from the German, *Mein Kampf* means *My Struggle*. After Marx, Communism, or Bolshevism, was primarily influenced by the writings of **Vladimir Lenin**. During this semester, we will explore the similarities and differences between Fascism and Communism, and contrast them with the **philosophy** and structure of our American Republic. By contrasting our American system of government with those two alien ideologies, you will gain a better appreciation of what makes America so exceptional in world history."

"Where does **socialism** fit into this, Miss Newton?"

"Good question, John. **Socialism** is an economic system in which the government owns the means of production – in other words, the factories and businesses – with the purported goal of spreading the wealth. It's the economic basis of communism. In other words, forced economic equality. Socialism can take many forms. Under social democratic governments, the goal of **purported** economic justice is advanced by taxation and the redistribution of wealth through government welfare programs. In its more extreme form – communism – government not only owns the factories, but makes all major economic decisions. In theory, such systems are supposed to be run by workers' cooperatives, or councils, but, that's all an **obfuscation** because, in reality, power in such systems generally **devolves** to a small ruling **elite** that claims to act in the name of the people. That's what we now have in the Soviet Union, which uses socialist **doctrine** as a **smokescreen** for a system in which a dictator – Joseph Stalin – makes those decisions."

"Another **virulent** form of government is **fascism**, a political regime that exalts the nation, and race, above the individual, and institutes a **centralized**, **autocratic** government headed by a dictatorial leader. What distinguishes **fascism** from **socialism** or **communism** is that it employs severe economic and social **regimentation** of private industry in place of outright ownership of the means of production. Private ownership of the means of production exists in name only, with the Nazi government calling the shots. It is the German government and not the **nominal** owners, that exercises all the substantive powers of ownership, including what is to be produced, in what quantities, by what methods, and how it is to be priced. **National Socialism** builds its Utopia upon the *Volk* – that's German for people – and the purity and solidarity of the tribe. That's where Hitler derives his concept of the **Master Race**, that he believes is destined to rule the world.

"Communism, on the other hand, builds its utopian vision upon a class foundation, the morally purified New Man or New Woman, which they collectively refer to as the **proletariat**, or working class. Their enemies are referred to as the **bourgeoisie**, a class which includes capitalists, business owners, shopkeepers, the middle class, and farmers who may own a couple more cows than their neighbors. But, the ultimate goals of the fascists and the Communists are essentially the same – to exalt the state above the freedom of the individual, all in pursuit of **collectivist** utopian goals. Thus, fascism and communism are both what we would classify as **left-wing** movements. They enforce their will by the firing squad, the concentration camp, and the use of slave labor. So, don't be deceived by the fact that they are fighting each other at the present time. They are simply two totalitarian visions competing for dominance. After World War I, for example, they were in league with each other against the liberal political order of **bourgeois** Europe. The Communist leadership of the Soviet Union ordered their German party members to **collaborate** with the Nazis to bring down the **Weimar Republic**, which Hitler did in 1933.

"The novelist **Arthur Koestler** gets at the heart of the similarities between communism and fascism in his novel *Darkness at Noon*, which was published in 1940, shortly after the Hitler-Stalin pact was signed. The lead character, Rubashov, is dreaming about the last time he was arrested, by the Gestapo, and cannot determine which of the two hostile dictators is after him this time. Rubashov, you see, is an old Bolshevik, but arrested, imprisoned, and tried for treason against the very government he helped create twenty years before. Now, he has become a victim of Stalin's 1938 Purge. Koestler draws upon his knowledge of the Soviet police state and his experience of imprisonment in Franco's fascist Spain a few years before. Curiously, his assertion of the basic sameness of the two regimes was written at a time when he still considered himself a Soviet sympathizer, and had not yet broken with the party. Eventually, the youthful **ardor** he felt for communism and the Soviet **utopia** evaporated as he came to grips with the appalling evil of the regime. I know it's difficult for those of us in the United States to conceive that such **totalitarian regimes** are in control of much of the world, but such is the age in which we find ourselves.

"We, of course, live in a Constitutional Republic with a free market economy, in which economic decisions are made by people in their individual capacities. Decisions about what to produce and how those products are to be priced are based on millions, if not billions, of individual market choices. Imagine going into your local A & P, and choosing between Wheaties and Kellogg's Pep. The decisions about how much of each to produce and how they are to be priced are based on consumer demand and open competition, not on government **fiat**. In a socialist or fascist economy, the government might decide that everyone should eat Wheaties: The Breakfast of **Commissars**. Under socialism or communism, the government would own the factory that produces Wheaties, and make every other decision regarding its production and distribution. Under fascism, the government would tell the private business to produce Wheaties. Same result. Naturally, this produces greater societal unrest as people are forced to fight through the political process to ensure that their choices are given preference. In a free market, everybody decides what cereal they want and the government stays out of the way, except to ensure that laws are obeyed, contracts are enforced, and **monopolies in restraint of trade** are outlawed. I use this simple example merely to illustrate what happens when the government steps in to make economic decisions best left to a free people. In the real world, of course, such decisions are far more significant than cereal choices, and affect the lives and fortunes of millions of people around the world.

"It is clear that communism and fascism have much in common. Both are **comprehensive** political ideologies that **advocate** violent revolution, but only until the ruling **clique** is firmly **entrenched**. After that, the rulers **decry** what they call 'counter-revolutionary tendencies' that might threaten their dominance. Both believe in the necessity of an **elite vanguard** being in control, both have disdain for what are termed 'bourgeois' values, for private property, and both have **totalitarian** ambitions. The most important consideration in both systems is that the state – that is, the government – is all-powerful, and the individual is important only insofar as he or she serves the state, like a cog in the vast machinery of government.

"By the way, how many of you have seen Charlie Chaplin's film *Modern Times?* Raise your hands. Most of you, I see. Good. Well, you may recall the scene where Charlie is working in a factory and is sucked into the **cogs** of a giant piece of machinery. That image is an accurate reflection of the modern totalitarian state where citizens are mere cogs in the state apparatus. Incidentally, when I use the word 'state' in this sense, I refer to **sovereign** political entities – nation states, or countries – rather than to the forty-eight states in the United States.

"The **irony** in all of this is that the United States is now in an alliance with one of these **totalitarian states,** or **regimes**, for the purpose of defeating the other totalitarian regime. Our system of government has nothing in common with communism, yet we are linked in a wartime alliance with it. It was the 19th century editor, **Charles Dudley Warren**, who was responsible for the **aphorism** that 'politics makes strange bedfellows.' Nowhere is that more true than in our current alliance with the mass murderer, Joseph Stalin. Sadly, President Roosevelt embodies a troubling **naïveté** that Stalin's regime is some kind of **crude** Asiatic New Deal that will come around in the post-war era. He uses the term 'Convergence' to describe what he believes is the inevitability of our two systems coming together, or meeting in the middle, perhaps after the war is concluded. Why, he even considers British **imperialism** a greater threat to world peace. Yet, he seems to typify the attitude of many experienced democratic politicians around the world, as well as scholars and intellectuals, who are **lamentably sanguine** about the nature of communist **ideology** and Soviet behavior. Such is the power of **myth** or **utopianism** and its hold upon the human **psyche**.

"Our system of government in the United States is the **antithesis** of ideology. This has effectively **inoculated** us in large measure from the **pernicious** influences of a **totalitarian** worldview. While our system of government obviously has certain philosophical underpinnings, those underpinnings are rooted in freedom, limited government, separation of powers, free markets, and individual liberty. Our Constitutional Republic leaves to a free people what in a communist or fascist regime is dictated by the government, or its dictator. Our system is not based on some **utopian** ideal that must be imposed on the people against their will, but on individual free choice.

"During this semester, we are going to explore the philosophical ideas that motivated the Founding Fathers to produce the greatest experiment in Ordered Liberty ever devised by man. I'm talking about our **United States Constitution** that was drafted in 1787. We'll look at the ideas of St. Paul, John Locke, the Baron de Montesquieu, William Blackstone, Sir Edward Coke, Cicero, Plutarch, and other **progenitors** of the ideas that motivated the Founders. These are the writers with whom the Founders were most **conversant**. Their **Revolutionary** experience made them deeply suspicious of power, whether exercised by kings, or mobs. They feared the tyranny of an **oppressive** majority as much as they feared the tyranny of kings, or **oligarchs**. That's why they created a **Republic**, not a democracy, because they feared mob rule. And that's why they created a system of **checks and balances**, to prevent any one branch of government from becoming all-powerful. Unfortunately, we have seen **unconstitutional** assaults on that system, such as when President Roosevelt attempted to pack the Supreme Court to advance his progressive agenda.

"You are the heirs to that great experiment. Whether it continues for future generations rests on your shoulders. Some of you young men may be called upon to serve your country on foreign shores, just as those of previous generations were called upon. It's called the price of liberty. Indeed, many Emerson graduates are already serving in various branches of the military, including, perhaps, some of your own family members. Others will be called upon to do their part on the home front, whether helping to produce the steel that fuels our war effort, buying war bonds or stamps, taking part in scrap drives, or in complying with the **ration system**. But, all of you need to fully comprehend the reasons why we are fighting.

"Some of you may have seen director **Frank Capra**'s film *Prelude to War,* the first in a series of documentary films entitled *Why We Fight.* If you have not already seen it, I urge you to do so. In that first installment, he explains the differences between democratic and fascist states, between free states and slave states. One thing you will notice, however, is that our government is downplaying the true nature of Soviet communism in **deference** to our wartime alliance. But, don't let that deceive you. I want to **underscore** that the Soviets are every bit as evil as the Nazis, perhaps even more so. Yet, President Roosevelt persists in using a variety of **euphemisms** to describe our wartime ally – like 'Uncle Joe.'

"This war is not your typical **balance of power** struggle of the kind we experienced in previous centuries. This is total war, driven by the urge to **subjugate** whole nations and bring them under the domination of an alien **ideology**. And this urge to subjugate other nations and peoples is driven by the **utopian** visions of dead philosophers who thought they knew best how we should live our lives.

"I'm not **sanguine** enough to expect that our problems will end when, and if, we defeat Nazi Germany and Imperial Japan. You have to imagine what a post-war world will look like with Joseph Stalin commanding vast **swaths** of European territory. Indeed, what will happen to Poland, Lithuania, Hungary, Serbia, Romania, Greece, and other countries in close **proximity** to the Soviet Union when the war ends?"

Ellen sat transfixed by Miss Newton's **trenchant** and **lucid explication** of the current **conflagration** in Europe, and the world, and the **objective** manner in which she **elucidated** the complex subject matter. But, she was also struck by the passion of her explanation and how similar Miss Newton's worldview mirrored that of Miss Satterfield back at Stratford High. She raised her hand.

"Yes, Ellen... Anderson."

"Miss Newton. I think we have only to look at how the Soviet Union treated little Lithuania, a nation of perhaps four million people, under the terms of the non-aggression pact between Nazi Germany and the Soviet Union. I mean, shortly after it was signed, the Germans marched into western Poland and the Soviets into eastern Poland. And less than a year later, the Soviet Union occupied Lithuania and the other Baltic countries. According to a Lithuanian friend of mine, it appears they had a secret agreement all along to divide up Eastern Europe. Since then, the Soviets have killed, or deported thousands of Lithuanians and other Baltic peoples to Siberia, as a means of bringing the country under its heel. They focus on arresting the professional and educated classes in an effort to **decapitate** potential opposition. They've also **profaned** and **desecrated** their houses of worship and arrested their priests. It's insidious!"

"Quite right, Ellen. That's the tragedy of the small nations that are trapped between these two military **behemoths**. They are virtually powerless to resist the death and wanton **pillaging** suffered at the hands of the warring forces. Their only hope is that the western democracies can ultimately triumph and restore their freedom and independence. But, right now, that prospect looks **daunting** if the post-war world shapes up the way I envision.

"After the **devastation** of the **Great War**, it was President Wilson's dream that a **League of Nations** would prevent future wars. And while it was a noble vision, it was unable to prevent a number of conflicts in the years leading up to the Second World War, including Italy's invasion of **Ethiopia** in 1935, and the **Spanish Civil War**. And, of course, it was totally **ineffectual** in stopping the aggression of the **Axis Powers** in the present conflict. The fact that the United States Senate failed to ratify the **League of Nations** reflected the dominant **isolationist** sentiments that prevailed at that time. Whether the League of Nations would have had any **appreciable** influence on the course of world politics in the years leading up to the invasion of Poland is, of course, a subject of considerable **conjecture**.

"So you see, class, you are living in trying times. The oceans separating us from Europe or Asia, and the **insularity** we have enjoyed up to now, have given us a false sense of security. We initially resisted becoming embroiled in World War I because we viewed it as Europe's conflict. **Ironically**, when President Wilson ran for re-election in 1916, his campaign slogan was 'He kept us out of war.' And, after the war, we **blithely** returned to a policy of **isolationism** that left us unprepared for Pearl Harbor. It's hard to imagine that, prior to the Japanese attack, the sentiment of the American public was so strongly opposed to **intervention** that we would have allowed Europe to be trampled by the Nazi war machine, and China by the Imperial Japanese Army. The **America First Committee** was a reflection of that deep-rooted isolationist **sentiment**. While the oceans may provide us with a measure of security, most of the world is not so fortunate. Whether it's the Far East, or North Africa, Norway, France, or Eastern Europe, the world is an extremely dangerous place.

"So, the study of civics takes on a **heightened** importance today as we contrast the brilliance of our Constitutional Republic and the freedom and prosperity we enjoy in America, with the war, devastation and cruelty that citizens in most parts of the world suffer on a daily basis because of the **insidious** effects of totalitarian ideology on the minds of men."

As the class drew to a close, Miss Newton distributed the civics textbook for the semester: *The Story of American Democracy,* written by two Connecticut authors: Mabel B. Casner of Washington School, West Haven, and Ralph H. Gabriel, Professor of History at Yale University. Ellen could have sat and listened to Miss Newton's **impassioned** lecture for hours, but her attention was rudely interrupted by the 3:10 bell, reminding her that her last period physical education class was about to begin.

Ellen's 3:15 physical education class met in the girls' lower gymnasium. **Gertrude Reynolds**, her physical education teacher, stood at the door of her

office, with her little pet terrier at her feet. After the bell rang signaling the start of class, she blew her whistle and brought the class to attention.

"Line up girls, in three rows, at arm's length from each other. Welcome to last period physical education. My name is Gertrude Reynolds, but you may call me Miss Reynolds. Most of you have already had me for physical education so you know how I conduct my classes. I regret to inform you that we have lost two of our faculty members since June. Miss Esther File joined the **WAVES** and is now serving at the **Great Lakes Naval Training Center**, and Miss Vogt left us to get married. But, we will **persevere**.

"Now, for some housekeeping details. You will all be expected to wear the standard green gymsuits in order to pass inspection. Those of you who need gymsuits can get them from the school store on the first floor. If you have not already done so, please be sure to stitch your last name and first initial above the breast pocket."

As Ellen stood in the second row next to Melanie, she heard an audible groan emitted by some of the girls in the back row when the subject of gymsuits was **broached**. It appeared that, for some, the regulation green gymsuits required

of female athletes failed to meet their current **sartorial** standards. Most, however, simply accepted them as a **rite of passage**.

"Your gymsuits will cost you $3.50," Miss Reynolds explained **succinctly**. "Unless you have a financial hardship, you will be expected to pay for your uniform by the end of next week. If you cannot afford $3.50, please see me. Fall sports will include field hockey, swimming and basketball, along with a healthy dose of calisthenics. Each of you will be expected to participate in at least two sports each semester. Sally, here, will see that you are assigned a locker on the balcony. It is up to you to purchase a padlock. Any questions? If not, you are dismissed for the day."

Melanie took Ellen by the arm and walked with her to their second floor lockers where they retrieved some of the textbooks they had acquired that day. Ellen's mind was still preoccupied with the **profusion** of ideas presented by Miss Newton in Civics, ideas that made her physical education class seem **jejune** by comparison.

Then, suddenly, the bell rang. A few seconds later, the hallways were filled with students leaving their last period classrooms, accompanied by the sound of trumpets echoing through the hallways. Ellen, Melanie, and the rest of the students in the second floor hallway froze in place as three trumpet players in R.O.T.C. uniforms marked the end of the school day with the traditional *Retreat*. Outside, a detachment of R.O.T.C. members lowered the American flag from the 40-foot flagpole that stood to the right of the school's main entrance. As the last note faded away, and the momentary stillness was broken by the **resumption** of student chatter, the girls continued down the front steps, out to 7th Avenue, and on their way home.

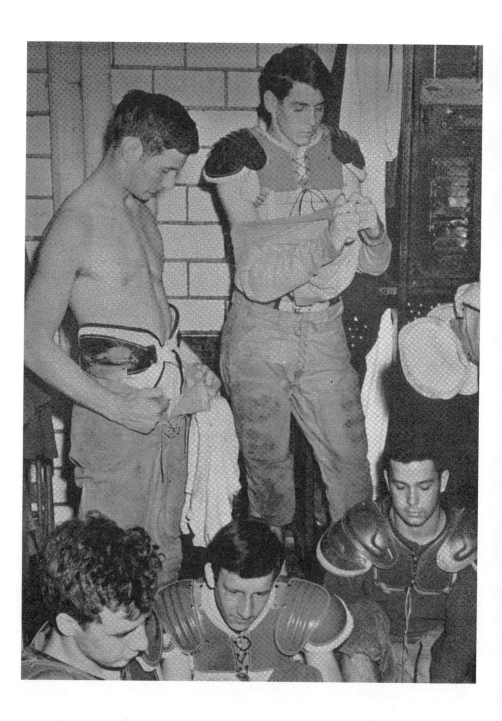

Chapter 30

Eavesdropping at the Sokolov's

For the remainder the week, Ellen was consumed with her classes, home-work, and some after school activities, leaving little time for sleuthing. On Friday, her friend, Melanie, was off to Maywood, Illinois, west of Chicago, with the rest of the cheerleading squad for Emerson's opening **gridiron** contest with Proviso High School. Ellen contemplated going to the game, but decided to stay home and listen to the play-by-play on the radio. She curled up in one of the overstuffed chairs in the parlor with the intention of reading *Macbeth* while she listened, but never got beyond Act II, Scene 1. Her father joined her, perusing the *Post-Tribune* while listening to the game. The **Golden Tornado** scored an impressive 20-0 victory, behind a balanced offensive attack and a **staunch** defense. Midway through the third quarter, with Emerson on its opponent's ten-yard line, Ellen heard Mrs. Matheus calling her from the rear stairway.

"Ellen... telephone for you!"

"Coming, Mrs. Matheus."

She scurried down the rear steps and into Mrs. Matheus' front room. The telephone receiver was resting on the oak end table.

"Hello? This is Ellen."

"Ellen, this is Tanya Sokolov. I promised to call you if I learned anything important. Well, this is important."

"Where are you calling from? Can you speak freely?"

"Yes. I'm using the pay phone at Diamond's confectionary on 11th Avenue, a few blocks from our house. My stepfather's at home and our phone is in the living room where he does his reading – mostly Communist party literature and ideological **tracts**."

"So, what's happening?"

"The local cell has called a meeting for Saturday night at our house, and I have an idea how we can eavesdrop on the proceedings."

"How's that?"

"Well, they meet in our basement and I've figured out a way to listen from my bedroom closet. There are several loose floorboards which I can remove temporarily to make it easier to hear their conversation."

"Say, that's **ingenious**. But, what if we're discovered?"

"My stepfather almost never comes into my room and, besides, we can replace the boards when the meeting is over. The thing is, you'll have to bring Natalia along to translate. They almost always speak in Russian, and I don't understand the language very well. My real father was Russian, but he almost never spoke the language around me. He was insistent that I learn to be a good American. Anyway, they plan to meet at eight o'clock, so it would be best if you and Natalia could be here no later than seven thirty. We can go into my bedroom and close the door. If my father discovers that I have visitors, I can tell him that we're doing homework, or some such thing. I can also turn on the radio to cover our movements, but I suspect that he'll be preoccupied in the basement getting things ready for the meeting. He's in charge of distributing copies of the *Daily Worker* to the members of his group. Each member has a **quota** to sell on street corners."

"I'd feel better if we arrived a little earlier, so we don't bump into any of his associates – say, seven fifteen?"

"Sure. That's a good idea. I'll have the floorboards loosened already so there's no chance of them hearing us. I'll depend on you to bring Natalia."

"You can count on me. This is just the break we've been waiting for. We'll be there promptly at seven fifteen. **Tardiness** is not part of my vocabulary. We'll see you then."

As soon as Ellen hung up, she dialed Natalia's number. After about a half dozen rings, somebody answered.

"Natalia?"

"No, this is her Aunt Veronika. Is this Ellen?"

"Yes, Mrs. Boroskova. May I speak to Natalia, please?"

"Of course. She's in her room. Let me call her."

"Hi, Ellen. I thought you might have gone to the Emerson football game with Melanie."

"I was thinking about it, but she already had a car full of cheerleaders. The game's being played about twenty miles west of Chicago – not so easy to get to without an automobile. But, I've got some news far more exciting than football. Tanya Sokolov called me a few minutes ago to say that the local Communist cell will be meeting in her basement tomorrow night at eight o'clock, and that she has found a way to listen in on their conversation from her bedroom closet."

"Fantastic! That's just the opportunity we've been waiting for. I expect you'll need me to do the listening?"

"That's right. Tanya's comprehension of Russian is limited, she says."

"No problem."

"O.K. I'll be at your house at seven o'clock and we'll walk over to Tanya's. We have to get there in plenty of time before her father's guests arrive."

When Ellen returned to her apartment, she informed her father that she would be out most of Saturday, having already made plans to go to the movies.

"Melanie's invited me to join some of the cheerleaders and football players at the movies tomorrow afternoon, with dinner afterwards. I hope that's all right?" She refrained from saying anything about her plans later that evening.

"You go right ahead, honey. I expect to be tied up at the plant all day. We have a deadline coming up on Monday and I still have some drawings to complete. I'm taking a lunch with me. It's good you're fending for yourself."

On Saturday afternoon, Ellen joined Melanie, Virginia Kelley, Frank Roman, Jim Swan, George Mihal and three other members of the Golden Tornado football squad for an **impromptu** celebration of the team's 20-0 trouncing of Proviso High School the night before. In **deference** to the boys, the girls **unanimously** agreed to see *Sergeant York,* starring Gary Cooper, which was

still playing at the Grand. It was the story of the hillbilly sharpshooter who became the most decorated hero of World War I, singlehandedly taking out 32 machine guns, killing 28 German soldiers and capturing 132 others. Gary Cooper played the role of Alvin York brilliantly. When the picture was over, the young people filed out of the theater shaking their heads in disbelief at the **audaciousness** of his heroics. Then, they all descended on Princess Confectioners, next door, for an early dinner. The receptionist directed them to a large round booth at the front of the restaurant.

"I wish I had gone to the game, Frank," Ellen lamented, "but I did listen to it on the radio. I'll bet Coach Rolfe doesn't think you stink, now," she added.

"Oh, he never lets us off the hook until the end of the season. He's tough, but fair, and he knows when we're not pulling our weight. But, beneath that tough exterior is a heart of gold. Without him, we'd be just a bunch of undisciplined high school kids. Mihal, here, can tell you."

"You bet. We complain like the devil about him, but wouldn't trade him for the world. He encouraged me from the time I was a freshman and made me what I am today."

"Which is what, Mihal?"

"Very funny, Swan. You tell me. I just know I never would have made varsity without him yelling at me. There's something about a coach yelling at you that makes you want to do your best. Besides, Coach knows the game is all about emotion, and hard work. You not only have to execute your plays, but you also have to have the will to win. If you get overconfident, or fail to take your opponent seriously, it can be disastrous. I'm just glad I'm wearing my helmet when he whacks me on the head with that aluminum clipboard of his."

"What do you think of the Tolleston team," Virginia inquired.

"Well, we beat 'em 54-7 last year, but then we lost a lot more starters than they did. I think this year's going to be a lot closer," Jim Swan replied.

"I remember their team razzing us and making **snide** comments from their bus when we walked over to Gleason Field in our cleats – trying to **precipitate** something. Coach told us to keep our cool. But, we were **unflappable** and wanted to pay 'em back. And we did – big time!" Mihal added. "Our defense was **tenacious**, and frustrated them at every turn. Never mess with a Tornado. It might just blow you into the next county."

"Hey, don't forget that breathing all that dust from the coke plant made men out of us," George Nabhan replied. "Compared to us, those guys from Tolleston are a bunch of cookie pushers."

The gang ordered burgers and fries all around. Most ordered chocolate malts, some ordered Cokes. Ellen enjoyed the conversation. It made her feel more a part of the gang, and **acutely** aware of what life was like growing up in a steel town. The students took it as it came and made the best of it, soot and all. As six thirty approached, however, she excused herself to catch the Tolleston streetcar.

"Going so soon, Ellen?" asked Frank, who appeared to have taken a shine to the visitor from Connecticut.

"I promised to meet a friend at seven and don't want to **procrastinate** or I'll miss my streetcar. So, I guess I'll see you all in school on Monday."

"Hasta la vista, señorita," shouted George.

"Sounds like Mrs. Reyher finally taught you something, George," **mocked** Melanie. "And this after how many years of Spanish?"

"Very funny, McGuire. You should go on Jack Benny."

"No, not Jack Benny. I'd rather go on Edgar Bergen. You could sit on my knee and I could pull the string at the back of your neck and put words in your mouth."

"Really? Do I look like Charlie McCarthy?"

"The spittin' image, but I'll buy you a tux and a top hat."

As her friends persisted in their **lighthearted banter**, Ellen paid her check and scurried over to the streetcar stop at the corner of 8th and Broadway, in front of the LaSalle Hotel. The Tolleston car arrived about ten minutes later.

The sun was low in the sky and cast an **eerie** glow across the neighborhood by the time she got off at 11th and Pierce and walked to the Boroskova's. She looked at her watch. It was six fifty-five. Natalia was sitting in the front parlor, reading the *Gary Post*-Tribune when Ellen rang the bell.

"Hi, Ellen. I'm ready to go! Uncle Stan and Aunt Veronika went to the movies. The Roxy in Glen Park is showing *Nazi Agent*, with **Conrad Veidt**.

It's about German spies, if you can believe it."

"Conrad Veidt, eh? My favorite movie villain. Too bad it's not about Soviet spies," Ellen suggested, "but close enough."

"That's a good point. How many movies are there about Soviet spies?"

"None that I know of. Stalin's our ally, after all," Ellen **mused**, "and Hollywood's gotten the message, with pressure from the Roosevelt administration."

"So, Tanya's at 1176 Tyler, correct?"

"That's right. She said it's a brick bungalow similar to yours, just a few houses north of the park, on the alley. Tanya said she'd be sitting on the front porch to guide us in, just in case her stepfather's prowling about upstairs."

It took the girls about five minutes to walk to Tanya's house, where they found her sitting on the front porch, as promised. She scooted them inside the front door and into her bedroom before even her mother noticed. She could hear her stepfather arranging folding chairs in the basement. She closed and locked her bedroom door, then opened her clothes closet. Dresses and skirts hung from a clothes rod, allowing an occupant to easily conceal herself within, amidst the odor of mothballs.

"I've already removed the floorboards," Tanya said in a barely **audible** whisper. "You can see the light from the basement through the cracks in the subfloor. I suggest you get yourself situated now and I'll close the door. Here's a pillow to make yourself more comfortable. When the meeting starts, you can put your ear to the floor. Ellen and I can look at my postcard and doll collections in the meantime. When the meeting's over, you can dictate and I'll type up what you've heard."

"That sounds like a excellent plan," replied Natalia. "See you later, girls."

After Tanya closed the closet door, she walked to her desk and showed Ellen the typewriter her mother had given her. It was a late Underwood Standard Manual, World's Fair Model.

"Did I tell you I'm up to 70 words per minute? Having my own typewriter has been a real **boon** to my typing skills. Let me show you. Just keep an eye on the second hand of my alarm clock."

Tanya took a seat at her desk, opened an issue of the *Saturday Evening Post* and placed it on her left, next to the typewriter. When the second-hand reached twelve she began typing. Her fingers raced across the keys. A minute later, she stopped, and pulled the paper out of the carriage. Ellen examined it, counting the words. She looked in vain for mistakes, but couldn't find any. She counted 78 words.

"That's a new record. I'm aiming for 90 words per minute by the end of October."

"I'm very impressed, Tanya. Typing has never been my strong suit. I'm more of a hunt-and-peck typist. Who wouldn't want to hire you?"

Tanya smiled. "That's what I'm hoping for. I turn sixteen in March, and then I can get my work permit."

Tanya invited Ellen to sit on her bed and look at her collection of post-cards.

"We used to do a lot of traveling when my father was alive. I've been to Chicago, of course, Milwaukee, the Wisconsin Dells, Indiana Dunes State Park, Indianapolis, Brown County, Saugatuck, Detroit, Niagara Falls, Mount Rushmore, Gettysburg, Williamsburg, Washington, DC, Philadelphia, and New York City. Here's a postcard of the Statue of Liberty. We even went up into the crown. And we also took a boat ride all around Manhattan Island."

As Tanya passed postcards to Ellen, the girls heard the front doorbell ring. It was ten minutes of eight, and the guests had begun to arrive. Most of the voices were too soft to be recognizable, with the exception of Galina Borovsky, whose raspy voice – probably from cigarette smoking – was unmistakable. The girls detected nine people coming to the door. Ellen had memorized only seven names. That meant two new ones were downstairs.

"Where's our coffee?" Tanya's stepfather shouted from the basement.

"It's on the kitchen stove," her mother replied.

"Then, bring it to our guests."

"My Mother hates it when he invites them over here. She knows what it's all about, but is terrified of saying anything."

The girls heard Tanya's mother walking down the basement stairs, presumably with the coffee pot.

"It's about time. Now, get out of here and leave us in peace."

"See what I mean, Ellen?"

"Wow! How can she stand it? I'd hit him over the head with a frying pan."

Before she retired to her bedroom, Tanya's mother knocked on the Tanya's bedroom door.

"Did I hear voices in there? Do you have company, Tanya?"

Tanya unlocked the door and opened it a crack.

"Yes, Mother, I have a friend visiting. We're looking at my postcard collection. We'll be quiet."

"That's all right, dear. I didn't mean to pry. I'll be in my bedroom." Tears flowed down her mother's face.

"Mom's become such a **timorous,** creature. Or, at least my stepfather has made her into one. She didn't used to be like that when my father was alive. She walks on eggshells whenever my stepfather's around, and becomes so **laconic.** And when he has meetings here, she's beside herself. He's so **tactless** and treats her like a servant. I'm surprised she doesn't go visit my Aunt Grace in Glen Park when he has guests, to spare herself the **humiliation.** Say, I'm dying to know what they're talking about."

When Tanya had finished showing Ellen her postcards, she took her dolls down from her bookshelf. She had a Shirley Temple doll, and a collection of dolls in various European national costumes – Greek, Italian, Russian, Swedish, Irish, German, Spanish, Polish, Serbian, and Hungarian.

"My mother's been buying these for me since I was seven years old. I'm very proud of them. My goal is to have a doll for each of the nationalities in Gary."

As Ellen observed the pride which Tanya displayed toward her collections, she realized what a strong liking she had taken to the girl. She was a very sweet, sincere girl caught in an impossible domestic situation. Upon reflection, it was somewhat **akin** to the relationship she enjoyed with Christine Applegate, back in Stratford. Like Tanya, Christine had lost her father to a **tragic** accident. But, unlike Tanya, Christine's home life was loving, and not **compromised** by all these political **machinations.** Ellen felt terribly **solicitous** toward Tanya and wished she could do something to help **extricate** her from her **dilemma.** Unfortunately, there didn't seem to be any immediate solution.

"How's school going so far?"

"It's great. As you know, I'm taking a commercial course: typing, shorthand, and English. But, I'm also taking world history, general science, auditorium, and physical education."

"Does Froebel offer business law?"

"Yes. I plan to take it next year. I figure that will help me if I want to get a job in a law office."

"Remember what I said about law school. There's no reason why you can't pursue a career in the law if you have **persistance**. Perhaps, you'll start out as a legal secretary and learn the ropes. I had a neighbor in Stratford who started out as a legal secretary. She often knew more legal procedure than her boss and got him out of all sorts of **predicaments** when it came to drafting and filing legal documents and such. You simply have to have a game plan. It may take you a few more years than someone who goes straight to college, and then to law school, but it can be done, if you have the will. Don't hesitate to seek advice from people who understand the field and can give you solid guidance. And build on the skills you are learning in school. Be the best at whatever you do, whether it's typing or shorthand, or business law. Don't **shelve** your **ambitions**, or let anyone stand in your way. And once you reach eighteen, and leave Froebel, don't be afraid to go out on your own and escape this **oppressive** home environment."

"You've really opened my eyes, Ellen, and given me a sense of confidence I've never had before. I'm just afraid of what will happen to my Mother if I'm not around to **temper** my stepfather's outbursts. The abuse he **metes** out will undoubtedly get worse if there's no one around to **restrain** him."

"Well, I think you have a few more years before you have to confront that eventuality. Who knows? Your circumstances may change before that."

Tanya began putting her dolls back on the shelf when the girls heard steps on the basement stairs. It appears the meeting had concluded and her father's guests were in the process of departing. It was nine thirty-eight. Then, they heard Galina speaking, but in English.

"Remember what I told you, Boris. Get those paintings to New York before someone traces them to Chicago. The local police know that no one in their right mind would try to fence them in Gary. That leaves Chicago as the logical distribution point and makes us vulnerable to detection. I know for a fact that they have already alerted the Chicago police to be on the lookout for the paintings, and have given them the complete inventory. So, by moving them out of the Midwest, you can kill two birds with one stone."

"Understood."

Confident that Galina Borovsky was the last to leave, Tanya opened her closet door and helped Natalia up off the floor.

"Boy, did I get an earful," Natalia exclaimed, in hushed tones.

"What did they say? What did they say?" Ellen asked, anxiously.

"Wait, let me put some paper in my typewriter first," Tanya urged, softly. Then, as Natalia spoke, quietly, Tanya began typing.

"First of all, they're planning to transfer the entire collection of paintings to the East Coast. Once there, they plan to distribute them to agents in a dozen cities, where their sale will be far less **conspicuous,** or likely to arouse suspicion."

"How do they plan to get them there?" Tanya inquired.

"Your stepfather has been elected to drive them there, with two others on board: one to ride in the cab with him and the other to ride in the back of the truck. They plan to deliver them to a warehouse in Jersey City, across the Hudson from New York City, but they didn't mention the exact address."

"When are they leaving?"

"About the first of October, provided their plans fall into place."

"So, who else is going besides Tanya's father?" Ellen inquired.

"Mike Ivanski – you know, the one from Johnson Street, and a Chicago member named Peter... Peter... Oh, what was his name now? Peter Milosz. That's it."

"Did they have anything to say about atomic research?" Ellen persisted.

"Yes, it appears that they are close to securing detailed diagrams of the **prototype** of the first **atomic reactor** from some of their **confederates** working on the inside of the project being conducted at the University of Chicago. From what I understand, it hasn't been tested yet. They intend to transport these to New Jersey in the same manner, with the idea of transferring them to an **Amtorg** freighter in New York harbor. The plans will be in the care of one of the project scientists with an understanding of atomic fission. He's a Hungarian national by the name of Molnar – Miklos Molnar. Apparently, he's got government security clearance and everything. He's taking the train to New York City and plans to meet up with them there."

"Who else was at the meeting besides Mike Ivanski and Galina Borovsky?"

"Let's see, there was Iggy Eisenberg, Konstantin Ivanov, Alex Kropotkin, Gene Alexandrov, Peter Milosz. And, oh, yes, Dimitri Poliakov came down from Chicago. He also had someone with him who sounded important. I only caught his first name – Hyman. He seemed to be giving directions to the others. Perhaps Uncle Stan might know the name?

"There's something else you should know, and it's not good. They know about me. At least, that I was on the train to Chicago and disappeared in Marshall Field's with two other people. Tanya, that would be Ellen and her father."

"Did they **intimate** that they might know your whereabouts?" Ellen inquired.

"Not that I could **discern**. But, they knew my last name and suggested that they should begin a search of area telephone directories for a relation. And that poses a real problem because Boroskova is an extremely uncommon name whether in Chicago, or the United States. It may just be a matter of time before they track me down. So, unless I change my name or move somewhere else, they'll be able to trace me to my uncle and aunt's home."

"What can they do to you, Natalia?" Tanya inquired.

"That's anyone's guess. They tracked me onto the 20th Century Limited in New York and followed me to Chicago. They were after secret documents I brought with me from England, but those are now in the hand of my Uncle Stan and his friends. The cat's out of the bag, so to speak. It's possible they'll just want to question me, but I don't want to find out."

"Did they have anything else to say?"

"Yes, but it was rather **opaque** and **indecipherable** – mostly about party doctrine. Oh – I almost forgot – they're looking for recruits to engage in industrial espionage, mostly about steelmaking processes."

"It's obvious you'll need to consult with your uncle before deciding how to proceed," Ellen suggested. "In the meantime, we've got to get out of here."

"Let me make sure my stepfather's still in the basement," Tanya suggested. "Then, you can slip out the front door. Wait here." Tanya could see that the basement light was on and could hear her stepfather still rummaging around down below.

"The coast is clear. Out this way. We'll be in touch," she whispered.

Ellen and Natalia spirited themselves out of the house and down Tyler Street to 13th Avenue. A few minutes later, they were back at the darkened Boroskova residence. Natalia's aunt and uncle had not yet returned from the movies.

"I don't feel comfortable leaving you here alone, Natalia. Why don't I stay with you until they come home, and then, perhaps, your uncle can drive me home. Besides, I'd rather not take the streetcar home at this hour."

"Yes, please stay until they get home. In the meantime, I'll make us some hot Ovaltine and we can listen to the radio."

In the time it took her to heat some water, Natalia returned with two warm mugs of the delicious chocolate beverage. "This should take off some of that evening chill."

"I'm worried, Natalia. If the Communists know your name, it wouldn't be difficult for them to track you here. You'll be like a sitting duck, that is, if you stay here."

"I agree. I got a cold chill when I heard them say that they knew my name. Uncle Stan said that there is only one Boroskova in Chicago, and they're not related to us. It shouldn't take them long to find my uncle through the telephone operator, and, through him, me."

"Then, why don't you come live at our place for the time being? I've got a double bed, and you can simply take the streetcar to Froebel for classes."

"Are you sure your father, or landlady, won't mind?"

"Of course not. When Dad hears the situation, he'll be totally supportive, and Mrs. Matheus is a peach. She'll enjoy having the extra company."

Shortly before eleven o'clock, Ellen and Natalia heard Stan and Veronika's sedan pull into the rear driveway. They entered the house through the back door.

"Well, hello, you two. How did you make out?" He and Veronika took a seat on the davenport, and leaned forward, anxiously.

"Great. We learned a lot. Our friends are planning to transport the art collection to New Jersey by truck," Natalia explained.

"I'm not surprised," Stan replied. "What about the atomic research?"

"It appears they have obtained some preliminary diagrams of the **prototype** of an **atomic reactor**, and have a basic **conception** of the process by which a **fission bomb** can be constructed. It appears they are aware of the work of **Robert Oppenheimer** and his team of scientists who have already concluded that such a fission weapon is a possibility. But, they are also aware that the plans are in a **nascent** stage. Apparently, Oppenheimer took over from another scientists who quit because of concerns about **operational security**. Obviously, his concerns were well-founded," she added.

"This **Robert Oppenheimer** is a potential problem," Stan observed. "We've known him as a member of a number of Communist front organizations. My sources tell me that he has attended meetings in the homes of known Communists on the West Coast, and has been sympathetic to Communist causes in the past, including the **Loyalist** cause during the **Spanish Civil War**. Since his days as a professor at the University of California at Berkeley, he has knowingly **consorted** with Communists and **fellow travelers**, not the least of which is his wife, Kitty. It makes me very uncomfortable to know that he's so intimately involved in this work."

"We have some other news that is far more troubling to us personally. It appears that the local cell members have been made aware of my name by members of the Chicago cell and are making an effort to **ascertain** my whereabouts. Ellen and I have come to realize that the name 'Boroskova' is a bit unusual in these parts. Why, there's only one in the Chicago telephone directory, and we are the only one in Gary. This should make it rather easy to track me down through you, Uncle Stan. Under the circumstances, Ellen has invited me to live at her apartment for the time being."

"I feared that this might happen, particularly after you were followed onto the 20th Century. I'm sure they got your name from the passenger manifest when you made the crossing from England. Not surprisingly, there are Communist agents working on most ocean liners. Unfortunately, there's little we can do to protect you from these **miscreants,** save assigning a bodyguard to you twenty-four hours a day. But, what will you do about school? You'll still have to return to the neighborhood."

"We've already figured that out. I can take the Tolleston streetcar every day and get off at 11ᵗʰ and Madison. It's only a seven block walk to Broadway from Carolina Street and two blocks from 11ᵗʰ Avenue to Froebel. I can handle that. And I'll just leave my violin at school. It's not like I need to practice every day. I've been playing since I was six."

"That sounds like a reasonable solution. This is assuming that Ellen's father has no objections to your moving in with them, and won't mind if your aunt and I visit you periodically."

"Of course not," Ellen replied. "We would love to have you. Besides, my Dad really enjoys your company."

"Fine. Then, why don't you get packed now, Natalia, and I'll drive you both over to the East Side."

Natalia packed enough clothes to last her a couple of weeks, her schoolbooks, and a assortment of books her Uncle Stan had given her, including Sergey Melgounov's *Red Terror in Russia*, and Eugene Lyons' *Assignment in Utopia*.

It was nearly midnight when Stan's car pulled up in front of 750 Carolina. Ellen's father was still up, listening to radio **pundit** E.V. Kaltenborn and perusing Saturday's *Gary Post-Tribune*. He was startled when Ellen and the entire Boroskova **entourage** walked through the kitchen door.

"Hi, Dad, I have a surprise for you. Natalia's going to be living with us for a while."

"Oh!"

"Yes! We just discovered that the members of the local Communist cell know her name and should have little difficulty tracing her to Uncle Stan and Aunt Veronika's home. There aren't too many Boroskovas in the United States and almost none in the greater Chicago area. It would have been just a matter of time before they found her. Under the circumstances, I hope you don't mind?"

"Of course not. Natalia can stay here as long as necessary."

"That's awfully nice of you, Eric," Stan interjected. "We're very concerned about her safety and this seemed to be the only **viable** short-term solution. She's brought along some of her things. But, it's late and we don't want to keep you up. We'll say 'goodnight,' and see you all soon."

à Pablo Sarasate.

Introduction
et
Rondo Capriccioso.

Violin.

CAMILLE SAINT - SAËNS, Op. 28.

Andante malinconico. (♩ = 52)

Chapter 31

An Unexplained Disappearance

In a seedy, rat-infested warehouse on Chicago's South Side, three members of the Chicago cell huddled in a tiny office on the second floor. One was examining a Chicago telephone directory.

"I spent the morning at the Chicago Public Library on Michigan Avenue," one of them reported. "I looked at practically every Chicago area telephone directory in their collection. There are almost no Boroskovas to be found. It's not a common name. There's one on the North Side of Chicago, near Wrigley Field, and one in Milwaukee, but neither one is related to Vladimir Boroskova, this young woman's father. I found one possibility in Gary – a Stanislaus Boroskova, and his wife, Veronika. I'm waiting for a call from the Russian embassy in Washington, DC to confirm if Vladimir had a brother named Stanislaus. If he did, then we've got our girl. She may have eluded us in Marshall Field's, but she can't hide from us indefinitely."

"How soon will you know?" asked a dark-skinned man with deep-set eyes.

"I hope by Tuesday morning. Then, we must be ready to move. Slava insists that we find out what she knows."

"What if she won't talk?"

"That won't be an issue once we have her. We have very effective means of persuasion."

The dark man with the deep-set eyes just smiled.

~~~~~~~~~~

For Ellen, growing up as an only child had its benefits, not the least of which was having her own bedroom, clothes, toys, books, and the undivided attention of relatively **indulgent** parents. But, those benefits were accompanied by the emotional **void** of having no **siblings** with whom to share her life. The presence of Natalia in the apartment filled that emotional void, **albeit** temporarily. She and Ellen proved to be highly compatible roommates and companions, with shared interests and a common worldview. Besides, Natalia was extraordinarily polite and thoughtful. After years in the Soviet Union, with all its wartime **deprivation** and poverty, living in the United States was the realization of a previously unimaginable dream.

With the exception of their contrasting hair colors, Ellen and Natalia might have been mistaken for sisters. Being of similar height and build, they soon began trying on each other's clothes. It was as if their wardrobes had doubled overnight. Ellen offered Natalia the opportunity of wearing some of the smart new dresses she had purchased at Howland's, and Natalia **reciprocated** by offering Ellen some of the new dresses and skirts she had purchased at H. Gordon & Sons in Gary. On Sunday, Natalia began pitching in with the housework and meal preparation, and even offered to run errands to the local A & P, or Rubin's, for Mrs. Matheus. And, despite attending different high schools, the girls' class schedules and previous education reflected a remarkable degree of **congruity**. They were both taking English, civics, and Auditorium. Both had studied Latin and were talented musically – Ellen with her voice and guitar, Natalia as an accomplished violinist. Ellen also enjoyed sharing her love of American history with a recent Russian immigrant whose previous high school education on the subject was both limited and **corrupted** with heavy doses of Soviet propaganda. Natalia was gratified, but not surprised, to learn that the United States was far from the capitalist **ogre** that it had been **caricatured** in the Soviet educational system and state-controlled press.

Ellen also introduced Natalia to the world of American popular culture: the radio programs, the big bands, Frank Sinatra, the Andrews Sisters, Glenn Miller and Tommy Dorsey. Hollywood films were also a revelation to a girl who had spent her high school years confined to the **insular** world of **Socialist realism,** the propaganda-laced films of **Eisenstein** and Pudovkin, and a cultural environment that suffered from tightly controlled **bureaucratic censorship and repression.** Ellen and Natalia also shared a **discriminating** passion for classical music and opera that set them apart from their peers, a passion that was reinforced during their Auditorium classes and the opportunities they had to hear radio broadcasts of the NBC Symphony Orchestra under conductor **Arturo Toscanini**.

Ellen anxiously awaited the opening of the Metropolitan Opera's Saturday afternoon broadcast season, and looked forward to introducing it to a friend who shared her passion. Although her favorite tenor, **Jussi Björling**, had been forced by war to return to Sweden in 1941, a galaxy of Met stars beckoned from across the **ether**, including Kirsten Flagstad and Lawrence Melchior in Wagner's *Siegfried*, the *Flying Dutchman*, and *Die Meistersinger*, Lilly Pons in Delibes' *Lakme*, Leonard Warren in *Pagliacci,* the delightful Brazilian soprano, Bidu Sayão, in *Don Giovanni* and *La Traviata*, American tenor Jan Pearce in Puccini's *Tosca*, and Zinka Milanov and Giuseppe Martinelli in Verdi's *Aida*.

Ellen and Natalia also spent long hours in their room talking about history and current affairs, particularly the state of the war in Europe. Ellen got a first-hand account of what it was like inside the Soviet embassy in London from the perspective of the daughter of a leading diplomatic official.

"How often did you visit your father at the embassy?" Ellen inquired.

"About once a week when I wasn't away at school. The mood was always **somber**, however. Except for my father's secretary, the staff viewed me with suspicion, as if I were an **interloper**. They were a humorless and **taciturn** lot. Naturally, I was not **privy** to any of their confidential communications, but my father occasionally opened up to my mother and me during unguarded moments. We lived about a block from the Soviet embassy, off Kensington Palace Gardens, in what is probably the most exclusive neighborhood in London. The building where we lived was owned by the Soviet government and housed diplomatic staff exclusively. And while father became more vocal in his criticism of the Soviet government generally, and Marshal Stalin in particular, he rarely did so in our apartment, with the certainty that listening devices had been implanted in the walls. During our walks in Hyde Park, however, he became progressively more outspoken, mostly about the fate of former associates who had been recalled to Moscow, and subsequently vanished. My mother and I **instinctively** sensed that it was leading to some kind of emotional **catharsis**. Yet, ultimately, it was as if the **NKVD** could read his mind, despite all the precautions he took."

"Isn't it **ironic** that with all the **repression** inside the Soviet Union, and the surveillance of Soviet officials working outside the country, Soviet spies are able to operate with virtual **impunity** inside the United States, often with help from domestic traitors?" Ellen observed. "I mean, just look at your own dilemma."

~~~~~~~~~~

Natalia was up at seven o'clock on Monday morning, giving herself sufficient time to have breakfast before walking to Broadway to catch the Tolleston trolley. In orchestra on Friday, she had learned that Mr. Resur had scheduled seating auditions for the first violin section on Tuesday. Auditions for the second violins, violas, cellos and string basses had already been concluded the previous week. The auditions would consist of scales, sight-reading, and a piece of the student's own choosing. After some **deliberation**, Natalia chose the *Introduction and Rondo Capriccioso*, Op. 28 by **Camille Saint-Saëns**, which she had once played for an audition at her high school orchestra back in Moscow.

When Tuesday arrived, she awaited her last period orchestra class with great anticipation. She was the third member of the first violin section called upon to play. She walked to the front of the room and took her place at the music stand. After breezing through the scales, she quickly navigated the brief sight-reading passages Mr. Resur placed in front of her, from the second movement of Brahms *Third Symphony.*

"And what piece have you chosen to play for us, Natalia?"

"*The Introduction and Rondo Capriccioso* by **Camille Saint-Saëns.**"

"Excellent! Please proceed."

Pausing briefly to collect her musical thoughts, Natalia launched into the melodious Andante of the Saint-Saëns, playing it from memory. By the time she had navigated the Animato passage, her fingers flying across the fingerboard with supreme confidence, her fellow musicians knew they were in for a rare treat. Mr. Resur, who normally cut auditioning students off at the two-minute mark, just let her play, so taken was he with her expressiveness and technical **virtuosity.** Nine minutes later, having breezed through the entire piece, **double stops** and all, she took the violin from her chin and placed it under her arm. The room burst into an enthusiastic round of applause. Mr. Resur stepped to the front of the room and gave Natalia a warm embrace.

"Natalia, that was superb! You have such a warm, rich tone, and your **intonation** is flawless. And to think that you carried it off with one of our inexpensive student violins. I can only imagine what you might have accomplished with a truly fine instrument."

The choice of a new **concertmistress,** under the circumstances, was a foregone conclusion, and potential jealousies **evaporated**, even before Mr. Resur posted the seating chart. The role of **concertmistress** would, naturally, involve new responsibilities for Natalia. In that regard, Mr. Resur asked her and the other newly selected string section leaders to meet with him after school on Wednesday to review orchestra policies and procedures, and their new responsibilities.

When classes ended on Wednesday afternoon, the five section leaders remained in the orchestra room for a meeting with Mr. Resur: Natalia representing the first violins; Helen Popa, second violins; Olga Dominkos, violas; Shirley Bias, cellos; and Catherine Fritts, string basses. Emerging from his office, Mr. Resur pulled up a chair and sat in front of the students.

"Thank you for staying after, people. I promise not to keep you. I'd like to take a few minutes to review your responsibilities as section leaders so you'll know what is to be expected of you and the players under your leadership. You are responsible for taking attendance at all rehearsals and concerts and submitting your records to me prior to the end of each grading period. I will also expect you to monitor the progress of your section, particularly when we break for sectional rehearsals. If players aren't pulling their weight musically, I will expect you to encourage more **assiduous** practice after school, or at home. Bow markings will also be your responsibility. And, finally, it is up to you to see that each member of your section is properly dressed for each public performance. Pay particular attention to those who are new to concert orchestra this year so that they receive the proper guidance."

"Do we know yet where we will be performing this year, Mr. Resur?"

"Yes, Helen. Our fall schedule has been finalized. Our first appearance will be on Saturday, September 28 at Holy Angels Church. This will be followed by a concert on Saturday, October 24 in the Miramar Ballroom for **Club SAR**'s annual banquet. We'll also be playing for the annual Teachers' Tea, which will be held in the girls' gymnasium on November 13. Our annual fall concert will take place on Friday, December 4 in the Auditorium. The spring schedule is still being **formulated**.

"Our fall repertoire will consist of the following pieces: the *Overture to Die Meistersinger* by Wagner, which we've already started working on, the first movement of Schubert's *Unfinished Symphony,* the *Two Elegiac Melodies* by Edvard Grieg, the *Grand March* from *Aida*, and a Victor Herbert medley, including *Toyland, Romany Life, A Kiss in the Dark*, and the *Italian Street Song.* I would also like to feature a violin soloist at most of our concerts, if she's willing." He looked directly at Natalia and smiled. She reciprocated. The other section leaders nodded enthusiastically.

"I think that takes care of everything for now. Please see me if you have any questions about what is to be expected of you." With that, he dismissed the group until the following day's rehearsal.

"Oh, Natalia, would you please stay a few minutes more?"

"Certainly, Mr. Resur."

"I'm serious about wanting you to be our soloist. I realize you're only going to be with us for one year, but I want to take full advantage of your marvelous talent. I hope you will accept."

"Of course, Mr. Resur. I would be honored."

"Then, why don't you think about what you'd like to play. Or, perhaps, I can make some suggestions. A piece for violin and piano would be appropriate. I'll give you wide **latitude**, but I might suggest something **romantic** like Fritz Kreisler's *Schön Rosmarin*, Dvorak's *Songs My Mother Taught Me*, or, perhaps, the *Meditation* from *Thais* by Massenet. Those are certainly great crowd pleasers. Mrs. Lee will be happy to accompany you. She's a gifted pianist. I take it you are familiar with those pieces?"

"Well, I have played the Dvořák, and some Kreisler as well. But, it was the

Liebeslied, not the one you mentioned.

"Well, the *Liebeslied* would be fine too, but you think about it. In fact, you may want to prepare several pieces so you can alternate them during the course of the year. I've got some anthologies of violin solos in my office you can borrow."

"Thank you, Mr. Resur." Natalia added the violin anthologies to the stack of books under her arm. "I'll see you tomorrow."

~~~~~~~~~~~

Once the members of the Chicago cell had obtained confirmation that Stan Boroskova of 1334 Lincoln Street was the brother of Vladimir Boroskova, late of the Soviet diplomatic corps, they began to set the trap for his niece. With a number of **discreet** inquiries around the Froebel neighborhood, they were able to determine that she was a student at Froebel High School and a member of the school orchestra. From there, it was simply a matter of springing the trap.

For nearly an hour, a black, **nondescript** panel truck cruised the streets around Froebel School and pulled up in front of 1352 Jackson Street, opposite the building's west entrance. Alexei Kropotkin emerged from his apartment at 1342 Jackson and climbed into the front passenger seat. The driver cast his eyes in the direction of the school's doorway. It was four o'clock, fifteen minutes prior to the end of the school day.

A few minutes earlier, Hyman Petrov, a member of the Chicago cell, entered the building by the front entrance and identified himself as Natalia's uncle to the office staff. With an impressive **flair f**or the dramatic, he convinced Mattie MacArthur, one of the attendance clerks, that Natalia's aunt had been taken to Mercy Hospital with an attack of **appendicitis**. Employing this successful **ruse**, he was directed to the orchestra room where Mr. Resur was concluding his three fifteen orchestra rehearsal. At the end of the second floor hallway, Petrov hovered outside the fire door at the far end of the corridor where he could **surreptitiously** observe those leaving the orchestra room. He knew that recognizing Natalia would not be a problem, having already shadowed her from New York to Chicago on the 20th Century Limited. Apparently, several of Mr. Resur's students were staying after class for a meeting with their teacher, and Natalia was among them. He would have to be patient.

Finally, with three books and the violin anthology tucked under one arm, and her violin in the other, Natalia emerged from the orchestra room, and made her way down the west end stairwell, and out the door to Jackson Street. Petrov followed behind, but maintained a safe interval between himself and his **unwary** prey. Natalia was totally **oblivious** to the **imminent** danger. She was in a **euphoric** mood, having not only been selected concertmistress, but asked by Mr. Resur to be the orchestra's soloist. There was a natural **buoyancy** to her step. As she approached Jackson Street, Petrov signaled to his confederates to turn their truck around and follow her. The dark-haired Petrov followed at a discreet distance as she walked down Jackson Street and alongside the Froebel athletic fields on her way to the 11th Avenue streetcar. The dark van followed slowly behind as she approached 13th Avenue and began crossing the street near the Greek church. Suddenly, without warning, the van accelerated, pulled up at an angle across the sidewalk in front of the church, and cut off her path. Her pursuer, Hyman Petrov, now sprinting, reached the van just as the side doors were opened, and pushed her inside. The strong hands of Alexei Kropotkin reached across her mouth with a strangely scented cloth before she was able to scream. She struggled briefly, but was soon overcome by the scented fumes. A few seconds later, she passed out on the floor of the van as it sped away. The **chloroform** had done its work.

Unbeknownst to the occupants of the van, and Hyman Petrov, a little boy had seen it all from behind the black wrought-iron fence that separated his apartment house at 1157 Jackson Street from the yard surrounding the Greek church. Fearfully, he crouched down in the gladiola bed that bordered the fence and peaked out over its concrete base, the fence partially shielding him from detection – not that any of the kidnappers would have noticed any witnesses due to the swiftness of the operation. When the van pulled away, Corky got up, ran to the side entrance of his English basement apartment and hurried inside. His mother, Alvida Zvingilas, was sitting at her sewing machine in the bedroom.

"Mommy, Mommy, they took a girl away. They took a girl away."

"Calm down, Corky. What do you mean, they took a girl away?"

"A black truck went on the sidewalk by the church and a man pushed a girl inside. Then, it drove away."

"Where did it go?"

"It went down Jackson Street to the corner. Then, it turned by the funeral parlor."

"Did you see what the girl looked like?"

"She was a big girl, a high school girl. And she was carrying books and a black case."

"A black case? What kind of case?"

"Like for a musical instrument. Like a trumpet."

"Are you sure about that?"

"No. I just know that they put instruments in a little suitcase. It was like that."

"So, you're sure it was some kind of musical instrument case?"

"Yea. Mike Matunas next door has one. He plays the trumpet."

"I think we need to call the police. I think someone's been kidnapped."

"Kidnapped? What's that?"

"It's when they take somebody where they don't want to go. Quick, we need to use Grandma's phone."

Alvida and Corky ran out the side door and up the front concrete steps to Corky's grandmother's second-floor flat.

"Hi, Mom, we need to use your telephone. It's an emergency."

"Sure. You use it." she said, in her foreign-laced accent.

Alvida quickly found the number for the police department in the front of the directory, and dialed 7506.

"Hello? Police department? I want to report a kidnapping."

"O.K. lady. What's your name?"

"Alvida Zvingilas. I live at 1157 Jackson Street, right next to the Greek church."

"What's your telephone number?"

"2-1033"

"O.K. Sit tight. We'll have a squad car over there in a few minutes."

A Gary Police Department squad car pulled up in front of 1157 Jackson five minutes later. Alvida had been standing outside the apartment house, pacing anxiously. Corky was at her side.
Two officers jumped out of the car and approached her.

"Sergeant Art Brewer, M'am. And this is Sergeant Billick. Are you the lady who just called us about a kidnapping?"

"That's right, Sergeant."

"Please, tell us what you saw."

"Actually, I didn't see it. My son, Corky, here, saw it all."

Sergeant Brewer raised his eyebrows and directed a **disdainful** look at his partner. He had had experience with **precocious** youngsters before, occasionally **embellishing** the truth. "I hope this isn't a **hoax**." He knelt down to talk to Corky.

"Now, tell me, son, how old are you?"

"I'm four years old."

"And what did you see?"

"There was this truck and it drove on

the sidewalk, which is only for people and bikes. Then, a man ran up and pushed the girl inside."

"What color was the truck?"

"Black."

"Was it a big truck or a little truck?"

"It was kind of little – the kind that Uncle Sam uses to deliver groceries."

"Who's this Uncle Sam he's talking about, lady? I hope not the guy in the red, white and blue suit?"

"No, that's my husband's brother, Sam Zvingilas. He makes deliveries for Bill Schwimmer, a grocer on the East Side."

"Oh, yea, we know the place, on East 8th Avenue. And what kind of truck does he drive?"

"I think you'd call it a panel truck, officer. It has double doors on one side and in the back."

"And was there any writing on the truck, Corky?"

"No, it was just black. It wasn't like a truck that says Dixie Dairy on the side. It was just plain."

"Can you tell us about the girl, young man? What did she look like?"

"My name's 'Corky.'"

"O.K., Corky, what did the girl look like?"

"I don't know. It happened so fast. But, I remember she had on a blue dress. And she was carrying some schoolbooks and a case for a musical instrument. That's all I could see."

"Did you see her face?"

"No. It happened so fast."

The officers walked with Corky and his mother to the sidewalk in front of the Greek church.

"Is this about where it happened, Corky?"

"Yes. It was by the gate." Some light skid marks on the sidewalk marked the spot where the van stopped, a few inches short of the wrought-iron fence that was embedded in a concrete base.

Sergeant Peter Billick reached down and picked up some schoolbooks, one of which was *American English Grammar,* by Charles Carpenter Fries. It was lying upside down on the sidewalk, at the base of the fence.

"Looks like Corky here is telling us the truth."

"I always tell the truth. It's a sin to tell a lie. Isn't that right, Mommy?"

"That's right, Corky."

"O.K. It looks like we have the abduction of a female student walking home from school with books and a musical instrument case. We need to **ascertain** her name as soon as possible. I'd like to get over to the office at Froebel before it closes."

Officer Brewer knelt down, again, to speak to Corky.

"I want to thank you, Corky, for being such a good little detective. I hope we can find the girl and bring her home safely. Tell your Mother you deserve a big dish of ice cream for helping the police."

Corky beamed with pride as he and his Mother waved 'goodbye' to the officers. His mother took his hand and led him back into their apartment.

"Well, Mommy?"

"Yes, Corky, you may have some ice cream – after dinner."

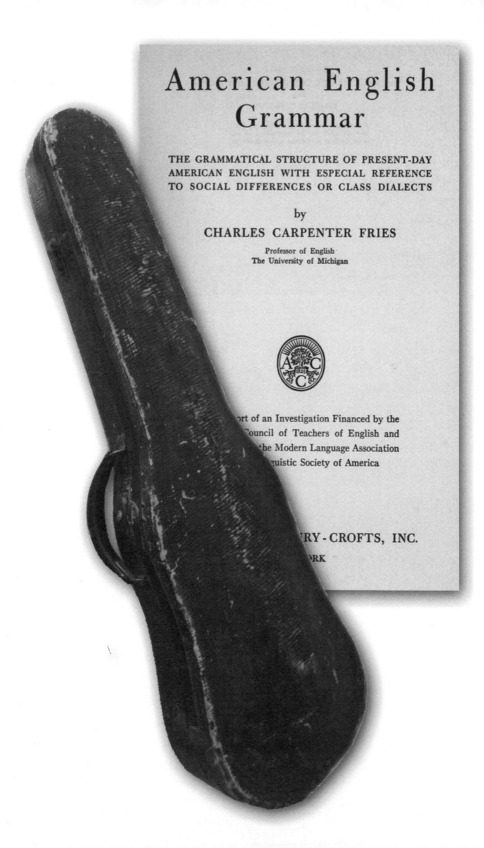

American English Grammar

THE GRAMMATICAL STRUCTURE OF PRESENT-DAY AMERICAN ENGLISH WITH ESPECIAL REFERENCE TO SOCIAL DIFFERENCES OR CLASS DIALECTS

by

CHARLES CARPENTER FRIES

Professor of English
The University of Michigan

...ort of an Investigation Financed by the
...Council of Teachers of English and
...the Modern Language Association
...guistic Society of America

...RY - CROFTS, INC.
...ORK

Chapter 32

The Investigation Continues

Officers Billick and Brewer knew that they didn't have a moment to waste, and that any delay might prove fatal. Hopping into their squad car, they drove to Froebel's front entrance, on 15th Avenue, and ran inside. They found Miss Nikolich still on duty as they entered the second-floor office.

"Yes, officers, may I help you?"

"I'm Sergeant Brewer and this is Detective Sergeant Peter Billick. We've got a kidnapping in progress and need to identify one of your female students."

"Oh, my word! Certainly. What's her name?"

"Unfortunately, that's the problem. We have only limited information to go by. She appears to be a high school girl, and was observed carrying schoolbooks and a case which may have contained a musical instrument of some sort. She had on a blue dress. Also, she dropped this book."

"Mmmmm... *American English Grammar,* by Fries?"

"Can you tell us what classes use this textbook?"

Miss Nikolich went to a file cabinet and retrieved a list of textbook assignments for high school level English classes. "Let me see... that book is used by Frances Uncapher in her senior English classes."

"Do you have a list of the students enrolled in those classes?"

"Yes, Sergeant, we keep very detailed records here. We can tell you where every student is at each hour of the day, unless, of course, they're playing **hooky**." A few moments later, she produced a list of students in each of two senior English classes taught by Frances Uncapher and placed them on the counter in front of the officers. Officer Brewer counted 32 students on one list, 17 of whom were girls, and 34 on the other list, 19 of whom were also girls.

"We appreciate your help. I know it must be

past your closing time."

"Not at all, Sergeant. Think nothing of that. This is an emergency, after all. If one of our students has disappeared, we'll do everything in our power to help you find her."

"We're going to need to match the names on this list with the names of students in band and orchestra. May we also see those lists?"

"Certainly," she said, pulling additional class lists from the files. "As you can see, the lists for concert orchestra and concert band are much longer."

The officers took the class lists and began scanning them for the names of girls appearing on both.

"I wish we knew what kind of instrument case it was. That would make our job that much easier."

"Here's one: Marie Camba. She plays clarinet in the band and is in Frances Uncapher's English class," Sergeant Billick cried.

"Ditto for Eva Vorkavich. Plays clarinet in the orchestra."

"Miss Nikolich, there is something you can do for us right now," Sergeant Brewer asked.

"Anything."

"As we find girls in either band or orchestra who are also in one of Miss Uncapher's English classes, we'll need you to call their homes immediately to determine if they've arrived home safely. You can start with Sophia Drakos and Margaret Kirla."

"Add Natalia Boroskova to the list," shouted Sergeant Billick. "She plays violin in the orchestra."

"And Eva Vorkavich and Marie Camba."

Miss Nikolich started writing down the names, pulling their student records from the files, then dialing their homes.

"Here's two more: Helen Poulos and Rose Popa," added Sergeant Brewer.

"That appears to be every girl in both English classes who's also taking instrumental music," concluded Sergeant Billick. The officers waited while Miss Nikolich continued making the phone calls.

"Thank you, Mrs. Poulos. We just wanted to make sure Helen was all right."

"How many more, Miss Nikolich?" Sergeant Brewer inquired.

"Two more."

"Yes, hello, Mrs. Vorkavich? This is Miss Nikolich at Froebel High School. We just wanted to make sure that Eva has arrived home safely... She has?... Yes, I know, it is a bit unusual for us to be calling, but the circumstances are a bit out of the ordinary in this case. I can't say any more right now. Thank you so much."

"One more to go." She dialed. "I got a busy signal last time... Hello, Mrs.

Boroskova? This is Anne Nikolich at Froebel High School. We're just calling to make sure than Natalia has arrived home safely from school. ... What? ... You haven't seen her? ... What's that you say? ... She's living on the East Side!"

Putting her hand over the mouthpiece, she spoke to the officers:

"I think you'll need to talk to her. She says her niece is living on the East Side temporarily, near Emerson School, so she's not aware if she's made it home yet, or not."

"Let me speak with her."

"Hello, Mrs. Boroskova? This is Sergeant Brewer of the Gary Police Department. We have reason to believe that your niece, Natalia, has been kidnapped. We have an eyewitness who observed her being dragged into a panel truck at the corner of 13th and Jackson ... Yes, that's right ... No, we have no idea where the truck has gone. It could be miles from Gary by now. I understand that she plays violin in the Froebel Orchestra. Is that correct? It is.

"That explains the violin case in her possession when she was taken. So, tell me, where is she living now? ... 750 Carolina? ... That's a bit outside the Froebel district, isn't it? ... Yes, I understand, it's only temporary ... No, you're not going to get in trouble with the school authorities. That's the last of our worries right now. Is Mr. Boroskova at home? ... He's working day shift, eh ... All right. Let me explain. My partner and I are going over to Carolina Street right now. I want you to explain the situation to your husband as soon as he gets home from work, and meet us there as soon as possible, O.K? ... Good. We'll see you there." *Click.*

"You got that address, Peter? Apparently, Natalia has been staying temporarily with an Emerson High School student. She just moved her things over there on Sunday. She says the girl's name is Ellen Anderson. I want to get over there immediately. The Boroskovas will join us when the husband gets off work."

"Thank you, Miss Nikolich. You've been a big help. Anytime you want a job down at Police headquarters, you let us know. You're very efficient."

"Glad to help, Sergeant Brewer. I hope you find her quickly. If I recall, she's the new girl who escaped from the Soviet Union. Her parents were liquidated by Stalin during the Great Purge, you know."

"How horrific! I wonder if there could be some connection?"

Sergeants Brewer and Billick hurried out of the building and jumped into their squad car. A few minutes later, they were knocking on the door to 750 Carolina. Mrs. Matheus had not yet returned from Dr. Bills' home, and Ellen's father was still at work. Ellen, who was doing trigonometry problems in her front parlor, observed the squad car from her chair. She hurried anxiously down the stairs and opened the front door.

"Ellen Anderson?"

"Yes, I'm Ellen Anderson. Is something the matter?"

"I'm Sergeant Brewer and this is Sergeant Billick. Are you familiar with a girl named Natalia Boroskova?"

"Yes, she's been staying with me. Has something happened to her?"

"She's disappeared. In fact, we have reason to believe that she's been kidnapped."

"Kidnapped! Oh, my goodness! It's just as we feared!"

"Oh, yea? May we come in?"

"Of course." Ellen led the officers upstairs to her apartment.

"Please have a seat. Can I offer you something to drink?"

"No, thank you."

"Please, tell me what happened."

"Apparently, Miss Boroskova was walking home from Froebel School when she was grabbed from behind and pushed into a black van in front of the Greek church at 13th and Jackson. The eyewitness was a four-year-old boy by the name of 'Corky.' He saw the whole thing from his front yard."

"Well, how about that! I think I know that boy! I met a 'Corky' and his mother on the streetcar several weeks ago, just after I arrived in Gary. What else?"

"We were able to identify her at Froebel School from an English textbook she dropped on the sidewalk in front of the church and from the fact that she was carrying a musical instrument case, apparently a violin."

"That's right. She plays the violin."

"We narrowed her name down from a half dozen possibilities after calling students' homes. Her aunt, Mrs. Boroskova, informed us that she has been living here with you since Sunday. Is that correct?"

"Why, yes, it is."

"What else would you like to tell us?"

"I can tell you that she escaped from the Soviet Union earlier this year, and has apparently been on the radar of Communist agents in this country. You see, her father was a Soviet diplomatic official who was **liquidated** by Stalin's henchmen during the **Great Purge**, as was her mother. She's lucky to have made it out of the Soviet Union alive. My father and I met her a few weeks ago on the 20th Century Limited out of New York City. We helped her elude Soviet agents in Chicago and accompanied her to her aunt and uncle's home in Gary. However, she recently discovered that they knew her name and were trying to locate her. Under the circumstances, she could no longer risk staying with her aunt and uncle because she would be too easy to trace. You see, there aren't many Boroskovas in the Chicago area. I offered to put her up here."

"Where do her aunt and uncle live?"

"On Lincoln Street – the 1300 block – across from St. Casimir's Church. Apparently, the Communists believe she is in possession of secret documents stolen from the Soviet Embassy in London. That's why they've been following her."

"Why didn't she bring this to the attention of the F.B.I., or at least the Gary Police Department before now?"

"Because Natalia is a very private person and didn't want to call attention to herself. She's tired of always looking over her shoulder, and fearful of enemy agents. She thought she could put it all behind her by remaining as **unobtrusive** as possible in Gary. The fact that they followed her onto the 20th Century, however, made her a bit **paranoid**. She's confided in my father and me, and her aunt and uncle, of course, but has been **reticent** about sharing the details of her story with the authorities."

As Ellen related Natalia's story to the officers, she realized that she was sitting on a powder keg of information, including not only the theft of the Emerson art collection, but, possibly, the Communists' efforts to infiltrate the top-secret research at the University of Chicago. Knowing that timing was everything at this critical **juncture,** she decided to keep that information to herself for the time being. Much depended on what she could learn from Tanya Sokolov, about how close the Communists were from obtaining plans of the atomic reactor, and moving the art collection to New Jersey. She feared that, if she informed the police prematurely, it would force the Communists into hiding and make it difficult to **foil** their plans.

"Do you have any idea where she may have been taken?" asked Sergeant Brewer.

"If I had to guess, I'd say somewhere on the South Side of Chicago."

"Why Chicago?"

"Well, naturally, because it's a big city, with lots of places to hide. And because the Communist cells in Gary and the South Side are operating in **tandem**."

"There's a Communist cell operating under our noses, in Gary?"

"That's right. I'm surprised you didn't know that already. I can give you names and addresses of several local Communists to question. And Natalia's Uncle Stan can also help you. He was a former member of the White Russian Army and **loathes** the Communists for what they have done to his country. He can tell you a lot more."

Shortly after five o'clock, the front doorbell rang. Ellen escorted Mr. and Mrs. Boroskova upstairs and into the presence of the officers.

"Mr. and Mrs. Boroskova, I'd like to introduce Sergeants Brewer and Billick. They've just informed me that Natalia was kidnapped this afternoon in front of the Greek Orthodox Church at the corner of 13ᵗʰ and Jackson."

Natalia's uncle sat **transfixed**, unable to conceal his **anguish** and horror that this could have happened to his beloved niece. Veronika Boroskova was equally **distraught**.

"I blame myself. For all my sophistication about the Soviet menace in this country, I failed to appreciate the Communists' ability to trace Natalia to us. I should have known better. After all, they knew enough to follow her onto the 20ᵗʰ Century Limited and apparently knew her identity before that. I also failed to realize how rare the name 'Boroskova' is in the United States. Of course, even had we changed our name, it would have been too late to make a difference. It would have been easy enough to find us in the prior year's city directories. Any detective or spy would have had no difficulty in tracing her to our home on Lincoln Street."

"Can you give us any leads as to who might be implicated in this crime, Mr. Boroskova?" asked Sergeant Billick.

"You can start with Gene Alexandrov at 1333 Adams Street, Galina Borovsky at 1573 Fillmore, Iggy Eisenberg at 1121 Jefferson, and Alexei Kropotkin at 1342 Jackson. And check out the owner of Crimean Imports, Konstantin Ivanov, at 1334 Washington Street. He lives at 900 Arizona Street in Aetna."

"I'm writing this all down, Mr. Boroskova. Where did you say this Iggy Eisenberg lives?

"1121 Jefferson. And it's Ignace Eisenberg, to be correct."

"Sounds like you've been keeping close watch on these people, Mr. Boroskova, to know their addresses by heart?"

"That's right. And I know what they're up to."

"What about their Chicago connections?" Sergeant Brewer continued. "Ellen suggests that Natalia may have been taken to Chicago?"

"I'm convinced of it. In fact, a member of the Gary cell recently moved to Chicago. His name is Dimitri Poliakov. The last we knew he was living at 5468 S. Woodlawn Avenue in Hyde Park, near the University of Chicago. He's definitely a person you need to **interrogate**."

"What can you tell us about the secret documents that Natalia supposedly brought to this country from the Soviet Embassy?"

"Primarily that they contain the names and addresses of Soviet agents in the United States and Europe. They were imbedded in a book that Natalia's father left for her in London should she manage to return to England. How the Soviets learned of it is anyone's guess – perhaps, by **electronic surveillance**. The documents are over four years old by now, but should still be useful."

"How can we get our hands on these documents?"

"I've got them at my home. And a back-up set is in the home of one my associates, a photographer, in Tolleston."

"Excellent. We'll be by tomorrow to examine them. In the meantime, we need to questions these suspects. We have your phone number, so we'll be in touch."

"We'll do anything to bring Natalia home safe and sound," Stan replied.

Chapter 33

In the Darkness

When Natalia awoke, she had no idea where she was or how many hours had **elapsed**. With her hands tied behind her back and a blindfold over her eyes, she was helpless and terrified. She was still in a semi-lucid state and had almost no memory of what had transpired earlier that day – or, was it the day before? She **vaguely** remembered the black van jumping the curb in front of the church and blocking her path, and being shoved inside by someone who surprised her from behind. But, she never saw his face. She also remembered the cloth being put over her face and the strange scent that caused her to lose consciousness. After that, it was all blackness.

She scooted her body across the floor and felt the walls with her bound hands. Then, she stretched out her legs to gauge the dimensions of the space. It couldn't have been more than four feet square – a closet, perhaps? The walls were unfinished, with nothing between the studs. The first thing she wanted to do was get the blindfold off her eyes in an effort to restore her sense of **equilibrium**. She placed her head firmly against one of the two-by-fours and tried to push the cloth off her head. After repeated attempts, she finally managed to maneuver it over her forehead and toss it off with a quick flip of her head. It took several minutes for her eyes to adjust to the darkness. It was a closet all right, empty, with a single shelf and a horizontal pole for hanging clothes. The ceiling was probably eight feet high. Though groggy, she managed to stand and reach for the doorknob. Not surprisingly, it was locked. A sliver of light peaked in from the bottom of the door. Placing her ear to the door, she detected garbled voices coming from some distance away. She made a **futile** effort to attack the bonds that secured her wrists, but they were tied too tightly, causing her hands to lose sensation. Resigning herself to her **predicament** for the time being, she lowered herself to the floor and waited for her captors to make the next move.

It was some minutes before she heard voices again, this time far more **audible,** in both Russian and English. Suddenly, a key was inserted into the lock and the door was opened. Artificial light flooded the small space, temporarily blinding her. As her eyes adjusted to the brightness, she saw two **intimidating** men of **formidable** size hovering over her.

"Ah, Miss Boroskova! What a pleasure to meet you at last. That was quite a chase you led is on – and through Marshall Field's no less. But, no matter.

It was just a matter of time before we tracked you down. Too bad your Uncle Stanislaus has such an unusual name in this part of the world. It made our task so much easier. Had your name been Smith, or Jones, or... Anderson, we might have had a lot more difficulty finding you. Permit me to introduce myself: Hyman Petrov of the **NKVD**. And this is my associate, Alexei Kropotkin, who has been shadowing you from his apartment on Jackson Street, across from Froebel School. You thought you were being very clever moving out of your uncle's home to Carolina Street. You see, it wouldn't have made any difference. You were like a mouse in a maze of our creation. We had only to reach out and grab you by the tail," he continued, his voice laced with **sarcasm**. "Well, it's about time you came out and met the other members of our fraternity."

Petrov and Kropotkin each grabbed one of Natalia's arms and dragged her out of the closet and down a flight of wooden stairs from the balcony. They were in a large, **cavernous** space, a warehouse, perhaps, with ceilings that stood more than two stories high, and storage shelves that lined the perimeter. A half dozen windows were covered with black shades. A large double-door, big enough to admit a tractor-trailer, stood at one end of the space; and what appeared to be offices were at the other. Lined up along one wall was a series of wooden crates that immediately caught Natalia's attention. *If only her captors knew what she knew.* And if she hadn't recognized them immediately, the identifications in black crayon gave them away. Each was inscribed with the name of an artist: Kilgore #1, Dudley #3, Nyholm #8, Buehr #19, Tellander #27, and so on, all names Natalia had seen in the *Gold and Gray Book* that listed the original oil paintings in the Emerson art collection. *They had captured the school's priceless art collection, and now they had captured her.*

A solitary armless wooden chair stood in the middle of the warehouse, apparently earmarked for her. Her handlers pushed her down roughly and tied her to the back. Her arms and wrists already **chafed** from the ropes confining them. She counted nine men in the room, each dressed in a suit and tie. *How civilized*, she thought.

"We've been waiting for you, Miss Boroskova," Kropotkin said, in a exceedingly **churlish** tone. Petrov tells me you led him and his men on a merry chase through Marshall Field's. Had we done our research sooner, we would have known you were headed for the Illinois Central Station and the South Shore railroad. You thought you were being clever – but not clever enough for the **NKVD.** We consume traitors like you for breakfast. But, enough of this. We want information, and you're going to give it to us. We know from our surveillance, that your late father was a traitor to the Soviet Union, and that he left documents in London for you to retrieve before making your way to the United States. We want those documents, and we want to know to whom you gave them."

Natalia sat **dumfounded** by the **predicament** in which she now found herself. She planned to **disavow** any knowledge of secret documents and, indeed, had no intention of telling her **captors** anything. But, then she feared what they might do to her. She had heard all the stories about methods of torture used on political prisoners at the time of the Great Purge. She also knew that even the strongest of men **succumbed**, eventually.

"Cat got your tongue? I warn you, Miss Boroskova, you had better tell us what we want to know or it will not go well for you, or your family."

"What makes you think I have documents? All I wanted to do was get out of the Soviet Union, and the sooner the better. I don't know where you got your information, but you're totally mistaken. We're not in the Lubyanka now, but in a civilized part of the world. Your strong-arm tactics won't work here."

"Please, Miss Boroskova, spare us your **insipid histrionics**. We are not **neophytes** at interrogation. Every person we have taken into custody starts out professing innocence, or ignorance, but eventually succumbs to – how shall I say it – persuasion. I guarantee, you will be no different. You can tell us now, and spare yourself a lot of pain and **anguish**, or tell us later and then try to put your body back together again. Incidentally, I notice that you have very delicate fingers – fingers that move effortlessly across the fingerboard of a violin. Am I correct? This is your violin, is it not?" Natalia nodded, hesitantly. Kropotkin took the violin from its case, gripped the neck with one hand, and smashed it against one of the building's support beams, shattering it into pieces. "It would be such a shame to break those fingers – one by one – making it impossible for you to ever play the violin again."

Now, Natalia began to break into a sweat. *They wouldn't really do that, would they? Surely her uncle and her friends in Gary would find her before that could happen. She needed to hold on until then.*

"Come, Miss Boroskova, spare yourself the pain that is **inevitable** if you refuse to cooperate."

Natalia sat silently, trying not to **antagonize** them. Most of the faces surrounding her were unfamiliar ones. She recognized three from the photo taken in Norton Park, including her **inquisitor**, Alexei Kropotkin, Iggy Eisenberg, and Yevgeny Alexandrov, but the other faces were new ones. They were hardened faces, **callous** faces, **countenances devoid** of human emotion that were accustomed to **meting** out violence against their enemies without **compunction**.

"Gene, it's your turn. Why don't you let her hang for a while, and see if that takes some of the **obstinacy** out of her."

Hang? What did he mean by 'hang?' she thought. She found out quickly enough. Alexandrov removed the ropes that confined her to the chair and threw a longer coil of rope over one of the ceiling rafters. He tied one end around her wrists and pulled her arms up behind her until the pain was **excruciating**. Then, he tied the other end to a hook on one of the warehouse's support beams pulling her several inches off the ground in the process. One of the other men stuffed a gag into her mouth. *Are they going to leave me like this? And, if so, for how long?*

"We'll be back in a few hours, my dear. By that time, I expect you'll be ready to tell us what we want to know."

Alexandrov grabbed Natalia by her delicate chin and forced her to look into his hardened **visage**.

"When we return, you're going to **furnish** us with everything we want to know. Do you understand?" Natalia stubbornly refused to nod in **assent**.

The pain was already unbearable, though she tried her best not to show it. Then, Petrov and his **subordinates** filed out of the warehouse and left her suspended. Try though she might, she could not touch the floor. As tears rolled down her face, all she could do was to **bemoan** her fate, and pray.

~~~~~~~~~~~~

Much though she appreciated the efficiency of Sergeants Brewer and Billick and the speed with which they had discovered Natalia's disappearance, Ellen couldn't wait to speak with Natalia's aunt and uncle before commencing her own plan of attack.

"I can't say I'm surprised, Mr. Boroskova, particularly after Natalia herself learned on Saturday they were hunting for her. Your last name provided the Communists with all the information they needed, and there's nothing you could have done about it. The question is: what do we do now? Tanya Sokolov already told me that they're planning to move the entire art collection to New Jersey, and that the only thing **constraining** them is that they have yet to acquire the plans of the nuclear reactor. Once they have those plans in their filthy hands, Tanya's father has been assigned the job of driving the load to New Jersey. The paintings will be dispersed among art dealers in the New York metropolitan area, and the plans will be delivered to an **Amtorg** freighter headed for **Archangel**. One of the things I fear is that it would be a simple enough task to return Natalia to the Soviet Union by the same means.

"I had the same thought. We've got to stop that truck before it ever leaves the Hyde Park warehouse," Stan replied.

"Let me get Tanya on the phone right now. Perhaps, she has some more up-to-date information about their plans. Wait here while I use Mrs. Matheus' phone."

Ellen scurried down the rear stairs and knocked on Mrs. Matheus' door.

"Come in, Ellen."

"Mrs. Matheus, I need to use your telephone. It's an emergency."

"Of course, dear. Go right ahead."

Ellen had memorized the number and dialed 2-3465. On the fifth ring, someone picked up.

"Hello, may I speak with Tanya?"

"Who may I say is calling?"

"Ellen Anderson – a friend from school."

"Hold just a moment ... Tanya! ... Ellen Anderson is on the phone."

"Hi, Ellen, this is Tanya."

"Good. Can you talk?"

"Fortunately, yes. My stepfather's in Chicago. I think this is the real thing. Apparently, he was summoned by the higher-ups this afternoon. He left late this afternoon and told my mother he wouldn't be back for a week, or so. If I had to guess, I'd say they have the plans and are ready to move them and the art collection to the East Coast."

"Tanya. I can't tell you how vital your information is – not only for the Emerson art collection, and national security, but for Natalia. The Communists kidnapped her this afternoon, and I'm certain they've taken her to the warehouse in Hyde Park."

"Oh, my goodness! How awful. How did it happen?"

"Apparently, they grabbed her on Jackson Street in front of the Greek Orthodox Church. A little boy saw the whole thing and reported it to the police."

"What are you going to do?"

"Well, we've already spoken with the police department, but I have a plan of my own in the works. Wish us luck."

"Certainly. But, be careful. These people are ruthless."

When Ellen returned to her apartment, she proceeded to lay out her plan for Mr. and Mrs. Boroskova. They nodded their approval. Ellen's father had not yet returned from work.

"You're welcome to follow us, if you wish. If not, you know the address – 815 E. 52nd Street. We'll be there as soon as I can round up the troops," said Ellen.

Ellen's next stop was Melanie's house. She knocked on her front door.

"Hi, Ellen, what was that police car all about?"

"Natalia has been kidnapped by Communist agents."

"I don't believe it! Kidnapped?"

"It's true. She was grabbed this afternoon walking home from school. I'm convinced she was taken to a warehouse in Hyde Park, the same place where the Emerson art collection was taken."

"What can we do?"

"Well, the police have already been alerted, but they still don't know where the warehouse is. And we can't wait for the F.B.I. or the Chicago police to respond. Tanya Sokolov has informed me that they're ready to move the art collection to the East Coast and they'll probably take Natalia with them. If they do, they'll undoubtedly put her on board a Soviet freighter and take her back to the Soviet Union."

"Oh, how awful! And after what she's already been through..."

"We need to get Frank Roman and the football team to help us. If we show up with overwhelming force, we can stop them in their tracks."

"I know Frank will help us, and if he says 'yes,' the rest of the team will follow. They should be finishing up their afternoon practice just about now. We need to get over to the gym right away!"

Ellen and Melanie ran all the way to school and down into the boys' lower gymnasium. They approached the locker room door cautiously.

"Are you guys decent? We need to talk to Frank Roman. It's an emergency," Melanie shouted.

"Yea, we're decent," replied George Mihal. "Frank's right here."

Frank was drying his hair with a towel as he emerged from the locker room "What is it, Melanie? You look distressed."

"Ellen's friend Natalia Boroskova – you know, the girl from the Soviet Union – was kidnapped by Soviet agents this afternoon, on her way home from Froebel. Ellen's convinced she's been taken to a warehouse in Hyde Park, near the University of Chicago. We need you and the rest of the football team to help us rescue her."

"You mean the dark-haired girl who was with you at the beach?"

"That's the one."

"Of course, we'll help. All we need to do is round up some automobiles and baseball bats."

"That's great, Frank," Ellen cried, as she patted him on the shoulder.

Frank poked his head back into the locker room and shouted to his players.

"Hey, guys, Melanie and Ellen need our help. Their friend Natalia Boroskova has been kidnapped by a gang of Communist thugs and taken to a warehouse in Chicago. They need our help to rescue her. Are you with me?"

"You bet, Frank," came a chorus of shouts from team members.

"Mihal, you've got a car, or least access to one," Frank shouted. "Jim Swan, you, too. Who else can get a car on short notice?"

"I can," shouted Bill Biernat.

"Me, too," added Henry Sobol.

"We need a couple more, besides mine. How about you, Gerometta?"

"Sure, my Dad will let me take his."

"Bailey, you've got a car, right?"

"Yep. '39 Studebaker."

"I can get my Dad's '36 DeSoto," yelled Russell Bailey.

"That's the spirit, guys," Frank shouted over the din.

Ellen stepped in front of Frank and looked out over the crowd."

"I have something else to tell you guys. We've found out that these are the same criminals who stole our art collection." Her words elicited an immediate reaction from the locker room and the undivided attention of the other team members.

"That's right. I'm sure they've taken Natalia to the same warehouse where they stashed our paintings. I just learned that they're planning to move the whole collection out tonight to somewhere on the East Coast. And, they're probably going to take Natalia with them and put her on a freighter bound for the Soviet Union."

At that moment, Coach Art Rolfe came out of the equipment locker.

"I heard everything, guys. You're going to need some clubs. This could get nasty. Why don't I issue each of you boys a baseball bat so you can knock these Commies out of the park, **figuratively** speaking, of course."

"That's swell coach. Would you like to join us?"

"Wouldn't miss it for the world."

"Say, Ellen, where is this warehouse?"

"It's at 815 E. 52nd Street, a few blocks northwest of the University of Chicago campus. If Melanie and I ride in your car with coach, we can lead the rest of our **entourage** to the spot."

"Did you hear that, guys?"

"Yep, we heard: 815 East 52nd Street," shouted Art Gerometta. "That's the time the school day starts – eight fifteen."

"O.K. Here's what we need to do," shouted Frank. "You guys with cars, bring 'em here as soon as you can and line 'em up along Carolina Street between 6th and 7th. I'll be parked first in line at the corner of 6th and Carolina, across the street from the Shops building. Just fall in behind me. Those of you without cars, just wait on the sidewalk until we see how many cars we have."

"I counted 27 bats in the equipment locker," shouted Coach Rolfe. "Those of you with bats at home, bring 'em. Nabhan, you can help me by loading up the bat bags and carrying 'em out to the street."

"Sure thing, coach."

By six fifteen, eight cars were lined up along Carolina Street, between 6th Avenue and the Emerson driveway, near the handball courts. While the team members were retrieving their automobiles, Ellen ran home to grab her Chicago map. By the time she returned, forty-six team members were stuffing themselves into the assortment of coupes and sedans in the procession. At Coach Rolfe's urging, most brought along their football helmets in the event the **altercation** got out of control. Frank Roman sat behind the wheel of his Dad's 1940 Oldsmobile, with Coach Rolfe riding shotgun, and  Ellen and Melanie in the back seat. After **reconnoitering** with Ellen and her map, Frank jumped out to bark some final instructions:

"All you drivers, come over here. Here's the plan, guys. Stay close behind me on Highway 20 until it merges with Highway 41 in Whiting. We're going to follow Highway 41 to Lake Shore Drive as far as the Museum of Science and Industry. I want you all to pull into the Museum parking lot to make sure we're all together. From there, we're going to follow E. 53rd Street west until we get to S. Drexel Avenue. At that intersection, we're going to leave our cars on the street, grab our baseball bats and march down East 52nd Street. I don't want to hear a word from anyone until we make our move. I want this to be a complete surprise. Understood?"

"You bet!" cried George Mihal.

"O.K. Let's move out!"

Chapter 34

A Chicago Field Trip

Natalia had been hanging nearly an hour with her arms wrenched behind her back when her captors returned. Her arms were numb and she was on the verge of losing consciousness. Tears filled her eyes, clouding her vision. Forced to confront the limits of human **endurance,** she was nevertheless fully aware that they were prepared to do far worse. Indeed, they had already **intimated** that her fingers might be next. Hyman Petrov, agent of the NKVD, took up where Alexandrov had left off:

"So, Miss Boroskova, are you ready to cooperate, or shall we try more violent methods? It's your call."

Natalia tried to ignore him in a **valiant** effort to buy time, but her **stamina** had begun to **flag,** and she was gripped by a **profound malaise.** And with the gag still stuffed in her mouth, she found it difficult to breath. Petrov approached her sagging body, grabbed her by the chin, again, and smacked her **maliciously** across her left cheek. She stubbornly refused to cry out, though stunned by the **grievous** blow. Then, he did it again, this time on the right cheek. She gritted her teeth. Tears rolled down her face.

"I've got all night, Miss Boroskova. I've done this many times, usually in the basement of the Lubyanka. They all crack eventually. You will, too. Why don't you spare yourself the pain and **humiliation?**"

Before Petrov could strike her again, there was a soft knock on the side door. A blond-headed man in a dark blue trench coat entered the room with a manila envelope under his arm.

"I've got them," he said. "What you've been waiting for."

"Let's see what you've got," Petrov commanded.

Natalia counted thirteen men in the room by now, most of them powerfully built, with hardened faces. They walked over to a wooden table in the far corner of the warehouse. The blond-haired man removed papers from the envelope and began unfolding them. He spread the papers on the table, smoothed out the folds, then turned the diagrams in Petrov's direction.

"This is it," the blond-haired man explained. "The prototype of the nuclear reactor. I know it's hardly **intelligible** to most of you, but our Soviet scientists will be able to make sense of it. I've also got detailed design specifications for the reactor and the latest information on the potential for constructing a fission bomb – all neatly summarized for our Soviet scientists."

The grim-faced men studied the **cryptic** diagrams with **befuddled** interest.

"Our efforts have finally paid off. It's time we were on our way, comrades," Petrov urged. "This is what we've been waiting for. Time to load the truck with the paintings, the plans, and Miss Boroskova."

Petrov again approached Natalia, and took her face into his outstretched palms.

"If you're going to remain **obdurate**, how would you feel about paying a little return visit to your homeland, my dear? We have a ship waiting for us on the Jersey City docks, and you're going to be on it when it sails."

"Nooooooooo!" screamed Natalia, through the gag. The prospect of being returned to the Soviet Union had not even occurred to her. She had anticipated the more likely prospect of winding up at the bottom of Lake Michigan, or the Chicago River, but not being sent back home. Indeed, she now considered the United States her home and had **resigned** herself to never seeing her homeland again.

While Natalia grappled with this **horrendous** revelation, the men in the warehouse proceeded to load the truck with crates containing the Emerson art collection, thirty-two paintings in all. Three men were assigned to accompany the truck to the East Coast, with Tanya Sokolov's father driving.

"Cut her down," Petrov shouted to Gene Alexandrov. The **subordinate** pulled out a switchblade and sliced the rope that held her suspended from the ceiling rafter. She fell to the floor like a hundred pound sack of rice, bruising her shoulder in the process.

"Tie her hands in front of her, and tie her ankles as well. Then, place her in the truck," Petrov ordered. "I want her healthy enough to make the voyage to **Archangel**, and to Moscow for questioning."

When they had cut her loose from her bonds, Natalia had barely enough time to shake some of the numbness from her aching limbs before being tied up again. Then, she was lifted by two pair of strong hands and passed to two other men standing on the truck's lift gate. They placed her outstretched body on the floor and secured her wrists and ankles to ring bolts along the inside wall of the truck. She tried to rest and allow some of the feeling to return to her aching arms and shoulders. Then, her mind began to drift into horrific speculation. *Was this what fate had in store for her? Once the truck left the warehouse, its route and destination would be unknown to all but a few people. And once they got to New Jersey, it would be all over. She would be on her way back to the Soviet Union. Would they allow her to live and, if so, would she spend the rest of her life in a slave labor camp in Siberia along with millions of others?*

~~~~~~~~~~~~

It had taken the procession of automobiles slightly more than an hour to wind its way on Rt. 12 through Gary, East Chicago, Whiting, Hammond, and South Chicago, before pulling into the parking lot in front of the stately Museum of Science and Industry, the last remnant of the **Columbian Exposition** of 1893. Along the way, Ellen explained more fully to Frank and Coach Rolfe the remarkable story of Natalia's escape from the Soviet Union, her journey to Gary, and the steps they had taken to ascertain the location of the stolen art collection. After the cars reached the parking lot, they formed a circle. Frank climbed out of the lead car and took a tally to make sure all the cars were accounted for.

"Just follow my car, guys. If we get separated, just make sure you drive west on 53rd Street until you come to Drexel Avenue. You got that? – Drexel Avenue. That's where we'll park our cars. We'll go the rest of the way on foot. Ellen knows the way. But, before we take off, Coach has something to say to you."

"Let's not try to break any skulls, men. A swift blow across the solar plexus will knock the wind out them. If necessary, you can also give them a whack across their kneecaps. It should be easy enough to overpower them after that. I've got enough rope here to tie up half an army before the police arrive."

"Are you ready, men?"

"Ready, Coach!"

"Then, let's go!"

The entourage proceeded slowly through the Hyde Park neighborhood that bordered the northern edge of the University of Chicago. Ellen's heart began to pound rapidly as their car neared the appointed intersection. Melanie looked at her with a heightened sense of anticipation and **foreboding**. When they got to Drexel Avenue, the lads pulled their cars to the curb, grabbed their helmets and baseball bats, and assembled at the corner of 52nd Street. The Boroskovas were there to meet them. It would have been a novel sight for any passersby to witness more than forty helmeted football players marching down the sidewalk, each brandishing a baseball bat. A new sport, perhaps?

Ellen led Coach Rolfe and Frank Roman at the front of the small **gridiron** army. When they approached the warehouse, the only light they could discern was squinting out from the edges of the shades that covered the three side windows. The large double-door that stood below the words 'Hyde Park Moving

& Storage,' was shut tight. Ellen had already formulated a plan. She turned around and, with a finger to her lips, urged silence on the team. Moving slowly toward the side door, she directed the boys to flatten themselves against the brick wall. She knocked.

"Western Union – Special Delivery!" yelled Frank.

Not more than three seconds later, as she heard the door about to open, Ellen leaped out of the way. One of the occupants of the warehouse opened the door. It was Boris Sokolov, Tanya's stepfather.

"Yes, that's one of them," shouted Ellen. "This is the place."

It was fateful mistake on Boris Sokolov's part, one of many he would later come to regret. Nearly four-dozen football players, joined by Coach Rolfe, flooded the warehouse, swinging baseball bats as they advanced.

Frank Roman struck a blow at the stomach of Gene Alexandrov and dropped him to the floor with a single swing, finishing him off with a solid right hook to the jaw before he could catch his breath. Comrade Petrov came at George Mihal, fists swinging, and suffered a similar fate. Gasping for breath, he was quickly subdued by Jim Swan and Art Gerometta who pulled his arms behind his back and secured them with a length of rope thrown them by Coach Rolfe. One by one, each occupant of the warehouse met a similar fate, either by a blow to the stomach or being **grappled** or gang tackled by charging linemen. The Golden Tornado had struck with a **ferocity** not seen since last year's Tolleston game, which they won by the lopsided score of 54 to 7. In this case, the score was 13-0.

In less than two minutes, every member of the **hapless** gang had been cap- tured and **subdued**, with their arms tied behind their backs. Pushed to the floor by team members, they sat silently, clearly **befuddled** by the sudden turn of events. Coach Rolfe quickly located the telephone in the adjacent office and dialed both the Chicago Police and the local F.B.I. offices.

Ellen yelled "Natalia! Natalia!" Hearing a muffled sound coming from the truck, Ellen wasted no time in climbing onto the rear of the truck and finding Natalia, bound hand and foot, a gag stuffed in her mouth. After removing the gag, Natalia **emitted** a **protracted** sigh.

"Oh, Ellen, I prayed that you would find me before they drove away from here. Would you believe, they were planning to take me back to the Soviet Union? I had almost given up hope." Ellen gave her a warm embrace.

Frank Roman jumped into the truck as well and cut Natalia free of her bonds with his pocket knife. Natalia quickly got to her feet and hugged them both.

"Frank, help me push one of these crates to the edge of the truck," Ellen urged. "Here, guys, lower it to the floor. Anybody got a crowbar?"

"Here's one," shouted Jim Swan. After he pried the top open, Jimmy Maxwell and Manuel Manos slid the painting out of the crate and set it on the floor. The team members were **dumbfounded**. The brass plate read: *Gary Mills at Night, by Alexis Jean Fournier, donated by the Class of 1930.*

"And there are 31 more where that came from," cried Ellen. "And, one more in Konstantin Ivanov's home in Aetna. That makes thirty-three in all."

"And one more thing," cried Natalia. "There should be a manila envelope around here somewhere."

"Like this?" shouted Bill Biernat.

"Let me see it," Natalia replied. She reached inside and pulled out a number of documents, including the **cryptic** plans of what was doubtless the atomic reactor.

"What is it?" Bill inquired, anxiously, while the others crowded around.

"Secret plans stolen from a government project. And enough evidence to put these guys safely behind bars for espionage," Ellen added. "The F.B.I. will be **elated** to get their hands on material that these guys were planning to send to the Soviet Union."

"No kidding? And I thought we came here just to rescue Natalia," Frank replied.

"No, Frank, you and the boys have done a lot more than that," Ellen replied. "You not only saved our precious art collection, but you threw an enormous wrench into the gears of the Soviet spy apparatus. Allies or not, these guys are not our friends – just wait till the war's over. You can think of it as the biggest interception of your career."

"The police are on their way," Coach Rolfe shouted.

I almost forgot," cried Ellen. "We need to call Sergeant Brewer." She grabbed the phone from the coach and dialed the Gary Police Department.

Four Chicago Police squad cars and a half dozen F.B.I. agents arrived within ten minutes of each other, arresting all thirteen members of the spy ring. Together, Ellen and Natalia were able to help them identify Alexei Kropotkin, Yevgeny Alexandrov, Mikhail Ivanski, Iggy Eisenberg, Boris Sokolov, Peter Milosz, Dimitri Poliakov, and Hyman Petrov. The other five – members of the Chicago cell – were also identified after a brief interrogation.

"Petrov is the ringleader of the bunch and the one who tortured me before you all arrived," Natalia instructed the F.B.I. agents. "He's an officer in the **NKVD**. Isn't that right, Hymie?" She couldn't resist grabbing Petrov by the chin. He was **uncharacteristically** mute.

"NKVD? What that?" asked Art Gerometta.

"The Soviet Secret Police," Natalia replied.

"Holy cow!"

"There's another person you need to pick up – Miklos Molnar. He's a

Hungarian scientist working on the inside of the Project. The plan was for him to accompany the documents to the Soviet Union," Ellen explained.

Officers Brewer and Billick arrived within the hour. To say they were **flabbergasted** by the developments would have been a gross **understatement**. They were startled to learn that the Emerson art collection had been recovered and secret government plans intercepted.

"To think these guys were operating under our very noses in the Central District leaves me speechless," exclaimed Sergeant Brewer. "We've come to expect the usual gambling, **larceny**, **bootlegging**, and **numbers rackets**, but this enemy espionage is certainly beyond our **ken**. Of course, there's a lot that goes on there about which we haven't a clue, particularly when it takes place in languages we don't comprehend."

"Sergeant Brewer, there are at least two more back in Gary connected to this gang," Ellen added. "Konstantin Ivanov, the proprietor of Crimean Imports, 1334 Washington Street, and Galina Borovsky, who, you will be surprised to learn, works as a matron down at police headquarters. She lives at 1573 Fillmore. I'd have them picked up before they can skip town. And you'll find the last of the paintings in the bedroom of Ivanov's home at 900 Arizona Street, in Aetna."

"We'll do that, as soon as we get back to Gary," Sergeant Billick promised.

"It sounds to me like you've got a career in law enforcement in your future, young lady," observed one of the F.B.I. agents.

"That's my intention," Ellen said, beaming.

"Would it be O.K. if we drove the art collection back to our school, officers?" Frank inquired. "We'll be happy to testify whenever you want us."

"I have no problem with that," said one of the federal agents. "We have more than enough to charge these men with, including kidnapping, assault, and espionage. It's going to be a long time before they see the outside world again."

"We'd be happy to give you a police escort," Sergeant Brewer added.

"That would be swell," Ellen replied.

By this time, a paddy wagon had pulled up in front of the warehouse and the thirteen handcuffed **malefactors** were crammed inside, on their way to a federal **detention** facility **pending** their **arraignment**.

"Coach, if you'll drive my car back home, I can handle the truck," Frank Roman suggested. "Rhetorik and Hovanec are going with me."

"It'll be a pleasure, particularly with three pretty girls in the back seat."

"Oh, Coach, you're such a flatterer. But, I'll be happy to sit up front with you," Melanie replied, taking him by the arm.

Once the truck was loaded and secured, the boys opened the warehouse door and released it into the cool September evening. Sergeants Brewer and Billick led the entire convoy back to Emerson. It was just shy of midnight when they pulled into the parking lot at the rear of the school.

To their surprise, Principal Everett Spaulding was already waiting for them when they arrived; and his secretary, Maureen Link, was at his side. The expressions on their faces were priceless. They were both beaming from ear to ear.

"Mr. Spaulding," Melanie cried, "how did you know?"

"Coach called me from Chicago. I've been waiting anxiously for your arrival. I've already unlocked the rear door. Why don't you boys carry the crates to the boy's upper gymnasium. I'll have the night janitor give you some tarps to put down first so we don't scratch the floor. We can sort them all out in the morning. Then, you'd all best be getting home and getting some sleep. You've earned it."

Before they could leave the boy's gymnasium, Ellen and Natalia were **besieged** by reporters from the *Gary Post-Tribune, Chicago Herald-American, Chicago Tribune,* and *The Chicago Daily News.* The girls politely answered the reporters' questions for more than a half-hour before Principal Spaulding stepped in to run interference so they could make a dash for home.

Chapter 35

Something to Celebrate

Ellen's father and Mrs. Matheus were both waiting anxiously in the second-floor apartment when they heard Ellen coming up the back stairs. Eric had gotten a call earlier in the evening from Stan Boroskova who informed him of Natalia's kidnapping, but had no idea what plans Ellen, Melanie and their Emerson friends had **concocted** for her rescue.

Breathlessly, Ellen rushed into the living room and plopped herself down in one of the soft wing chairs.

"You won't believe it, Dad. You simply won't believe it."

"Try me. You forget I'm used to this by now. You remember – agita?"

"Natalia is safe and sound. We found her tied up in a Hyde Park furniture warehouse, where she had been taken by a gang of Communist thugs. What they didn't take into account was the Emerson football team, rushing them all at once and **brandishing** baseball bats. Can you imagine? They got the tar knocked out of them in a matter of minutes. The scary thing is that they were ready to drive Natalia to the East Coast and put her on a freighter bound for the Soviet Union. We got there just in the nick of time. The Communists were no match for forty-six club-wielding members of the Golden Tornado. You should have seen it. By the time the Chicago Police and F.B.I. arrived, the boys had them **subdued** and all **trussed** up like calves at a rodeo. It was terrific! And we can thank that little boy on Jackson Street who witnessed the kidnapping in front of the Greek Church."

"Jackson Street? What little boy?" Mrs. Matheus exclaimed.

"His name is Corky... Corky Zvingilas."

"Why, that's my grandson, Corky, my daughter Alvida's boy!"

"No kidding? Well, he saw the whole thing from his yard, and, if he hadn't reported it to the police, Natalia would be on her way to New Jersey by now and, eventually, back to the Soviet Union."

"Thank goodness," exclaimed Mrs. Matheus. "The poor girl. She must have been terrified."

"Yes, she was! We found her all bound and gagged in a truck when we arrived. They'd already been torturing her before we broke into the warehouse, but she refused to tell them a thing. They even threatened to break her fingers if she didn't tell them what they wanted to know. Can you imagine? And Natalia a violinist!"

"How awful," Eric exclaimed. "I hope they put 'em behind bars and throw away the keys."

"Or worse," Ellen suggested. "You know what happened to those Nazi agents who were put ashore on Long Island back in April." She drew a finger across her neck. "These Communists did far worse, and were about to steal plans of the atomic experiments going on at the University of Chicago. Had we not arrived when we did, they would have been off to New Jersey with those plans, with Natalia and the Emerson art collection."

"That's amazing, Ellen," cried Mrs. Matheus. "How did you know they were in the warehouse?"

"It's a long story, Mrs. Matheus, but one that will have to wait until tomorrow. I'm ready to collapse. And, I didn't even finish my trigonometry homework."

"Well, I think that'll be the least of Miss Talbot's concerns tomorrow," Eric added. "I believe she'll cut you a little slack under the circumstances."

"I suppose you're right, Dad. Well, goodnight. See you in the morning."

As Eric walked Mrs. Matheus to the back door, he didn't know what to say.

"That's a remarkable girl you've got there, Eric. You must be very proud?"

"I am, of course. But, would you believe she promised to stay out of trouble on this trip?"

~~~~~~~~~~

When Eric awoke at six thirty the next morning, his first task was to run over to Rubin's and pick up several copies of the Chicago newspapers whose headlines **heralded** the daring raid on the South Side warehouse. The front-page story in the *Chicago Tribune* said it all:

Eric read, with pride, the article detailing Ellen's amazing exploits:

THEFT OF GOV. SECRETS ALSO FOILED

In a daring raid last night on a warehouse in Chicago's Hyde Park neighborhood, Ellen Anderson, a visiting student from Stratford, Connecticut, aided by Coach Arthur Rolfe and members of the Gary Emerson football team, recovered thirty-two paintings stolen from Emerson School nearly three weeks ago. One additional painting was recovered by Gary Police from the Aetna home of Konstantin Ivanov, a Central District furniture dealer who has been implicated in the crime.

Daytime Kidnapping

The raid was precipitated by the Wednesday afternoon kidnapping of Natalia Boroskova, 1334 Lincoln Street, a Gary Froebel High School student and recent refugee from the Soviet Union. In an as yet unexplained series of events, the daring daylight kidnapping of Miss Boroskova led Miss Anderson, forty-six members of the Emerson High School football team, and Coach Rolfe to the warehouse where Miss Boroskova was being held captive by Gary and Chicago Communist Party cell members.

Theft of Military Secrets

The raid also implicated the Soviet secret police and fifteen Gary and Chicago area Communist Party members who have also been charged with the theft of top secret government documents. According to Miss Anderson, the stolen documents, which have enormous national security implications, were slated to be transferred by truck to a Soviet freighter berthed on the East Coast and bound for the Soviet Union. By the same means, the Emerson art collection was to be placed in the hands of East Coast intermediaries for sale to art dealers in the New York metropolitan area, with the goal of funding Communist Party operations in the Midwest. The incident also presents a significant embarrassment to American-Soviet relations and their alliance against Nazi Germany. Neither the White House, not the Soviet embassy in Washington have responded to requests for comment.

Golden Tornado Busts Communist Ring

The Communist plans were brought to a screeching halt when forty-six members of the Emerson football team, led by quarterback Frank Roman and Coach Rolfe, burst their way into the Hyde Park warehouse with baseball bats to rescue Miss Boroskova. After subduing thirteen Communist Party agents, including a member of the Soviet secret police, the students not only freed the Froebel student, but recovered the Emerson art collection and **stymied** the theft of vital government secrets in the process.

Emerson Neighborhood Euphoric

The Emerson neighborhood is in a state of unbridled **euphoria** upon learning that their precious art collection had been recovered. Principal Everett A. Spalding credits Emerson student, Ellen Anderson, and Froebel student, Natalia Boroskova, with initiating the investigation that ultimately led to the collection's recovery. According to Miss Anderson, the trail led from Emerson to Crimean Imports, the Central District furniture emporium owned by Russian businessman, Konstantin Ivanov. Miss Boroskova reported that the art collection was transported last week to the Chicago warehouse in a truck owned by Mr. Ivanov. A second Emerson student, Melanie McGuire, also assisted in the investigation.

Kidnapping of Miss Boroskova

According to F.B.I. agents in Chicago, Natalia Boroskova is the daughter of the late Vladimir Boroskova, who had served as a high-ranking official in the Soviet embassy in London for seven years. He was also a member of the Soviet secret service until his liquidation in 1937 during Stalin's Great Purge. In a **scenario** one would generally assign to spy novels, Miss Boroskova managed to flee to the West earlier this year, only to be tracked by Soviet spies to her uncle's home in Gary. Her kidnapping was a part of a Soviet plot to return her to the Soviet Union via a freighter docked in New Jersey harbor, there to stand trial for treason against the Soviet Union.

By the time Ellen arrived at school on Thursday morning, the news of her exploits had spread quickly. All eyes were upon her as she walked up the steps to the front entrance. Dozens of students approached, warmly shook her hand and patted her on the back. Several students she didn't even know embraced her. After the opening Assembly sounded, she hurried off to her morning register where Miss Tinsman smiled broadly as she entered Room 204.

"Well, I'd say we had a celebrity in our register this morning." Ellen blushed.

"There are a few announcements this morning. Mr. Spaulding has called an **impromptu** assembly for tomorrow morning at ten fifteen for all juniors and seniors. The program will be repeated at twelve fifteen for freshmen and sophomores. I've been advised not to steal any of his thunder, so I'll say no more about that." She looked up at Ellen. "The freshman sock hop is this Friday at seven o'clock in the girls' lower gymnasium. All classes are invited. Admission is ten cents. Miss Reynolds, with Coach Rolfe's support, is holding the first ballroom dance class on Wednesday after school, also in the girls' lower gymnasium. Both boys and girls are encouraged to attend."

In her first period English class, Ellen was greeted with a bear hug from Mrs. Pierce.

"We can't thank you, enough, Ellen. And just when we thought we'd never see those paintings again. You know, it was my class that bought the first fourteen paintings in 1920, so this is personal to me."

Class proceeded as usual with a line-by-line **explication** of Act III of Shakespeare's *Macbeth*, followed by a review of **adverbial clauses**.

Mr. Flinn was similarly **effusive** in his praise at the opening of Ellen's nine fifteen physics class. "Military secrets, indeed! I've had students submit projects for extra credit before, but this one takes the cake! Who would have thought that a student of mine would become **embroiled** in **thwarting** the theft of military secrets by Communist agents. Perhaps, in a few days, you'll consent to **regale** the members of our class with tales of your **exploits**, Ellen. We could all learn something."

Friday came faster than Ellen might have ever imagined. At the end of her physics class, Ellen joined hundreds of her classmates in filing into the auditorium. There to greet local dignitaries and guests in front of the War Honor Roll, which recognized Emerson graduates currently serving their country, were Mr. Warrum of the Science Department, Principal Everett Spaulding, Minnie Talbot of the Math Department, Auditorium Head, Hazel Harrison, and Bertha Ade of Home Economics. The stage had already been arranged with a podium and a dozen chairs, for what Ellen assumed would be for visiting dignitaries. Members of the Auditorium Council, under the direction of

Miss Harrison, had decorated the stage with Emerson gold and gray streamers, reflecting Gary's sand dunes and steel mills. But, most impressively, they had lined the outside walls on both sides of the auditorium with the thirty-three paintings recovered from the Chicago warehouse, most of which Ellen had never seen before. It was a magnificent sight. Soon, every seat was occupied by students, teachers, guests, and members of the Emerson Alumni Association. The president of the student council approached Ellen and asked her to take one of the front row aisle seats. To her surprise, Natalia was soon escorted to the adjacent seat.

Soon, a procession of visitors filed in from the wings of the auditorium and took seats on the stage, Ellen's father and the Boroskovas among them. Also seated on stage were Mayor Schaible, the Chief of Police, Sergeants Brewer and Billick, School Superintendent Charles Lutz, Mildred Harter Wirt, and Mrs. Edith Dorman, representing the school board. The last person to walk out on the stage was four-year-old Corky, the little boy who had witnessed the kidnapping, and without whose timely intervention Natalia might have been on her way back to the Soviet Union. Finally, as Mr. Spaulding approached the podium, the audience members quieted themselves.

"Good morning students, faculty, honored guests. We are here to celebrate a truly grand occasion, the recovery of our precious art collection that was taken from us three weeks ago by a gang of Communist agents operating out of our very own city. When I conceived the idea of an art gallery back in 1911, I hoped that bringing great works of art into our school on a permanent basis would foster a deeper appreciation of the world's great artistic heritage. The Class of 1911 was the first to donate a work of art to our school – a copy of Rembrandt's *Mother*. After our first art exhibition in 1919, the graduating class of 1920 donated fourteen original oil paintings to the school, at a cost

of nearly $4,000. Subsequently, other classes have followed their example, donating more than $10,000 in original art works to grace our halls.

"I see some of our alumni in the audience today, people like Pauline Hilton and Frances Monfort, who were responsible for some of those donations. We honor their legacy and treasure those gifts that will, hopefully, grace the halls of our school as long as it stands as a symbol of educational excellence in this city.

"For you see, our school is more than bricks and mortar, more even than a collection of students and faculty that occupy our building today. A school – Emerson School – represents a **hallowed** legacy that extends over multiple generations, binding us all in our love for its history and traditions, and for its educational and cultural mission. We who serve the school today have a sacred responsibility to honor the legacy we were **bequeathed** by former graduates and teachers, and to pass it on to future generations. Our art collection is the most visible **manifestation** of that legacy.

"Today, we honor those who bear responsibility for the return of our beloved art collection to Emerson. At this time, I want to call upon the members of our varsity football team who took part in the raid on the Chicago warehouse, and their coach, Art Rolfe. Please come up to the stage so you can receive the grateful thanks of our assembly."

Rising from their seats throughout the auditorium were forty-six members of the varsity football squad, accompanied by Coach Rolfe. As they ascended the stairs and formed three lines across the length of the stage, the audience began a sustained round of applause that continued long after the last team member was in position. Then, as the applause began to **dissipate**, Coach Rolfe stepped to the microphone.

"On behalf of our Golden Tornado team members, I want to thank you for your **accolades**. But, at the same time, I want to say that what we did pales in comparison to the actions of two brave young ladies who are responsible for locating the art collection in the first place and leading us to the warehouse where it was hidden. To introduce these ladies, I want to bring our team quarterback, Frank Roman, to the microphone. Frank..."

Frank Roman stepped forward from the front row of team members and walked to the podium.

"I met Ellen Anderson on the first day of school. She and Melanie McGuire were having lunch at Rubin's, and I asked Melanie to introduce us. I have to confess that I thought she was kind of cute and was somebody I'd like to get to know. I soon learned that she was a visiting student, from Stratford, Connecticut and had a boyfriend back home. I had no idea at the time that she and her girlfriend, Natalia Boroskova, were already following clues that would eventually lead to the recovery of our art collection and the arrest of a gang of Communist agents that had already been responsible for a series of burglaries in Gary.

"Natalia Boroskova is a recent immigrant from the Soviet Union. What you probably don't know is that the Soviet Union does not voluntarily permit its citizens to leave the country. Its borders are sealed and its citizens are, in effect, inmates in a giant prison. Natalia had already experienced her share of tragedy. Her parents were **liquidated** by Stalin's henchmen during the Great Purge. And she almost lost a foot to frostbite during one of the frigid Russian winters while digging tank traps to halt the Nazi advance on Moscow. But, Natalia was not a person to sit **impassively** and submit to the dictates of a **brutal** and **repressive** government. She was resolved to escape to the West. So, at great personal risk to herself, she walked to Lithuania and managed to join a band of Jews in crossing the Baltic Sea in a fishing trawler. After a few months in Stockholm, she made her way to England, then New York, and, finally, to Gary, where her aunt and uncle live. By chance, Natalia met Ellen on the 20th Century Limited on her way to Gary. It was their friendship that **fortuitously** led to the restoration of the Emerson art collection.

"But there's another story, even more significant than the restoration of our art collection. Those same Communist spies were involved in an effort to steal sensitive military secrets from the United States government. Had the Germans stolen these plans, it would have had the potential to change the course of the war. And if the Soviet Union had managed to steal them, it would have presented a serious future threat to the United States in a post-war world. What Ellen and Natalia managed to accomplish was to confound months of espionage work against our own government. So, not just Emerson, but the entire country, owes them its undying gratitude. So, at this time, I would like to call Ellen Anderson and Natalia Boroskova to the stage to receive the grateful appreciation of the Emerson community."

As Ellen and Natalia walked to the stage, more than 800 students, faculty and guests rose **spontaneously** from their seats and began applauding with unbridled enthusiasm. Ellen acknowledged her father, sitting on the stage with the Boroskovas, his face beaming with pride. She thanked Frank for his introduction as she approached the microphone. She had to wait more than a minute before the applause died down sufficiently to begin speaking.

"I don't know what to say. This is all so unexpected. All I can tell you is that, from the first day I entered Emerson, I have never felt more welcome. You're like one big family and you've made me feel a part of it. Ironically, I barely had time to appreciate your art collection when it was stolen, three days after my arrival. It was Melanie McGuire who explained its history to me when she gave me a tour of the building the day I arrived. On the afternoon after the robbery, I spoke with several members of the Emerson Alumni Association who had been instrumental in making donations to the collection on behalf of their graduating classes. Their grief was **palpable**. I know what it meant to all of you, and how heartbroken you all were over its loss. It was on that afternoon that I resolved to find it and restore it to the school.

"I could not have done it without Natalia Boroskova, a young woman of **indomitable** courage whom I chanced to meet on the 20th Century Limited on my way to Gary. Natalia had already been through so much in her native land, yet was still being pursued by Soviet agents in this country. It was her kidnapping on Wednesday afternoon that **precipitated** our assault on the Chicago warehouse where both she and the Emerson art collection were being held. Yes, we were able to save her, but not before she was tortured by her captors who were planning to return her to the Soviet Union along with the stolen military secrets. But, I'll let her tell you about that in her own words."

"Thank you, Ellen. I can't tell you how grateful I am to Frank Roman, Coach Rolfe and the rest of the Emerson football team for believing Ellen's story and saving me from a **horrific** fate. Not only did the Communists plan to send me back to the Soviet Union, but they threatened to break my fingers if I did not divulge the secrets I had learned about Communist infiltration into your federal government – fingers I use to play the violin. In my despair, I prayed that Ellen would lead my rescuers to the warehouse where I was being held. Fortunately, God answered my prayers. I can't tell you how grateful I am for your bravery," she said, turning to acknowledge the members of the football team, with tears rolling down her face. "And, finally, I want to acknowledge the presence today of Mrs. Wirt whose late husband, William A. Wirt, **presciently** sounded the warning call of Communist infiltration into our federal government nearly ten years ago. That warning should be a lesson to us all that the freedom you enjoy in the United States is not shared by most people in the world, and that the Soviet Union is just as much a threat as Nazi Germany and Imperial Japan. In closing, I leave you with the words of your great president, Thomas Jefferson: 'The price of liberty is eternal vigilance.'"

As Natalia stepped back from the microphone, the audience again extended its **plaudits** by erupting into a thunderous roar of applause, prompting Mr. Spaulding to return to the podium. Several other speeches followed, each **effusive** in its praise for the young heroines, including a particularly **florid** one by Mayor Schaible. At their conclusion, Mr. Spaulding again returned to the podium.

"As we bring our assembly to a close, I'm going to ask Ellen and Natalia to stay after to accept your expressions of gratitude. All those who wish may form a line at the base of the stage where you will have an opportunity to thank them." Before Ellen left the stage, she warmly embraced her father. Similarly, Natalia hugged her aunt and uncle who were **dumbfounded** over what had transpired over the past 48 hours, and little Corky, who was beaming from ear to ear.

Following lunch in the cafeteria with the visiting dignitaries, Ellen and Natalia returned to the auditorium for a **reprise** of the morning program for the benefit of the freshmen and sophomore classes. By the time the day was over, she must have shaken hands with most of the school.

WESTBOUND

TIME TABLES

WINTER SCHEDULE
All trains operated on
CENTRAL STANDARD TIME

Trains to
CHICAGO
(SIX CONVENIENT STATIONS)
KENSINGTON
63rd STREET
53rd STREET
ROOSEVELT ROAD
VAN BUREN ST.
RANDOLPH ST.
from
SOUTH BEND
MICHIGAN CITY
GARY . . EAST CHICAGO
HAMMOND
(and intermediate points)

Connecting Motor Coaches to
Michigan City
from
BENTON HARBOR
ST. JOSEPH
(and intermediate points)

Chicago South Shore and South Bend Railroad

Schedule in effect September 29, 1942

Chapter 36

Heading Home

It took several days for the excitement around school to **dissipate**, by which time the paintings were restored to their proper places in the second and third floor hallways.

Ellen succeeded in re-focusing her attention on her studies and became progressively less a center of attention around school. Still suffering the lingering effects of the physical abuse she had received at the hands of the Communists, Natalia was taken to see Dr. Danielski at the Gleason Welfare Clinic for an **exhaustive** check-up. Detecting no permanent **musculoskeletal** damage, he treated her **abrasions**, prescribed some hot baths and soothing topical **emollients** to ease her pain. After a few days **recuperating** at home, she resumed her classes at Froebel School and her normal schedule of activities.

Not surprisingly, Friday evening football games now consumed an increasing amount of Ellen's and her father's attention. Coach Rolfe led his squad to successive victories over Tolleston (20-0), and Hammond (27-0), before losing a nail-biter to East Chicago Washington by a score of 20-19. Touchdown runs by George Settle and Jim Swan sparked the following week's victory over South Side rival Froebel at Gleason Field, at which they were joined in the stands by the Boroskovas. On October 16, the Golden Tornado's winning ways continued when they **vanquished** a highly rated West Rockford, Illinois team by a score of 13-12.

Ellen and her father had their first opportunity to hear Natalia and the Froebel Orchestra perform at Holy Angels Church on Saturday, September 28. For her solo, Natalia played an **exuberant** rendition of Fritz Kreisler's *Variations on a Theme by Corelli,* using an **Amati** violin Mr. Resur acquired for her from a **beneficent** Jewish refugee on Gary's West Side. So taken was the audience with her performance that she received multiple invitations to perform for various fraternal and civic organizations in the city. It was a

poignant reminder of how dramatically Natalia's life had changed for the better since her arrival in Gary, and how **resilient** she had been in the face of multiple **adversities**.

A month later, Ellen and her father heard Natalia and the orchestra perform, again, this time at the Miramar Ballroom for Club SAR, the Social, Athletic and Recreational organization on the city's South Side. On this occasion, her solo number was the *Csárdás* by Vittorio Monti, a work in Hungarian folk **idiom** that **resonated** with the club's Eastern European members. The orchestra also performed admirably with **nary** a sound of **dissonance**, a fitting **testament** to Mr. Resur's skilled direction.

Then, on Sunday, October 25, Ellen's father broke the news to her. His work was completed at Gary Armor Plate and they would be leaving for Connecticut on Saturday. The announcement was a bittersweet one for Ellen who had come to love her adopted city and its people, particularly Natalia, the Boroskovas, and her friends and teachers at Emerson High School. But, she also missed Ken, her mother and her friends back in Stratford. She was resigned to the fact that it was time to go home.

When her friends heard the news, they insisted on accompanying Ellen and her father to the South Shore station. By the time they were driven to the station the following Saturday morning, more than a hundred people had already arrived, including most of the varsity football team, Coach Rolfe, Melanie and her friends from Carolina Street, her teachers, Corky and his parents, Paul Baukus, Pop Rubin, Tanya Sokolov, Stasha Poliakov, dozens of Emerson students and, of course, Natalia and the Boroskovas. Joining them were Eleanor Matheus and her son, Ernest, who was home on leave from **boot camp** at Great Lakes Naval Training Station. Ellen had never hugged so many people in so short a time. The warmest and longest hug was reserved for Natalia, who had become Ellen's dearest friend. Most stayed to wave 'goodbye' as their train

pulled out of the station at twelve thirty-eight. When they arrived at the Randolph Street Station, it was one thirty-nine.

With their luggage safely checked through to New York City, and with more than three hours to spare before their next train, Ellen **cajoled** her normally **parsimonious** father into letting her do a bit of shopping at Marshall Field's. She reminded him that their previous visit to the magnificent shopping **emporium** was a rather hasty affair that had afforded them no time for shopping, their chief concern being to elude Communist agents.

"So, how much may I spend, Dad?"

"Fifty dollars, and not a nickel more," he replied, playfully. He handed her three twenties. Honestly, you deserve a lot more **remuneration** for what you've accomplished. In my opinion, you're worth at least $10.00 per spy."

"Fantastic! You're a peach, Dad!" she exclaimed, kissing him on the cheek. But, $50.00 is more than I expected. Where shall I meet you when I'm done shopping?"

"Meet me under the Marshall Field's clock at the corner of State and Randolph at four thirty."

"Isn't that the most famous meeting place in Chicago?"

"That's right. Don't be late now. The 20th Century Limited leaves promptly at six o'clock."

In a flash, Ellen was off to Field's, where she quickly navigated the store's directory and found the departments for misses' clothes. Ellen was not normally an **impulsive** shopper. In slightly more than two hours, however, she managed to **cull** out a half dozen casual dresses, a **smart** Sunday dress, two skirts, a pair of maroon wool worsted slacks, a twin sweater set in blossom blue, two embroidered white blouses in rayon satin, a pink satin nightgown, and a pair of blue kidskin shoes. She also bought a sweater and blouse for her mother, and a blouse for Grandmother Eliason.

From there, she rode the escalator to the fourth floor book department where she browsed the shelves of bestsellers, mysteries and books on history and current affairs. She selected Arthur Koestler's autobiographical account of the Spanish Civil War *Dialogue with Death*; Agatha Christie's *The Body in the Library*; Raymond Chandler's *The High Window*; Alexander Seversky's *Victory Through Air Power*; and a 1936 edition of Austrian economist Ludwig von Mises' *Socialism*, a devastating critique of **command economics** that had been recommended to her by 'Uncle' Stan. Four shopping bags later, Ellen made her way to the designated meeting place under the clock where she found her father waiting patiently.

"It looks like you've had a successful expedition. So, do you have any **superfluous** change for me?"

"Just a dollar and forty-three cents. I got a little carried way. But, you should see the great items I found. Besides, I bought a gifts for Mother and Grandmother."

"Smart thinking. I don't know how I would have made **restitution** if we had forgotten to bring them home something. I spent all my time at Kroch's & Brentano's book store on Wabash Avenue and bought a few books myself, including a fabulous limited edition monograph entitled *Himalaya*, containing plates of **Nicholas Roerich's** paintings. You know, I've always been fasci-

nated by Roerich's haunting depictions of the **Himalayan Mountains**. Well, I think we'd better grab a cab now and get over to the LaSalle Street Station. Our train leaves in an hour and a half. Why don't I relieve you of a couple of those bags?"

After a short cab ride to LaSalle Street Station, and a brief stop at the newsstand where Ellen's father picked up a copy of the *New York Times* and Ellen bought a 3 Musketeers to tide her over until dinner, the two found their train waiting on Track 1. They were promptly escorted to their compartment by another Pullman porter named George, who helped them get comfortable and took their dinner reservations. Ellen stowed her purchases in the overhead rack, removed her jacket and kicked off her shoes, then curled up in the lounge chair with part of the *New York Times* to await the train's departure. Promptly at six o'clock, she felt the train begin to crawl out of the station, then gradually accelerate as it left the rail yard behind. They were on their way home.

As the train crossed the border into Indiana, Ellen looked up from the section of the *New York Times* she was reading. "Say, Dad, did you see this article about the theft of the Roerich expedition map?"

No! Let me see that. Well, isn't that ironic? And to think that I just bought that book of Roerich reproductions at Kroch's and Brentano's. If you recall, Nicholas Roerich is the artist and mystic I told you about who conducted an expedition to Central Asia in the 1920s. Apparently, the map of that expedition has been stolen from the Roerich Museum in New York City, and the police have no clues as to its whereabouts."

"Just where is this museum?" Ellen inquired.

"On the Upper West Side... now, wait just one minute, young lady. I hope you're not entertaining any ideas about looking for that missing map. Haven't you had enough excitement for one trip?"

"Well, a girl can always dream, can't she?"

Epilogue

The once grand **edifice** of Emerson School, the flagship of William A. Wirt's Work-Study-Play system of education, now sits abandoned and neglected on Gary's crumbling East Side. Where once students and teachers occupied its classrooms, auditorium, gymnasia, swimming pool, hallways and athletic fields, now the **ravages** of nature, neglect and vandalism have taken hold. Arguably the most famous school building in America, Emerson opened its doors on September 13, 1909 and, within a few years, became the focus of the most famous educational experiment in American history. After 72 years, shrinking citywide enrollment forced the closing of the original Emerson High School in 1981. After a one-year **hiatus**, however, it was reopened as a magnet school for the arts, with students from grades five to seven. In 1987, the school board officially named it the Emerson School for the Visual and Performing Arts. Its first senior class graduated in 1988. Twenty years later, and after 98 years as an active school building, its doors were closed for good after the Gary Community School Corporation voted to transfer its student body to the Kennedy-King School in the Miller district. Shortly thereafter, in 2009, it was combined with the former William A. Wirt High School to form the William A. Wirt/Emerson School for the Visual and Performing Arts, where it thrives today.

Principal Everett A. Spaulding initiated the Emerson art collection in 1912, with the **acquisition** of a copy of Rembrandt's *Mother*. In 1920, with funds derived from the profits of the school cafeteria and art shows, Emerson acquired 14 original oil paintings. By 1931, a total of 38 paintings had been acquired at a cost of $14,093.00. By 1949, the collection comprised 44 oil paintings, including a portrait of Principal Spaulding, who retired in 1952 after 42 years service. When the building was closed in 2008, the Gary Community School Corporation placed the art collection in storage. In 2015, the Corporation contracted with The Conservation Center of Chicago to store Gary's entire collection of over 120 paintings, now estimated to be worth over a half million dollars. Ultimately, the Corporation hopes to have the collection inventoried, **catalogued**, and preserved so that this precious resource may be enjoyed by future generations.

What will be the fate of the historic structure on Gary's East Side? Will neglect and the **ravages** of time ultimately force its demolition, a fate that befell Froebel School in 2004? Or, will local politicians and civic-minded citizens come together to find a new purpose for this splendid monument to American educational history? Only time will tell.

For further information, visit: www.emerson65.com

Glossary of SAT Vocabulary Words

A

abase (v.) to humiliate, degrade

abate (v.) to lessen, to reduce

abdicate (v.) to give up a position, usually one of leadership

abduct (v.) to kidnap, take by force

aberration (n.) something out of the norm

abet (v.) to aid, help, encourage

abhor (v.) to hate, detest

abide (v.) to put up with; to remain

abject (adj.) wretched, pitiful

abjure (v.) to reject, to renounce

ablutions (n.) a cleansing with water or other liquid, especially as a religious ritual

abort (v.) to give up on a half-finished project or effort

abrasion (n.) a wound caused by superficial damage to the skin, no deeper than the epidermis. It is less severe than a laceration, and bleeding, if present, is minimal

abridge (v.) to cut down, shorten

abrogate (v.) to abolish or break, usually by authority

abrupt (adj.) sudden, unexpected

abscond (v.) to sneak away and hide

absolute (adj.) perfect in quality or nature; complete; not limited by restrictions or exceptions

absolution (n.) freedom from blame, guilt, sin

absorption (n.) the process of being absorbed, or incorporated

abstain (v.) to freely choose not to commit an action

abstemious (adj.) marked by restraint especially in the consumption of food or alcohol

abstract (adj.) conceived apart from matter and from special cases; theoretical

abstruse (adj.) hard to comprehend

absurd (adj.) unreasonable. nonsensical, foolish

abundance (n.) a large amount, more than sufficient, plenty

academia (n.) the life, community, or world of teachers, schools, and education, particularly at the college or university level

a cappella (n.) solo or group vocal or singing without instrumental sound

accede (v.) to agree to their request

accelerating (v.) to increase the speed of

accentuate (v.) to stress, highlight

accessible (adj.) obtainable, reachable

accessory after the fact (n.) a person who gives assistance or comfort to someone known to be a felon or known to be sought in connection with the commission of a felony

acclaim (n.) high praise

acclimated (adj.) accustomed to a new environment or situation; adapted

accolade (n.) high praise, special distinction

accommodating (adj.) helpful, obliging, polite

accomplice (n.) one who knowingly aids another in committing a crime

accomplish (v.) to succeed in doing (something)

accord (n.) an agreement

accorded (v.) to grant as suitable or proper; to concede; to award

accost (v.) to confront verbally or physically

accoutrements (n.) additional items of dress or equipment, or other items carried or worn by a person or used for a particular activity

accretion (n.) slow growth in size or amount

accumulate (v.) **to** gather together or acquire an increasing number or quantity of

accusation (n.) an allegation that a person is guilty of some fault, offence, or crime

Achilles heel (n.) a metaphor for a fatal weakness in spite of overall strength. An Achilles' heel is a deadly weakness in spite of overall strength, that can lead to one's downfall

acknowledge (v.) to take note of, to admit to be real or true; recognize the existence, truth, or fact of

acolyte (n.) a devoted fan or follower of someone or something famous, including a political or religious movement

acquiesce (v.) to agree without protesting

acquisition (n.) something acquired or owned

acrid (adj.) harsh, burning, or biting to the touch, taste or smell

acrimony (n.) bitterness, discord

acuity (n.) sharpness, keenness, acuteness

acumen (n.) keen insight

acute (adj.) sharp, severe; (adj.) having keen insight

adage (n.) an old saying; a maxim or proverb

adamant (adj.) impervious, immovable, unyielding

adept (adj.) extremely skilled

adhere (n.) to stick to something; to follow devoutly

adherents (n.) devoted followers

adjacent (adj.) close by; lying near, but not necessarily in direct contact with

admonish (v.) to caution, criticize, reprove

adorn (v.) to decorate

adroit (adj.) skillful, dexterous

adulation (n.) extreme praise

adverbial clause (n.) an adverbial clause is a group of words which plays the role of an adverb. Like all clauses, an adverbial clause will contain a subject and a verb

adversary/ies (n.) a person, group, or country one fights against an enemy

adverse (adj.) antagonistic, unfavorable, dangerous

adversity (n.) misfortune, hardship, great difficulty or trouble

advocate (v.) to argue in favor of something; (n.) a person who argues in favor of something

aerial (adj.) somehow related to the air

aesthetic (adj.) artistic, related to the appreciation of beauty

affable (adj.) friendly, amiable

affiliated (adj.) being in close formal or informal association; related

affinity (n.) a spontaneous feeling of closeness

afflicted (adj.) distressed with mental or bodily pain; trouble greatly or grievously

affluent (adj.) rich, wealthy

affront (n.) an insult

agent (n.) a person who acts in an official capacity for a government or private agency, as a guard, detective, or spy

agent provocateur (n.) an undercover agent who acts to entice another person to commit an illegal or rash act or falsely implicate them in partaking in an illegal act

aggrandize (v.) to increase or make greater

aggravated (v.) make (a problem, injury, or offense) worse or more serious

aggregate (n.) a whole or total); (v.) to gather into a mass

aggrieved (adj.) distressed, wronged, injured

agile (adj.) quick, nimble

agita (n.) a feeling of agitation or anxiety, from the Italian for heartburn or acid

agnostic (adj.) one who questions the existence of God

agriculture (n.) farming

aisle (n.) a passageway between rows of seats

akin (adj.) allied by nature; having the same properties; kindred

alacrity (n.) eagerness, speed

albeit (conj.) although; even if

alcoholic (n.) a person who frequently drinks too much alcohol and is unable to live a normal and healthy life : a person who is affected with alcoholism

alias (n.) a false name or identity

alignment (n.) a position of agreement or alliance

allay (v.) to soothe, ease

allegations (n.) assertions or claims made without proof;

allege (v.) to assert, usually without proof

allergy (n.) an abnormal reaction of the immune system that occurs in response to otherwise harmless substances

alleviate (v.) to relieve, make more bearable

allocate (v.) to distribute, set aside

allotted (adj.) assigned as a portion, set apart

alluded (v.) to refer to indirectly, to mention casually

alluring (adj.) highly attractive, tempting, charming

allusion (n.) a brief and indirect reference to a person, place, thing or idea of historical, cultural, literary or political significance

alma mater (n.) a school, college, or university at which one has studied and, usually, graduated; the school song; from the Latin for nourishing, or dear, mother

aloof (adj.) reserved, distant

altercation (n.) a dispute, fight

altered (v.) change or cause to change in character or composition, typically in a comparatively small but significant way

altruism (n.) unselfishly concerned with or interested in the welfare of others

amalgam (n.) a combination or mixture of different things; a mixture of mercury and other metals used for filling holes in teeth

ambiance (n.) the mood, character, quality, tone, atmosphere, etc.

ambiguous (adj.) uncertain, variably interpretable

ambitions (n.) an earnest desire for some type of achievement or distinction, as power, honor, fame, or wealth

ambivalent (adj.) having opposing feelings

ameliorate (v.) to improve

amenable (adj.) willing, compliant

amenity (n.) an item that increases comfort

amiable (adj.) friendly

amicable (adj.) friendly

amicably (adv.) showing friendliness or goodwill

amnesiac (n.) one who has lost his memory

amoral (adj.) lacking moral sensibility; not caring about right and wrong

amorous (adj.) showing love, particularly sexual

amorphous (adj.) without definite shape or type

amply (adv.) in an ample manner; sufficiently or abundantly

anachronistic (adj.) being out of correct chronological order

analogous (adj.) similar to, so that an analogy can be drawn

analytical (adj.) expert in or using analysis, especially in thinking

anarchist (n.) one who wants to eliminate all government

anathema (n.) a person or thing detested or loathed

ancestry (n.) family or ancestral heritage; descent

ancient (adj.) very old; having lived or existed for a very long time

anecdote (n.) a short, humorous account

anesthesia (n.) loss of sensation

anguish (n.) extreme sadness, torment

animated (adj.) lively

animosity (n.) strong hostility

animus (n.) a feeling of animosity, ill-will

annex 1. (v.) to incorporate territory or space; (n.) a room attached to a larger room or space

annihilation (n.) the state of being annihilated; extinction; destruction

anomaly (n.) something that does not fit into the normal order

anonymity (n.) the quality or state of being unknown or unacknowledged

anonymous (adj.) being unknown, unrecognized

antagonism (n.) hostility

antagonize (v.) to make hostile or unfriendly, to anger

antecedent (n.) an event or occurrence that precedes something similar in time, a forerunner

antediluvian (adj.) ancient; lit. before the biblical flood

anthology (n.) a selected collection of writings, songs, etc

anthropomorphism (n.) an interpretation of what is not human or personal in terms of human or personal characteristics

anti-fascism (n.) opposition to fascist ideologies, groups and individuals

antipathy (n.) a strong dislike, repugnance

antiquarian (adj.) of or relating to persons who study or deal in antiques or antiquities

antiquated (adj.) old, out of date

anti-Semitic (adj.) prejudice against or hostility towards Jews often rooted in hatred of their ethnic background, culture, and/or religion

antithesis (n.) the absolute opposite

antithetical (adj.) characterized by an extreme contrast, polar opposites

anxiety (n.) intense uneasiness

apathetic (adj.) lacking concern, emotion

aphorism (n.) An aphorism is a maxim, or original thought, spoken or written in a laconic (concise) and memorable form; literally a "distinction" or "definition

apocryphal (adj.) fictitious, false, wrong

apolitical (adj.) not involved or interested in politics

apoplectic (adj.) affected with, inclined to, or showing symptoms of stroke; greatly excited or angered

apostasy (n.) renunciation of a religious faith; abandonment of a previous loyalty; defection

appalling (adj.) inspiring shock, horror, disgust

apparatus (n.) the technical equipment or machinery needed for a particular activity or purpose; a complex structure within an organization or system

appease (v.) to calm, satisfy

appellation (n.) a name, title, or designation

appendicitis (n.) inflammation of the vermiform appendix; a medical emergency that requires prompt surgery to remove the appendix which will eventually burst, or perforate, spilling infectious materials into the abdominal cavity, leading to peritonitis

appraise (v.) to assess the worth or value of

appreciable (adj.) large or important enough to be noticed

apprehend (v.) to seize, arrest; (v.) to perceive, understand, grasp

apprehensive (adj.) anxious or fearful about the future; uneasy

apprise (v.) inform, to give notice to

approbation (n.) praise; approval

appropriate (v.) to take, make use of; (adj.) suitable or fitting for a particular purpose, person, occasion, etc.

aptitude (n.) skill, expertise, ability

aquatic (adj.) relating to water

arable (adj.) suitable for growing crops

arbiter (n.) one who can resolve a dispute, make a decision

arbitrary (adj.) based on factors that appear random

arboreal (adj.) of or relating to trees

arcane (adj.) obscure, secret, known only by a few

archaic (adj.) of or relating to an earlier period in time, outdated

ardor (n.) extreme vigor, energy, enthusiasm

arduous (adj.) very difficult, hard to accomplish or achieve

argumentative (adj.) given to arguing; disputatious

aristocratic (adj.) characteristic of an aristocrat; having the manners, values, or qualities associated with the aristocracy; a government of nobles, or principal men

armada (n.) a fleet of warships

armaments (n.) the arms and equipment with which a military unit or military apparatus is supplied

arraignment (n.) to call (an accused person) before a court to answer the charge made against him or her by indictment, information, or complaint

arrest (v.) to seize and hold under the authority of law, to check the expansion of, to hold back

arrogant (adj.) having or showing the insulting attitude of people who believe that they are better, smarter, or more important than other people

articulate (v.) uttered clearly in distinct syllables; using language easily and fluently; capable of speech

artifact (n.) a remaining piece from an extinct culture or place

artifice (n.) a deceptive maneuver, a craft ruse, a clever stratagem

artillery (n.) a class of large military weapons built to fire munitions far beyond the range of infantry's small arms

artisan (n.) a craftsman

ascent (n.) movement upward from a lower to a higher state, degree, grade, or status; advancement

ascertain (v.) to perceive, learn

ascetic (adj.) practicing restraint as a means of self-discipline, usually religious

aspirations (n.) strong desire, longing, or aims; goals; ambitions

aspire (v.) to long for, aim toward

assassination (n.) the targeted murder of a high-profile person, usually by surprise attack, and for political purposes

assault (n.) an attack, an unlawful physical attack upon another with or without a battery; a sudden attack by something

assent (n.) agreement, acquiescence, compliance

assertion (n.) a positive statement or declaration, often without support or reason

assess (v.) to evaluate

assiduous (adj.) hard-working, diligent

assuage (v.) to ease, pacify

asthma (n.) a lung disease that makes breathing difficult for millions of Americans, both young and old

astounding (adj.) causing amazement and wonder; bewildering

astute (adj.) very clever, crafty

asylum (n.) a place of refuge, protection, a sanctuary; (n.) an institution in which the insane are kept

atheistic (adj.) reflecting the rejection of belief in the existence of deities

atoll (n.) a coral island consisting of a reef surrounding a lagoon

atomic reactor (n.) a device to initiate and control a sustained nuclear chain reaction

atone (v.) to repent, make amends

atrocities (n.) appalling or atrocious actions, conditions, qualities

atrophy (v.) a wasting away or progressive decline

attain (v.) to achieve, arrive at

attribute 1. (v.) to credit, assign; (n.) a facet or trait

atypical (adj.) not typical, unusual

audacious (adj.) excessively bold

audible (adj.) able to be heard

augment (v.) to add to, expand

au naturel (adj.) in a natural state; without anything added; nude

aura (n.) a distinctive and pervasive quality or character; air

auspicious (adj.) favorable, indicative of good things

austere (adj.) very bare, bleak

austerity (n.) characterized by great self-denial, a situation in which there is not much money and it is spent only on things that are necessary

authoritarian (adj.) of, relating to, or favoring a concentration of power in a leader or an elite not constitutionally responsible to the people; dictatorial

autocrat (n.) an absolute ruler, especially a monarch who holds and exercises the powers of government as by inherent right, not subject to restrictions

autocratic (adj.) tyrannical, absolute, despotic

avarice (n.) excessive greed

avenge (v.) to seek revenge

averse (adj.) having an active feeling of repugnance or distaste

aversion (n.) a particular dislike for something

avuncular (adj.) suggestive of an uncle, especially in kindliness or geniality

awestruck (adj.) filled with awe, or an overwhelming feeling of reverence, admiration or fear

axiomatic (adj.) relating to or resembling an axiom; self-evident

B

baffle (v.) to confuse, bewilder, or perplex

balance of power (n.) a distribution and opposition of forces among nations such that no single nation is strong enough to assert its will or dominate all the others

baleful (adj.) portending evil and harm, sinister and forbidding

balk (v.) to stop, block abruptly

ballad (n.) a love song

balustrades (n.) a railing with supporting balusters

bankrupt (v.) to reduce (a person or organization) to bankruptcy

banter (n.) playfully teasing language, good-natured raillery

bard (n.) a poet, often a singer as well

bastion (n.) a fortified place; anything seen as preserving or protecting some quality, condition, etc.

battery 1.(n.) a device that supplies power; 2 (n.) assault, beating; 3 (n.) an artillery subunit of guns, men, and vehicles.

beckoned (v.) to signal, summon or direct; to lure

befitting (adj.) suitable, appropriate

befuddled (adj.) muddled or stupefies with or as if with drink

beguile (v.) to trick, deceive

beguiling (adj.) charming or fascinating, to delude, to influence by slyness

behemoth (n.) something of tremendous power or size

beleaguered (adj.) harassed, troubled, hassled, surrounded or beset with troubles

belie (v.) to give a false impression, to mislead or misrepresent

belligerent (n.) waging war; belonging to or recognized as a state at war and protected by and subject to the laws of war; inclined to or exhibiting assertiveness, hostility, or combativeness

bellwether (n.) an indicator of trends; a leader; one that takes the lead or initiative

bemoan (v.) to express deep grief or distress over

benefactor (n.) a person who helps people or institutions

beneficent (adj.) characterized by or performing acts of kindness or charity

beneficiary (n.) a person who receives a benefit, especially an inheritance

benevolent (adj.) marked by goodness or doing good

benign (adj.) favorable, not threatening, mild

bequeath (v.) to pass on, give

berate (v.) to scold vehemently

beseech (v.) to beg, plead, implore

besiege (v.) to crowd around; hem in; to harass or importune, as with requests

betray (v.) unintentionally reveal; provide evidence of; also, expose (one's country, a group, or a person) to danger by treacherously giving information to an enemy

bevy (n.) a group or an assemblage

bias (n.) a tendency, inclination, prejudice

bibliophile (n.) a lover of books, a book collector

birthright (n.) a right, possession, or privilege that is one's due by birth

blackmail (n.) an act, often a crime, involving unjustified threats to make a gain or cause loss to another unless a demand is met

bland (adj.) not highly flavored; mild; tasteless; lacking in special interest, dull

blatant/ly (n./adv.) brazenly obvious; flagrant; offensively noisy or loud

blight (n.) a plague, disease; (n.) something that destroys hope

blissful (adj.) extremely or completely happy; full of or causing bliss

blithely (adv.) carefree and lighthearted

blur (v.) make or become unclear or less distinct

boarder (n.) one who pays a stipulated sum in return for regular meals or for meals and lodging

body politic (n.) a group of persons politically organized under a single governmental authority

bohemian (adj.) a person who is known for unconventional behavior; a nonconformist

boisterous (adj.) loud and full of energy

bombastic (adj.) excessively confident, pompous

bona fides (n.) a person's honesty and sincerity of intention

boon (n.) a gift or blessing

boot camp (n.) a camp where people who have recently joined the U.S. Army, Navy, or Marine Corps receive their basic training

bootlegging (n.) to make, sell, or transport alcoholic liquor
for sale illegally

bourgeoisie (n.) the middle- or propertied class, capitalist

brandishing (v.) waving or flourishing (a weapon, for example) menacingly

brawler (n.) one who engages in noisy quarrels, or fights

brazen (adj.) excessively bold

breakfront (n.) a large cabinet or bookcase whose center section projects beyond the flanking end sections

breaking and entering (n.) The gaining of unauthorized, illegal access to another's premises, as by forcing a lock

brisk (adj.) quick and active; lively

broach (v.) to mention or suggest for the first time

broad (adj.) comprehensive, far-reaching, spacious, wide

brownstone (n.) a building made of reddish-brown sandstone

brusque (adj.) short, abrupt, dismissive

brutal (adj.) savage; cruel; inhuman

brutality (n.) the quality of being brutal; cruelty; savagery

buffet (v.) to strike with force; (n.) an arrangement of food set out on a table

bungle (v.) to act or work clumsily and awkwardly

buntings (n.) a coarse, open fabric of worsted used for flags, signals, etc.; flags

buoyancy (adj.) lightness or resilience of spirit; cheerfulness

bureaucracy (n.) administration of a government chiefly through bureaus or departments staffed with nonelected officials

bureaucratic (adj.) of, relating to, or characteristic of a bureaucrat or a bureaucracy; arbitrary and routine

burgeoning (adj.) growing or developing quickly

burnish (v.) to polish, shine

buttress (v.) to support, hold up; (n.) something that offers support

C

cache (n.) a group of things that have been hidden in a secret place because they are illegal or have been stolen

cacophony (n.) tremendous noise, disharmonious sound

cadence (n.) a rhythm, progression of sound

cajole (v.) to urge, coax

calamity (n.) an event with disastrous consequences

calculated (adj.) carefully thought out or planned

calculus (n.) the branch of mathematics that deals with limits and the differentiation and integration of functions of one or more variables

calibrate (v.) to set, standardize

calisthenics (n.) exercises for the muscles for the purpose of improving health, strength, and grace of form and movement

callous (adj.) harsh, cold, unfeeling

calumny (n.) an attempt to spoil someone else's reputation by spreading lies

camaraderie (n.) brotherhood, jovial unity

canard (n.) a false report; a rumor or hoax

candor (n.) honesty, frankness

cannon fodder (n.) soldiers, especially infantrymen, who run the greatest risk of being wounded or killed in warfare

canny (adj.) shrewd, careful

canvas (n.) a closely woven, heavy cloth of cotton, hemp, or linen, used for tents, sails, etc.; a piece of cloth on which an artist paints; (v.) to cover, inspect

capacious (adj.) very spacious

capitalism (n.) a free-market economic system based on the private ownership of capital and production inputs, and on the production of goods and services for profit.

capitulate (v.) to surrender, to give up, give in

capricious (adj.) subject to whim, fickle

captivate (v.) to get the attention of, hold

captor (n.) one that takes another as a captive; kidnapper

capture (v.) the act of taking and holding someone as a prisoner or of being taken as a prisoner

caricature (n.) A representation, especially pictorial or literary, in which the subject's distinctive features or peculiarities are deliberately exaggerated to produce a comic or grotesque effect

carouse (v.) to party, celebrate

carp (v.) to annoy, pester, complain fretfully

castigate (v.) to subject to severe punishment, reproof, or criticism

cataclysmic (adj.) something that causes great destruction, violence, etc.

catalog (v.) to list, enter into a list; (n.) a list or collection

catechism (n.) A book giving a brief summary of the basic principles of Christianity in question-and-answer form; a body

of fundamental principles or beliefs

categorically (adv.) in a very strong, clear, and definite way

catharsis (n.) discharge of pent-up emotions resulting in the alleviation of symptoms or permanent relief of the condition

caucus (n.) a meeting usually held by people working toward the same goal

cavalier (adj.) given to haughty disregard of others

cavernous (adj.) deep-set; containing caverns

cavort (v.) jump or dance around excitedly

celebrity (n.) fame; renown

censor (v.) to ban or cut portions of a publication, film, letter, etc., often on behalf of a governmental authority

censor (n.) a person authorized to examine publications, theatrical presentations, films, letters, etc, in order to suppress in whole or part those considered obscene, politically unacceptable, etc.

censorship (n.) the act suppressing speech or other communication which may be considered objectionable, harmful, sensitive, or inconvenient

centralized (adj.) to bring (something) under the control of one authority

central planning (n.) a centrally planned economy is an economy where decisions on what to produce, how to produce and for whom are taken by the government. It is generally associated with a Communist economy.

centrifugal force (n.) the apparent force that draws a rotating body away from the center of rotation. It is caused by the inertia of the body

cerebral (adj.) related to the intellect

cerebral hemorrhage (n.) a spontaneous bleeding into the brain tissue, either spontaneously or from trauma

chafe (v.) to irritate or annoy; to wear or abrade by rubbing

chagrin (n.) a feeling of being frustrated or annoyed because of failure or disappointment

channel (n.) a pathway through which information is transmitted, the bed of a stream, river, or other waterway (v.) to direct

chaos (n.) absolute disorder

chaotic (adj.) a condition or place of great disorder or confusion

chaperone (n.) a person, especially an older or married woman, who accompanies a young unmarried woman, or a mixed sex group, in public

character assassination (n.) the malicious and unjustified harming of a person's good reputation

charismatic (adj.) possessing a compelling and charming personality or traits that are attractive and alluring to others

chastened (adj.) Corrected by punishment or reproof; taken to task

checks and balances (n.) Under the U.S. Constitution, a system under which three co-equal branches of government exert a control that no one branch becomes all powerful

cherished (tr. v.) treated with affection

cherubic (adj.) like an angel, shown as a beautiful young child with small wings and a round face and body

chicanery (n.) actions or statements that trick people into believing something that is not true

chide (v.) to voice disapproval

chimerical (adj.) created by or as if by a wildly fanciful imagination; highly improbable

chloroform (n.) a colorless, volatile, nonflammable, slightly water-soluble, pungent, sweet-tasting liquid used to anesthetize, make unconscious, or kill

choreography (n.) the arrangement of dances

chronic (adj.) lasting for a long period of time or marked by frequent recurrence

chronicle (v.) to record in a factual and detailed way

chronological (adj.) arranged in order of time

churlish (adj.) not polite, vulgar, surly, rude, devoid of civility

circuitous (adj.) roundabout, indirect

circumscribed (adj.) bounded or limited; confined to a limited space

circumspect (adj.) cautious

circumspection (n.) caution, prudence, discretion

circumvent (v.) to get around

cirrus (adj.) a high-altitude cloud composed of narrow bands or patches of thin, generally white, fleecy parts

citation (n.) the act of citing or quoting a reference to an authority or a precedent, particularly in scholarly writing

civilian (n.) a person who is not on active duty with a military, naval, police, or fire fighting organization

clandestine (adj.) secret, not disclosed

class structure (n.) the organization of classes within a society

class struggle (n.) under Marxist doctrine, the continual conflict between the capitalist and working classes for economic and political power

classical liberalism (n.) a political philosophy in which primary emphasis is placed on securing the freedom of the individual by limiting the power of the government.

claustrophobic (adj.) afraid of being in a small or enclosed space

clemency (n.) mercy, forgiveness

clergy (n.) members of Christian holy orders

clientele (n.) a body of customers or patrons; clients of a professional person or practice considered as a group

clique (n.) a small set or group , usually one that is snobbishly exclusive

cloistered (adj.) separated from the rest of the world

coalesce (v.) to fuse into a whole

coalition (n.) a group of people, groups, or countries who have joined together for a common purpose

cobbler (n.) a person who makes or repairs shoes

codger (n.) an odd or peculiar person,

coerce (v.) to make somebody do something by force or threat

cog (n.) one of a series of teeth, as on the rim of a wheel or gear, whose engagement transmits successive motive force to a corresponding wheel or gear.

cogent (adj.) intellectually convincing

cognitive (adj.) knowing, conscious

cognizant (adj.) aware, mindful

coherent (adj.) logically consistent, intelligible

coincidence (n.) a striking occurrence of two or more events at one time apparently by mere chance

coke (n.) the solid product resulting from the destructive distillation of coal in an oven or closed chamber or by imperfect combustion

collaboration (n.) the action of working with someone to produce or create something; traitorous cooperation with an enemy

collateral (adj.) secondary; (n.) security for a debt

collectivization (n.) the forced consolidation of privately held farms into group enterprises in a failed attempt to boost agricultural production, such as in the former Soviet Union

colloquial (adj.) characteristic of informal conversation

collusion (n.) secret agreement, conspiracy

colonnade (n.) a series of columns placed at regular intervals

combustion (n.) the act or process of burning

comedic (adj.) of, pertaining to, or of the nature of comedy

comely (adj.) pleasing and wholesome in appearance; attractive

command economics (n.) economic system where the government, rather than the free market, determines what goods should be produced, how much should be produced and the price at which the goods will be offered for sale

commence (v.) to begin

commensurate (adj.) corresponding in size or amount

commissar (n.) the head of any of the major governmental divisions of the U.S.S.R.; called *minister* since 1946

commodious (adj.) roomy

commotion (n.) an agitated disturbance; a hubbub

communism (n.) a theory or system of social organization in which all property is held in common or by the state; during the 20th century, more than 100 million died under communist regimes

compassion (n.) a feeling of wanting to help someone who is sick, hungry, in trouble, etc.

compatriot (n.) a fellow countryman; a colleague or companion; peer

compelling (adj.) forceful, demanding attention

compensate (v.) to make an appropriate payment for something

compile (v.) to gather from different sources and put together in an orderly form; to organize

complacent (adj.) self-satisfied ignorance of danger

complement (v.) to complete, make perfect

compliant (adj.) ready to adapt oneself to another's wishes

complicit (adj.) being an accomplice in a wrongful act

compliment (n.) an expression of esteem or approval

comprehend (v.) to understand something, such as a difficult or complex subject

comprehensive (adj.) including everything, complete

compromise (v.) an endangering, especially of reputation; exposure to danger, suspicion, etc.; (n.) a settlement of differences by mutual concessions

compunction (n.) distress caused by feeling guilty

concede (v.) to accept as valid

conception (n.) a complex product of abstract or reflective thinking; an idea

concertmistress (n.) a female leader of the first violins in a symphony orchestra, who is usually also the assistant to the conductor; feminine of concertmaster.

concession (n.) an acknowledgment or admission

conciliatory (adj.) friendly, agreeable

concise (adj.) brief and direct in expression

concoct (v.) to fabricate, make up

concomitant (adj.) naturally accompanying or associated

condescension (n.) the attitude or behavior of people who believe they are more intelligent or better than other people

condiments (n.) something used to give a special flavor to food, as mustard, ketchup, salt, or spices

conduit (n.) a pipe or channel through which something passes; a channel through which anything is conveyed

confection (n.) a sweet, fancy food

confederate (n.) a member of a confederacy; an ally; one who assists in a plot; an accomplice

confer (v.) have discussions; exchange opinions; to bestow a title or honor

confidant (n.) a person entrusted with secrets

confinement (n.) the state of being confined; to shut or keep in, especially to imprison

confiscate (v.) to seize by or as if by authority; seized by a government; appropriated

conflagration (n.) great fire

conflate (v.) combine (two or more sets of information, texts, ideas, etc.) into one

confluence (n.) a gathering together

confound (v.) to frustrate, confuse

confrontation (n.) a situation in which people, groups, etc., fight, oppose, or challenge each other in an angry way

conglomeration (n.) a number of different things, parts or items that are grouped together; collection.

congregation (n.) a gathering of people, especially for religious services

congruity (n.) the quality of being in agreement

conjecture (n.) an opinion or conclusion formed on the basis of incomplete information

conjunction (n.) the state of being joined; a joint or simultaneous occurrence; concurrence

conk out (v.) to stop operating or functioning

connoisseur (n.) a person who, thorough study and interest, has a fine appreciation for something

conscientious (adj.) according to conscience, scrupulous, showing thought and care

conscription (n.) compulsory enrollment of persons for military or naval service; draft

consecrate (v.) to dedicate something to a holy purpose

conservative (n.) holding to traditional attitudes and values and cautious about change or innovation, typically in relation to politics or religion

consolation (n.) an act of comforting

consonant (adj.) in harmony

consort (v.) to associate; keep company

conspicuous (adj.) obvious, easy to see

conspiracy (n.) a planning and acting together secretly, esp. for an unlawful or harmful purpose, such as murder or treason

consternation (n.) a sudden and alarming amazement that results in confusion and dismay

constituent (n.) an essential part

constituent assembly (n.) The All Russian Constituent Assembly was a constitutional body convened in Russia after the October Revolution of 1917. It is generally recognized as the first democratically elected legislative body of any kind in Russian history.

constrain (v.) to forcibly restrict

consul/ar (n.) a government official whose job is to live in a foreign country and protect and help the citizens of his or her own country who are traveling, living, or doing business

consummate (v.) to complete a deal; to bring to completion or perfection; (adj.) complete or perfect; supremely skilled; superb

contemplate (v.) observe thoughtfully, reflect upon

contemporaneous (adj.) existing during the same time

contempt (n.) an intense feeling or attitude of regarding someone or something as inferior, base, or worthless; disdain

contender (n.) a person who tries to win something in a contest, especially a person who has a good chance of winning

contentious (adj.) having a tendency to quarrel or dispute

context (n.) the circumstances that form the setting for an event, statement, or idea, and in terms of which it can be fully understood and assessed

contradict (v.) to say the opposite of (something that someone else has said) : to deny the truth of (something)

contradiction (n.) a logical incompatibility between two or more propositions; assertion of the contrary or opposite; denial, inconsistency

contrite (adj.) penitent, eager to be forgiven

conundrum (n.) puzzle, problem

convalescence (n.) a period of recuperation from injury or sickness

convene (v.) to call together

convention (n.) an assembly of people; (n.) a rule, custom

convergence (n.) a coming together

conversant (adj.) familiar by use or study

conversational (adj.) an informal exchange or presentation of thoughts and feelings

convivial (adj.) characterized by feasting, drinking, merriment

convoluted (adj.) intricate, complicated

cordial (adj.) warm, affectionate

cordon (n.) a line of people, military posts, or ships stationed around an area to enclose or guard it

coronation (n.) the act of crowning or made ruler

corpulence (adj.) extreme fatness

corroborate (v.) to support with evidence

corrosive (adj.) having the tendency to erode or eat away

corrupted (adj.) debased in character; depraved; perverted; wicked; evil

cosmopolitan (adj.) sophisticated, worldly

coterie (n.) a small group of people who are interested in the same thing and are generally exclusive

counsel (n.) legal representation; advice, especially that given formally

countenance (n.) look, expression; support of encouragement, sanction

countermeasure (n.) an action or device that is intended to stop or prevent something bad or dangerous

counter-offensive (n.) an attack made in response to one from an enemy, typically on a large scale or for a prolonged period

counter-revolutionary (n.) one opposes a revolution or revolutionary government; a person who advocates or engages in a counter-revolution

coup (n.) a brilliant, unexpected act; (n.) the overthrow of a government and assumption of authority

courier (n.) a messenger, especially one on official diplomatic business; a spy carrying secret information

covet (v.) to desire enviously

covert (adj.) secretly engaged in

credentials (n.) documents which show that a person is qualified to do a particular job

credible (adj.) capable of being believed or accepted; plausible

credulity (n.) readiness to believe

credulous (adj.) willing to believe or trust too readily, especially without proper or adequate evidence; gullible

crescendo (n.) a steady increase in intensity or volume

criteria (n.) standards by which something is judged

cross-examine (v.) to examine by questions intended to check a previous examination; examine closely or minutely. 2. Law: to examine (a witness called by the opposing side), as for the purpose of discrediting the witness's testimony.

crude (adj.) Lacking tact, taste, sophistication or subtlety; blunt or offensive; rough

cryptic (adj.) difficult to understand; having or seeming to have a hidden meaning

cryptology (n.) science concerned with data communication and storage in secure and usually secret form, or secret codes

crystallize (v.) to take definite form or shape

cuisine (n.) a characteristic style of cooking practices and traditions, often associated with a specific culture

culinary (adj.) of or relating to a kitchen or to cookery

cull (v.) to pick out from others, to select

culmination (n.) the climax toward which something progresses

culpable (adj.) deserving blame

cult (n.) a group of people with extreme dedication to a certain leader or set of beliefs

cultivate (v.) to nurture, improve, refine

cultural literacy (n.) from a literary point of view, it is about understanding the meaning of a text based on a background of common knowledge that enables one to make sense of what is read

cunning (adj.) sly, clever at being deceitful

cupidity (n.) greed, strong desire

curry (v.) to seek or gain favor by fawning or flattery

cursive (n.) flowing often with the strokes of successive characters joined and the angles rounded; also known as handwriting or longhand.

cursory (adj.) brief to the point of being superficial

curt (adj.) rudely brief or abrupt, as in speech or manner

cynical (adj.) selfish and dishonest in a way that shows no concern about treating other people fairly

cynicism (n.) an inclination to believe that people are motivated purely by self-interest; skepticism

D

damask (n.) a rich patterned fabric of cotton, linen, silk, or wool

damper (n.) a person or thing that has a depressing, subduing, or inhibiting effect

daunting (adj.) intimidating, causing one to lose courage

davenport (n.) a large sofa, especially a formal one, often convertible into a bed

dazzle (v.) to amaze, overwhelm, or bewilder with spectacular display

dearth (n.) a lack, scarcity

debacle (n.) a disastrous failure, disruption

debauchery (n.) corruption by means of sensual pleasures

debilitated (adj.) to make (someone or something) weak; to reduce the strength of (someone or something)

debunk (v.) to expose the falseness of something

debut (n.) the first appearance of something, as a new product; a first public appearance on a stage, on television, etc.

decapitate (v.) to separate the head from the body

deception (n.) the act of deceiving or tricking, duplicity

decipher (v.) to change from code into ordinary language, to translate

decisive (adj.) very clear and obvious; causing something to end in a particular way

decorous (adj.) socially proper, appropriate

decry (v.) to criticize openly

deduce (v.) to derive as a conclusion from something known or assumed; infer

deemed (v.) to form or have an opinion; judge; think

defamatory (adj.) harmful toward another's reputation

defect (v.) abandon one's country or cause in favor of an opposing one

defector (n.) a person who gives up allegiance to one state in exchange for allegiance to another

defer (v.) to postpone something; to yield to another's wisdom

deference (n.) courteous regard for people's feelings

deferential (adj.) showing respect for another's authority

deficient (adj.) lacking some element or characteristic; defective

defile (v.) to make unclean, impure

definitive (adj.) authoritative and complete; precisely defined or explicit

deft/ly (adj./adv.) skillful, capable

defunct (adj.) no longer used or existing

degenerate (v.) having lost the physical, mental, or moral qualities considered normal and desirable; showing evidence of decline; decay

delegate (v.) to hand over responsibility for something

deleterious (adj.) harmful

deliberation (n.) careful thought or discussion done in order to make a decision

delicacies (n.) something delightful or pleasing, especially a choice food considered with regard to its rarity, costliness, or the like

delineate (v.) to describe, outline, shed light on

deluded (adj.) misled; deceived

demagogic (adj.) of, or characteristic of a demagogue, that is, a politician who seeks support by appealing to popular desires and prejudices rather than by using rational argument

demarcation (n.) the marking of boundaries or categories

demean (v.) to lower the status or stature of something

demeanor (n.) conduct, behavior

demise (n.) the end of existence or activity; death

democratic socialism (n.) a political ideology advocating a democratic political system alongside a socialist economic system, involving a combination of political democracy with social ownership of the means of production. Although sometimes used synonymously with "socialism", the adjective "democratic" is often added to distinguish itself from the Marxist–Leninist brand of socialism, which is widely viewed as being non-democratic.

demonize (v.) to turn into a demon or make demonlike, often for nefarious aims

demoralize (v.) to undermine the confidence or morale of; dishearten

demure (adj.) quiet, modest, reserved

denigrate (v.) to belittle, diminish the opinion of

denounce (v.) to criticize publicly

denunciation (n.) an act or instance of denouncing; public censure or condemnation

dependency (n.) Something dependent or subordinate; the quality of being dependent

deployed (v.) to spread out (troops) so as to form an extended front or line; to arrange in a position of readiness

deportation (n.) the expulsion of a person or group of people from a place or country

deportment (n.) the way that a person behaves, stands, and moves especially in a formal situation

depose (v.) to remove from office or power; to dethrone

depravity (n.) wickedness

deprecated (v.) To express disapproval of; deplore; to belittle; top disparage

deprivation (n.) the condition of being deprived, or not having something, such as food or shelter; privation; denial

deride (v.) to laugh at mockingly, scorn

derivative (adj.) taken directly from a source, unoriginal

desecrate (v.) to violate the sacredness of a thing or place

desolate (adj.) deserted, dreary, lifeless

despair (n.) loss all hope; overcome by a sense of futility or defeat

despot (n.) one who has total power and rules brutally

destitute (adj.) impoverished, utterly lacking

detection (n.) the act or process of discovering, finding, or noticing something

detention (n.) the act of detaining, confinement, temporary custody

deteriorate (v.) to become progressively worse

devastated (v.) to bring to ruin or desolation by violent action; to reduce to chaos and disorder, as by war or natural disaster

devious (adj.) not straightforward, deceitful

devoid (adj.) empty, void, or destitute; lacking

devolve (v.) to gradually go from an advanced state to a less advanced state

devour (v.) to eat voraciously, to consume greedily

devout (adj.) devoted to divine worship or service; pious; religious

dexterous (adj.) skillful in the use of the hands; done with skill or adroitness

dialect (n.) a variation of a language

dialectical materialism (n.) the Marxist interpretation of reality that views matter as the sole subject of change and all change as the product of a constant conflict between opposites arising from the internal contradictions inherent in all events, ideas, and movements.

dichotomy (n.) division into two mutually exclusive, opposed, or contradictory groups; division into two parts, kinds, etc.

dictator (n.) a ruler who assumes sole and absolute power (sometimes but not always with military control

dictatorial (adj.) of, relating to, or characteristic of a dictator or dictatorship; autocratic; domineering

didactic (adj.) intended for instruction; instructive

diffident (adj.) timid, lacking self-confidence

digress (v.) to stray from a topic in writing, speaking, or thinking; to go off on a tangent

dilapidated (adj.) falling to pieces, broken down, in disrepair

dilatory (adj.) inclined to waste time and be habitually late

dilemma (n.) a situation in which none must choose between equally unpleasant or unfavorable options

dilettante (n.) an amateur who engages in any activity without serious intentions, a dabbler

diligent (adj.) showing care in doing one's work

diminish/diminishing (v.) to make smaller or less; to detract from the authority, reputation, or prestige of

diminutive (adj.) small or miniature

din (n.) continuous, loud or annoying sound or uproar

diplomatic immunity (n.) the exemption from taxation and ordinary processes of law afforded to diplomatic personnel in a foreign country

directive (n.) an order or instruction, especially from an authority

dirge (n.) a mournful song, especially for a funeral

disaffected (adj.) rebellious, resentful of authority

disavow (v.) to deny knowledge of or responsibility for

discern (v.) to perceive, detect

discerning (adj.) demonstrating keen insight and good judgment

disconcerting (adj.) upsetting, frustrating

disciples (n.) those who accept and help to spread the teachings of a famous person; followers

disclose (v.) to reveal, make public

disconcerting (adj.) disturbing to one's composure or self-possession; upsetting, discomfiting; perplexing

discourse (n.) conversation, formal or orderly speech

discredit (v.) harm the good reputation of

discreet (adj.) cautious in one's speech or actions, tactful

discretion (n.) the quality of being reserved in speech or action; good judgment

discriminating (adj.) characterized by selective judgment, especially in matters of taste or judgment, sophisticated

discrimination (n.) an act or instance of discriminating, or of making a distinction; treatment or consideration of, or making a distinction in favor of or against, a person or thing based on the group, class, or category to which that person or thing belongs rather than on individual merit

disdain 1. (v.) to scorn, hold in low esteem; (n.) scorn, low esteem

disembark (v.) to get out of a vehicle or craft; to leave a ship, airplane, or train

disgorge (v.) to discharge or pour forth contents; To discharge violently; spew

disgruntled (adj.) displeased and discontented; sulky; peevish

disingenuous (adj.) characterized by giving a false appearance of honesty; deceptive

disgruntled (adj.) upset, not content

disheartened (adj.) feeling a loss of spirit or morale

disillusioned (adj.) having lost one's ideals, illusions, or false ideas about someone or something; disenchanted

disintegrate (v.) to break apart into many small parts or pieces

dismissive (adj.) showing indifference or disregard

disparage (v.) to criticize or speak ill of

disparate (adj.) sharply differing, containing sharply contrasting elements

disparity (n.) the condition of being unequal, a noticeable difference in age, income or treatment

dispatch (v.) to send off to accomplish a duty; to destroy; a written message, particularly an official communication, sent with speed

dispel (v.) to remove, to drive away or scatter

dispensary (n.) a place where medicine or minor medical treatment is given

disperse (v.) to scatter, cause to scatter

dispirited (adj.) affected or marked by low spirits; dejected

displaced (adj.) Moved or shifted from the usual place or position, especially forced to leave a homeland

disposition (n.) final settlement of a matter; bestowal, as by gift or sale

disrepute (n.) a state of being held in low regard

disrupt (v.) interrupt or upset, to cause disorder

disseminate (v.) to spread widely

dissent (v.) to disagree; (n.) the act of disagreeing

dissidents (n.) those who disagree or dissent, particular with regard to the government

dissipate 1. (v.) to disappear, cause to disappear; (v.) to waste

dissonance (n.) lack of harmony or consistency

dissuade (v.) to persuade someone not to do something

distinguish (v.) to mark off as different, to perceive clearly by sight or other sense; to discern

distortion (n.) something that has been presented in a way that makes it look different from the truth or in a way that makes it look different from normal

distraught (adj.) agitated with doubt or mental conflict or pain

distress (n.) extreme anxiety, sorrow, or pain

dither (v.) to be indecisive

diverse (adj.) of various kinds or forms

divine (adj.) godly, exceedingly wonderful

divisive (adj.) causing dissent, discord

divulge (v.) to reveal something secret

docile (adj.) easily taught or trained

doctor (v.) to falsify or change in such a way as to make favorable to oneself

doctorate (n.) the highest degree awarded by a university

doctrine (n.) a theory or set of principles actively taught and promoted by those who believe it

documentation (n.) the provision of documents or published information as proof or evidence

dogged (adj.) refusing to give up despite difficulties

dogma (n.) a belief or set of beliefs that is accepted by the members of a group without being questioned or doubted

dogmatic (adj.) aggressively and arrogantly certain about unproved principles

domestic (adj.) of or pertaining to the home, the household, household affairs, or the family; a household servant; the internal affairs of a home country

dominant (adj.) ruling, governing, or controlling; having or exerting authority or influence; occupying or being in a commanding or elevated position; predominant; main; chief

dormant (adj.) sleeping, temporarily inactive

dossier (n.) a collection of papers giving detailed information about a particular person or subject

double agent (n.) a person pretending to work as a spy for one government while actually working as a spy for another government

double stops (n.) the technique of playing two notes simultaneously on a bowed stringed instrument such as a violin, a viola, a cello, or a double bass

doubletalk (n.) deliberately evasive or ambiguous language

dour (adj.) stern, joyless

down-at-the-heel (adj.) looking or seeming cheap, poor, dirty or worn; shabby

drab (adj.) dull; cheerless; lacking in spirit, brightness, etc.

draconian (adj.) cruel, severe; of or relating to Draco and the harsh laws imposed by him

dross (n.) waste matter, refuse; a waste product taken off molten metal during smelting

drove (n.) a large group of people or animals that move or act together

drowsiness (n.) sleepiness

dry goods (n.) textile fabrics and related articles of trade, in distinction from groceries, hardware, etc.

dubious (adj.) doubtful, of uncertain quality

dumbfounded (adj.) to fill with astonishment and perplexity; confound

dupe (n.) a victim of deception, for example. American liberals who were deceived by communist propaganda

duplicity (n.) crafty dishonesty

duration (n.) continuance in time; the time during which something exists or lasts

duress (n.) hardship, threat

dynamic (adj.) actively changing

E

earnest (adj.) serious in intention, purpose, or effort; showing depth and sincerity of feeling

eau de Cologne (n.) a perfume originating near Cologne, Germany; a mildly perfumed toilet water

ebb (v.) a flowing backward or away; decline or decay

ebullient (adj.) extremely lively, enthusiastic

eccentric (adj.) deviating from conventional or accepted usage or conduct especially in odd or whimsical ways

ecclesiastical (adj.) of or pertaining to the church or the clergy; churchly; clerical; not secular

echelon (n.) a level of command, authority, or rank

eclectic (adj.) consisting of a diverse variety of elements

economical (adj.) marked by careful, efficient, and prudent use of resources; thrifty

ecstatic (adj.) intensely and overpoweringly happy

edict (n.) an order, decree

edifice (n.) building, especially a large or elaborate on

edifying (adj.) morally, spiritually or educationally instructive

eerie/eerily (adj./adv.) Inspiring inexplicable fear, dread, or uneasiness; strange and frightening

efface (v.) to wipe out, obliterate, rub away

effectuate (v.) to put into force or operation

effrontery (n.) impudence, nerve, insolence

effusive (adj.) gushing with unrestrained enthusiasm

egalitarian (adj.) characterized by belief in the equality of all people, especially in political, economic, or social life

egghead (n.) An intellectual, a highbrow, a highly educated person who may not know much about real life

ego (n.) an exaggerated sense of self-importance; conceit

egregious (adj.) extremely bad

elaborate (adj.) complex, detailed, intricate

elapse (v.) to pass or slip by (as in time)

elated (adj.) overjoyed, thrilled

electronic surveillance (n.) surveillance or the gathering of information by surreptitious use of electronic devices, as in crime detection or espionage

elicit (v.) to bring forth, draw out, evoke

elite (n.) the choice or best part of a body or class of persons

elitist (n.) a person or class of persons) considered superior by others or by themselves, as in intellect, talent, power, wealth, or position in society

elocution (n.) the study of how to speak clearly and in a way that is effective and socially acceptable

eloquent (adj.) expressive, articulate, moving

elucidate (v.) to make lucid or clear; throw light upon; explain

elude (v.) to evade, escape

elusive (adj.) cleverly or skillfully evasive

emaciated (adj.) very thin, enfeebled looking

emanating (v.) to flow out of, issue, or proceed, as from a source or origin; come forth; originate

emasculate (v.) to deprive of strength or vigor; weaken

embedded (v.) contained within, enclosed firmly in a surrounding mass

embellish/ing (v.) to enhance, to make more attractive with ornamentation

embezzle (v.) to steal money by falsifying records

embroilment (n.) to bring into discord or conflict; involve in contention or strife

emigrate (v.) to leave one country or region to settle in another; migrate

eminent (adj.) distinguished, prominent, famous; (adj.) conspicuous

eminent domain (n.) a right of a government to take private property for public use by virtue of the superior dominion of the sovereign power over all lands within its jurisdiction

emit (v.) to give out as sound; utter; to voice; express

emollient (adj.) soothing to the skin

empathy (n.) sensitivity to another's feelings as if they were one's own

emphatically (adv.) expressed or performed with emphasis; forceful and definite in expression or action

empirical (adj.) based on observation or experience; capable of being proved or disproved by experiment

emporium (n.) a store or shop; a store carrying many different kinds of merchandise

emulate (v.) to imitate

enamor (v.) to fill with love, fascinate, usually used in passive form followed by "of" or "with"

encapsulated (adj.) summed up in a short or concise form; condensed; abridged

enclave (n.) a country, or especially, an outlying portion of a country, entirely or mostly surrounded by the territory of another country; any small, distinct area or group enclosed or isolated within a larger one

encomium (n.) a formal expression of high praise; eulogy

encompass (v.) to include (something) as a part, to surround

encore (n.) the audience's demand for a repeat performance; also the artist's performance in response to that demand

encyclopedic (adj.) relating to all branches of knowledge

endeavoring (v.) to make a serious attempt or effort

endurance (n.) the ability to do something difficult or deal with pain or suffering for a long time

enervated (v.) exhausted, lacking physical, mental, or moral vigor

enforcer (n.) one who compels obedience or observance

enfranchise (v.) to grant the vote to

engender (v.) to bring about, create, generate

engrossed (adj.) to have absorbed the complete attention or interest of, fascinated

enigmatic (adj.) mystifying, cryptic

enlightening (adj.) making the truth or nature of something clear, freed from ignorance or prejudice, educational

enmity (n.) ill will, hatred, hostility

ennui (n.) boredom, weariness

enrapture (v.) give intense pleasure or joy to

ensconce (v.) establish or settle (someone) in a comfortable, safe, or secret place

ensemble (n.) all the parts of a thing taken together, so that each part is considered only in relation to the whole

ensnare (v.) to catch (an animal or person) in a trap or in a place from which there is no escape

ensued (v.) to follow in order, to come afterward

entail (v.) to include as a necessary step

enthrall (v.) to charm, hold spellbound

enticing (adj.) highly attractive and able to arouse hope or desire

entomology (n.) the scientific study of insects, a branch of arthropodology, which in turn is a branch of zoology

entourage (n.) a group of people who go with and assist an important person

entreat (v.) to ask (someone) in a serious and emotional way

entrenched (adj.) solidly established, dug in, strongly ingrained

enumerate (v.) to list one after another, court off, name individually

envelope (v.) to surround; something that envelops; a wrapper, or surrounding cover.

environs (n.) the area that is around a place (such as a city)

envoy (n.) a diplomatic agent; any accredited messenger or representative

ephemeral (adj.) short-lived, fleeting

epic (adj.) significant, consequential; pertaining to or having the qualities of a long, poem, novel or play, usually written in a dignified or elevated style, celebrating heroes and heroic deeds

epiphany (n.) a sudden, intuitive perception of or insight into the reality or essential meaning of something, usually initiated by some simple, or commonplace experience

epistolary (adj.) relating to or contained in letters

epitome (n.) a perfect example, embodiment

epitomize (v.) to serve as the typical or ideal example of

equilibrium (n.) mental or emotional balance; equanimity

equivalent (n.) equal in value, amount, function, meaning, etc.

equivocate (v.) to use ambiguous or unclear expressions, usually to avoid commitment or in order to mislead; prevaricate or hedge

eradicate (v.) to remove (something) completely : to eliminate or destroy

erratic (adj.) not regular or consistent, odd or peculiar

erroneous/ly (adj./adv.) incorrect, mistaken, wrong

erstwhile (adj.) former; one-time; long ago

erudite (adj.) learned

eschew (v.) to shun, avoid

esoteric (adj.) understood by only a select few, profound

espionage (n.) the practice of spying on others, the systematic use of spies by a government to discover secrets of other nations

espouse (v.) to take up as a cause, support

estrange (v.) to cause someone to be no longer friendly or close to another person or group

eternity (n.) infinite time; duration without beginning or end

ether (n.) a hypothetical substance supposed to occupy all space, postulated to account for the propagation of electromagnetic radiation through space; the upper regions of space; the clear sky; the heavens

ethereal (adj.) heavenly, exceptionally delicate or refined

ethnic (adj.) pertaining to or characteristic of a people, especially a group (ethnic group) sharing a common and distinctive culture, religion, language, or the like

ethos (n.) the fundamental character or spirit of a culture; the underlying sentiment that informs the beliefs, customs, or practices of a group or society; dominant assumptions of a people or period

etymology (n.) the history of words, their origin and development

eulogy (n.) a speech or writing in praise of a person or thing, especially a set oration in honor of a deceased person

euphemism (n.) the substitution of a mild, indirect, or vague expression for one thought to be offensive, harsh, or blunt

euphoria (n.) the state of being uplifted or elated

euphoric (adj.) elated, uplifted

evacuation (n.) the act of evacuating or the condition of being evacuated, or moved from one place to another, chiefly to one safer and more secure

evanescent (adj.) fleeting, momentary

evangelist (n.) an occasional preacher, sometimes itinerant and often preaching at meetings in the open air; a zealous advocate of a cause

evaporated (v.) to disappear; vanish; fade

evasive (adj.) meaning to evade, not forthright, indirect, intentionally vague

evenhanded (adj.) impartial, equitable

evince (v.) to show, reveal

evocative (adj.) characterized by using the power of imagination to call forth a memory

exacerbate (v.) to make more violent, intense

exalt (v.) to glorify, praise

excavate (v.) to dig out of the ground and remove

exceptional (adj.) extraordinary, outstanding

excessive (adj.) going beyond what is usual, normal, or proper

exclusive (adj.) admitting only certain people as friends, associates, or members, a select group

excruciating (adj.) extremely painful; causing intense suffering; unbearably distressing; torturing

excursion (n.) a trip or outing

execrable (adj.) loathsome, detestable

exemplary (adj.) worthy to serve as a model

exert (v.) to put forth or bring to bear, to bring pressure

exhaustive (adj.) careful and thorough, comprehensive

exhilaration (n.) the feeling or the state of being exhilarated, joyous, animated

exhort (v.) to urge, prod, spur

exhorting (v.) urging, advising, or cautioning earnestly; admonishing

existential (adj.) pertaining to existence; in philosophy, the fundamental doctrine that existence precedes essence; involving a person's or entity's very existence

exonerate (v.) to free from guilt or blame, exculpate

exorbitant (adj.) excessive; expensive

exotic (adj.) unfamiliar, strikingly different, from faraway places of the world, alien

expanse (n.) a wide and open space

expansive (adj.) having a wide range or extent; comprehensive; extensive

expedient (adj.) advisable, advantageous, serving one's self-interest

expertise (n.) specialized skill or knowledge

expiate (v.) to make amends for, atone

explicate (v.) to make plain or clear; explain; interpret.

explicit (adj.) clearly defined, definite, precise

exploit (v.) to use productively or to greatest advantage, even cynically; (n) a bold or daring feat

expose (v.) to reveal; to uncover

exposé (n.) a formal statement of facts; an exposure of something discreditable

expound (v.) to explain by giving detail, to express a point of view

express (train) (n.) sometimes referred to as "fast trains," usually meaning "faster than some other trains on the line in question, with more limited station stops

expunge (v.) to obliterate, eradicate

extant (adj.) existing, not destroyed or lost

extemporaneously (adv.) done, spoken, performed without advance preparation; impromptu

exterminate (v.) to destroy or kill (a group of animals, people, etc.) completely

extol (v.) to praise, revere

extract (v.) to remove with effort, to obtain despite resistance

extraction (n.) descent or lineage

extracurricular (adj.) not part of the regular course of study of a school or college

extravagant (adj.) excessive, immoderate, extremely wasteful

extricate (v.) to disentangle; to free or remove from an entanglement or difficulty

exuberant (adj.) effusively and almost uninhibitedly enthusiastic; lavishly abundant

exude (v.) to project or display conspicuously or abundantly; to radiate

F

façade (n.) the wall of a building; a deceptive appearance or attitude

facetious (adj.) meant to be humorous or funny; not serious

facile (adj.) easy, requiring little effort; (adj.) superficial, achieved with minimal thought or care, insincere

facilitate (v.) to make (something) easier

faculties (n.) powers or capabilities of the mind or body, either natural or acquired

fallacious (adj.) incorrect, misleading

familial (adj.) of or having to do with the family; hereditary

fanatical (adj.) excessively enthusiastic or devoted

fascism (n.) a governmental system where all political and economic power is centralized in the state and no dissent is tolerated

fashion (v.) to give something shape or form; (n.) a prevailing custom or style of dress, etiquette, socializing, etc.

fastidious (adj.) meticulous, demanding, having high and often unattainable standards

fatal (adj.) causing death; leading to failure or disaster

fatherland (n.) the nation of one's "fathers", "forefathers" or "patriarchs." It can be viewed as a nationalist concept, insofar as it relates to nations

fathom (v.) to understand, comprehend; (n.) a unit of length equal to six feet (1.83 meters) used especially for measuring the depth of water

faux (adj.) imitation, false

faux pas (n.) a slip or blunder in etiquette, manners, or conduct; an embarrassing social blunder or indiscretion

faze (v.) to disturb the composure of; upset

feasible (adj.) capable of being done or carried out

federalism (n.) a system of the government in which sovereignty is constitutionally divided between a central governing authority and constituent political units (like states or provinces)

federation (n.) a federated body formed by a number of nations, states, societies, unions, etc., each retaining control of its own internal affairs

feign (v.) pretend, fake, make believe

felicitous 1. (adj.) well suited, apt; (adj.) delightful, pleasing

fence (v.) to receive or sell stolen goods; (n.) one who engages in such activity

ferment (n.) to be in a state of agitation or intense activity

ferocity (n.) the state or quality of being ferocious; fierceness

fertile (adj.) productive, able to produce offspring, seeds, fruit, etc.

fervent (adj.) ardent, passionate

fervor (n.) a strong feeling of excitement and enthusiasm

festooned (adj.) decorated with strings or chains of flowers, foliage, ribbon, etc.

fiasco (n.) a total and ignominious failure

fiat (n.) an authoritative decree, sanction, or order: a royal fiat.

fidelity (n.) loyalty, devotion

figurative (adj.) symbolic

fiscal stimulus (n.) the use of government revenue collection (mainly taxes) and expenditure (spending) to influence the economy

fission (n.) the act of cleaving or splitting into parts; in physics, the splitting of the nucleus of an atom into nuclei of lighter atoms, accompanied by the release of energy

fission bomb (n.) atomic bomb; an explosive device that derives its destructive force from nuclear reactions, either fission or a combination of fission and fusion

flabbergasted (adj.) astounded

flag (v.) to experience a diminishing level of energy or strength, to submit or surrender

flagrant (adj.) offensive, egregious

flair (n.) a natural talent, aptitude, or ability; bent; knack

flamboyant (adj.) exaggerated, show, designed to attract attention

flattery (n.) excessive, insincere praise

flaw (n.) an imperfection or weakness and especially one that detracts from the whole or hinders effectiveness

fleeting (adj.) passing swiftly; vanishing quickly; transient

flippant (adj.) frivolously disrespectful, or lacking in seriousness; characterized by levity

florid (adj.) very fancy or too fancy, flowery

flout (v.) to disregard or disobey openly

fluency (n.) the ability to speak easily and smoothly, especially the ability to speak a foreign language easily and effectively

flummoxed (adj.) bewildered or perplexed

flustered (v.) nervous or upset

fodder (n.) feed for livestock, especially coarsely chopped hay or straw; a consumable, often inferior item or resource that is in demand and usually abundant supply

foil (v.) to thwart, frustrate, defeat

foist (v.) impose an unwelcome or unnecessary person or thing on

foment (v.) to promote the growth or development of

foolhardy (adj.) bold in a foolish and reckless manner

footnotes (n.) an explanatory or documenting note or comment at the bottom of a page, referring to a specific part of the text on the page, or citing sources

forage (v.) to graze, rummage for food

forbearance (n.) patience, restraint, toleration

forbidding (adj.) grim, sinister, menacing

foreboding (adj.) a feeling that something bad is going to happen

foreclose (v.) to hinder or prevent

foreign policy (n.) general objectives that guide the activities and relationships of one state in its interactions with other states

forestall (v.) to prevent, thwart, delay

forgery (n.) the act or legal offense of imitating or counterfeiting documents, signatures, works of art, etc. to deceive

forlorn (adj.) lonely, abandoned, hopeless

formidable (adj.) inspiring fear, dread or amazement; awesome

formulate (v.) to devise or invent; to express in systematic terms or concepts

forsake (v.) to give up, renounce

forthright (adj.) going straight to the point without hesitation

fortitude (n.) mental and emotional strength in facing difficulty, adversity, danger, or temptation; strength, guts

fortuitous (adj.) happening by chance, often lucky or fortunate

forum (n.) a medium for lecture or discussion

foster (v.) to stimulate, promote, encourage

foundry (n.) a building or factory where metals are produced

fractious (adj.) troublesome or irritable

frank (adj.) candid, open and honest

fraternal (adj.) of or relating to brothers; Showing comradeship; brotherly

fraught (adj.) filled or accompanied with

frayed (adj.) worn, tattered

frenetic (adj.) frenzied, hectic, frantic

frieze (n.) a sculptured or richly ornamented band (as on a building or piece of furniture)

frivolous (adj.) of little importance, trifling

frostbite (n.) a condition in which part of your body (such as your fingers or toes) freezes or almost freezes

frugal (adj.) thrifty, economical

fruitless (adj.) unsuccessful, useless, producing nothing

frustrate (v.) to make (plans, efforts, etc.) worthless or of no avail; defeat; nullify

fumigating (v.) to completely fill an area with gaseous pesticides to suffocate or poison the pests within

fundamental (adj.) serving as an original or generating source; primary; basic

funereal (adj.) of or suitable for a funeral; mournful; gloomy

furnish (v.) to provide something that is needed or demanded

furtive (adj.) secretive, sly

fuselage (n.) the framework of the body of an airplane

futile (adj.) of no use, ineffective, pointless

G

gallivanting (v.) to travel around for pleasure; to travel around with no purpose except enjoyment

galvanize (v.) to rouse to action, excite

gambit (n.) something done or said in order to gain an advantage or to produce a desired result

gambol (v.) to leap about playfully; frolic.

gang-tackle (n.) to bring down (a ball carrier in football) with several tacklers

gantry crane (n.) a large crane mounted on a platform that usually runs back and forth on parallel tracks astride the work area

garish (adj.) gaudy, in bad taste

garrulous (adj.) talkative, wordy

gauge (v.) measure, determine the exact dimensions, capacity, quantity, or force of; appraise

gauntlet (n.) an open challenge (as to combat); a glove worn with medieval armor

genocidal (adj.) characterized by the deliberate and systematic destruction, in whole or in part, of an ethnic, racial, religious, or national group

genre (n.) genus, sort, kind, style

genteel (adj.) elegant, courteous, refined

Gentile (n.) a person of a non-Jewish nation or of non-Jewish faith, especially a Christian as distinguished from a Jew

geometry (n.) a branch of mathematics concerned with questions of shape, size, relative position of figures, and the properties of space

ghetto (n.) a usually poor section of a city inhabited primarily by people of the same race, religion, or social background, often because of discrimination; an often walled quarter in a European city to which Jews were restricted beginning in the Middle Ages

glean (v.) to gather information or material bit by bit

glum (adj.) gloomy, moody, dejected

gluttony (n.) overindulgence in food or drink

goad (v.) to urge, spur, incite to action

godsend (n.) an unexpected thing or event that is particularly welcome and timely, as if sent by God

gothic (adj.) a style of architecture originating in France and spreading over western Europe from the 12th to the 16th centuries, and characterized by soaring heights, pointed arches, ribbed vaulting, and flying buttresses

gourmand (n.) someone fond of eating and drinking

gout (n.) a form of acute arthritis that causes severe pain and swelling in the joints

gramophone (n.) a phonograph, device that was most commonly used for playing sound recordings

grandeur (n.) magnificence, splendor

grandiloquence (n.) lofty, pompous language

grandiose (adj.) on a magnificent or exaggerated scale

grand larceny (n.) larceny in which the value of the goods taken is above a certain legally specified amount

grapple (v.) to engage in a struggle at close quarters, wrestle, vie

gratified (v.) to please or satisfy; to give what is desired to; indulge

gratuitous (adj.) uncalled for, unwarranted

gravely (adv.) to a severe or serious degree

gravitate (v.) to move or tend to move *to* or *toward* someone or something

gregarious (adj.) drawn to the company of others, sociable

gridiron (n.) in football, the field of play, or the game itself

grievous (adj.) injurious, hurtful; serious or grave in nature

grim (adj.) stern and admitting of no appeasement or compromise; fierce, savage, or cruel

guffaw (n.) a hearty, boisterous burst of laughter

guise (n.) an external form, appearance, or manner of presentation, typically concealing the true nature of something

gullible (adj.) easily deceived or cheated

H

habit (n.) a distinctive dress or costume, especially of a religious order; a recurrent, often unconscious pattern of behavior that is acquired through frequent repetition

hackneyed (adj.) unoriginal, trite

halcyon (adj.) calm and peaceful; tranquil

hallowed (adj.) revered, consecrated

hallucinate (v.) to see or sense something or someone that is not really there; to have hallucinations

hapless (adj.) unlucky

harbinger (n.) a precursor or forerunner, an indicator that someone or something is approaching

harrowing (adj.) greatly distressing, vexing

hasten (v.) to speed up, to accelerate

hasty (adj.) moving or acting with haste; speedy; quick

haughty (adj.) disdainfully proud

havoc (n.) widespread destruction

heartburn (n.) is a mild discomfort in the upper belly or abdomen, it occurs during or right after eating; indigestion

hedonist (n.) one devoted to the pursuit of pleasure, especially to the pleasures of the senses

hegemony (n.) domination over others

heinous (adj.) shockingly wicked, repugnant

heightened (adj.) to increase the degree or amount of; augment

henchmen (n.) trusted followers or supporters who performs unpleasant, wrong, or illegal tasks for a powerful person

herald/ed (v.) to praise or enthusiastically greet the arrival of something or someone

heresy (n.) opinion profoundly at odds with what is generally accepted, such as in religious beliefs

heretic (n.) a person who opposes accepted and established beliefs

heterogeneous (adj.) varied, diverse in character

heyday (n.) the peak of popularity and success of a movement, organization, person, fad, etc.

hiatus (n.) a break or gap in duration or continuity

hierarchy (n.) a system with ranked groups, usually according to social, economic, or professional status

highline (n.) elevated, or raised-bed, railroad tracks

histrionics (n.) an exaggerated and theatrical display of emotion

hit-and-run (adj.) involving a driver who does not stop after causing an accident

hither and yon (n.) from here to over there, especially to a farther place

hoax (n.) a trick or fraud, esp. one meant as a practical joke

Holocaust (n.) the genocide of European Jews and others by the Nazis during World War II

hooky (n.) unjustifiable absence from school, work, etc., as in *playing hooky*

horrendous (adj.) horrible, very bad or unpleasant

horrific (adj.) causing horror, awful

hostility (n.) expression of anger and confrontation; opposition or resistance to an idea, plan, project

hovered (v.) to float in the air without moving in any direction; to stay very close to a person or place

hubris (n.) excessive pride or self-confidence; arrogance

humiliating (adj.) to lower the pride, dignity, or self-respect of

hunkered (adj.) squatting close to the ground; to hide out or take shelter

hydraulic (adj.) operated by or employing water or some other liquid

hydroelectric (adj.) electrical power through the use of the gravitational force of falling or flowing water

hyperbole (n.) obvious and intentional exaggeration; an extravagant statement or figure of speech not intended to be taken literally

hypnotically (adv.) Inducing or tending to induce sleep; soporific

I

icon (n.) from the Greek for "image, it is generally a flat panel painting depicting Jesus, Mary, Saints and Angels, which is venerated among Eastern Orthodox, Oriental Orthodox, and in certain Eastern Catholic Churches

iconoclast (n.) a person who attacks cherished or popular ideas, traditions, or institutions

ideological (adj.) relating to or concerned with ideas; of, relating to, or based on ideology

ideology (n.) a body of doctrine, myth and symbols of a social movement, institution, or political philosophy

idiom (n.) a style or form of expression that is characteristic of a particular person, type of art, etc.

idiosyncratic (adj.) peculiar to one person; highly individualized

idling (adj.) not working or active; unemployed; doing nothing; not in use or operation; not kept busy

idolatrous (adj.) excessively worshipping one object or person

idyll (n.) a simple poem or other piece of writing that describes peaceful country life; happy and enjoyable scene or experience

idyllic (adj.) very peaceful, happy, and enjoyable

ignite (v.) to give life or energy to (someone or something); to set something on fire

ignominious (adj.) humiliating, disgracing

ilk (n.) type or kind; the same

ill-fated (adj.) having or destined to a hapless fate; unfortunate

illicit (adj.) forbidden, not permitted

illusion (n.) an erroneous concept or belief; the condition of being deceived by a false perception or belief

illusory (adj.) based on, or having the nature of an illusion; deceptive

immense (adj.) marked by greatness especially in size or degree

immerse (v.) to absorb, deeply involve, engross

imminent (adj.) about to occur; impending

immortal (adj.) not subject to death; never to be forgotten; everlasting

impassioned (adj.) filled with feeling and zeal, fervent

impassive (adj.) stoic, not susceptible to suffering

impeccable (adj.) exemplary, flawless

impecunious (adj.) having little or no money, usually habitually

imperative (adj.) necessary, pressing; (n.) a rule, command, or order

imperceptibly (adv.) barely noticeable, hardly perceived by the mind or senses

imperialism (n.) a policy of extending a country's power and influence through diplomacy or military force

imperil (v.) to put in peril or danger; endanger

imperious (adj.) commanding, domineering

imperturbable (adj.) incapable of being upset or agitated; calm.

impervious (adj.) impenetrable, incapable of being affected

impetuous (adj.) rash; hastily done

impetus (n.) the moving force behind something, a stimulus that moves something along

impishly (adv.) mischievously, in an appealing but bold manner

implement (n.) an instrument, utensil, tool; (v.) to put into effect, to institute

implacable (adj.) not to be appeased, mollified, or pacified

implicate (v.) to involve in an incriminating way, incriminate

implication (n.) an indirect indication; a suggestion; An implied meaning; implicit significance; an inference

impoverished (adj.) without money or resources

impromptu (adj.) made or done without previous preparation; improvised

impugn (v.) to criticize (a person's character, intentions, etc.) by suggesting that someone is not honest and should not to be trusted

impulsive (adj.) acting with a lack of forethought or deliberation, rash

impunity (n.) exemption from punishment; immunity from detrimental effects, as of an action

inaccessible (adj.) unable to be reached

inadvertently (adv.) accidentally, caused by lack of care

inanimate (adj.) not alive, not endowed with life or spirit

inarticulate (adj.) incapable of expressing oneself clearly through speech

incalculable (adj.) Impossible to calculate; too great to be calculated or reckoned

incarnate (adj.) existing in the flesh, embodied; (v.) to give human form to

incendiary (n.) a person who agitates; (adj.) inflammatory, causing combustion

incentive (n.) something that encourages a person to do something or to work harder

inchoate (adj.) unformed or formless, in a beginning stage

inclination (n.) a tendency, propensity

incompetence (n.) inability to function properly

incongruous (adj.) lacking harmony, inconsistent or incompatible with something else

inconsiderable (adj.) not large enough in size or amount to be considered important

inconsolable (adj.) not able to be comforted or alleviated

inconspicuous (adj.) not easily noticeable, not obvious

incontrovertible (adj.) indisputable

incorporate (v.) to include; to cause to merge or combine together into a united whole

incredulous (adj.) not able or willing to believe something

incriminating (adj.) charging or suggestive of guilt or blame

incumbent (n.) one who holds an; (adj.) obligatory

indecipherable (adj.) not understandable; incomprehensible

indefatigable (adj.) tireless, filled with an inexhaustible supply of energy

indelible (adj.) impossible to remove or forget; making marks that cannot easily be removed

indicative (adj.) serving as a sign or indication of something

indictment (n.) any charge, accusation, serious criticism, or cause for blame

indifferent (adj.) without interest or concern; not caring; apathetic

indigenous (adj.) originating in a region, native

indigent (adj.) very poor, impoverished

indigestion (n.) a term used to describe a feeling of fullness or discomfort during or after a meal. It can be accompanied by burning or pain in the upper stomach.

indignation (n.) anger sparked by something unjust or unfair

indiscreet (adj.) lacking discretion; injudicious

indispensable (adj.) not subject to being set aside or neglected; absolutely necessary

individualist (n.) one who advocates individual rights, freedom, and independent action; one characterized by individualism

indolence (n.) the state of having or showing a disposition to avoid exertion; slothful

indomitable (adj.) not capable of being conquered or dominated

induce (v.) to bring about, stimulate

inducement (n.) a thing that persuades or influences someone to do something

indulge (v.) to allow (yourself) to have or do something as a special pleasure

indulgent (adj.) characterized by excessive generosity; overly lenient and tolerant

industrious (adj.) hardworking, persevering

ineffable (adj.) unspeakable, incapable of being expressed through words

ineffectual (adj.) not effectual; without satisfactory or decisive effect

inevitable/inevitably (adj./adv.) unable to be avoided, evaded, or escaped; certain; necessary

inexhaustible (adj.) impossible to use up completely : impossible to exhaust

inexorable (adj.) unyielding or unalterable; incapable of being persuaded or placated

inexplicable (adj.) difficult or impossible to explain or account for

inextricable (adj.) hopelessly tangled or entangled

infamy (n.) notoriety, extreme ill repute

infatuated (adj.) possessed by an unreasoning passion or attraction

infectious (adj.) tending to spread from one to another

infiltrate (v.) to secretly enter or join something (an organization, etc.) in order to gain information or to do harm

infinitesimal (adj.) incredibly small, miniscule

infirm (adj.) of poor or deteriorated vitality; feeble from age

infirmary (n.) a place where sick people stay and are cared for in a school, prison, summer camp, etc.

inflame (v.) to cause (a person or group) to become angry or violent

inflicted (v.) to impose as something that must be borne or suffered

infusion (n.) an injection of one substance into another; the permeation of one substance by another

ingenious (adj.) clever, resourceful

ingratiate (v.) to establish (oneself) in the favor or good graces of others, especially by deliberate effort

inherent (adj.) belonging to the basic nature of someone or something

inhibit (v.) to prevent, restrain, stop

inhumane (adj.) lacking pity or compassion

inimical (adj.) being adverse often by reason of hostility or malevolence; hostile

initial (adj.) occurring at the beginning of something

initiate (v.) begin, start; to set going by taking the first step

initiative (n.) an introductory act or step; leading action

in loco parentis (adv.) in place of a parent

innate (adj.) inborn, native, inherent

innately (adv.) existing from the time a person or animal is born; existing as part of the basic nature of something **SAT**

innocuous (adj.) harmless, inoffensive

innovate (v.) to do something in an unprecedented way

innovations (n.) a new idea, device, or method

innovator (n.) a person who creates new inventions, ideas, or ways of doing things

innuendo (n.) an insinuation or intimation about a person or thing, especially of a disparaging or a derogatory nature

innumerable (adj.) too many to be numbered; countless

inoculate (v.) to introduce a microorganism, serum, or vaccine into an organism in order to increase immunity to illness; to vaccinate

inordinate (adj.) exceeding reasonable limits, going beyond what is usual, normal, or proper

inquisitive (adj.) given to inquiry or research; desirous of or eager for knowledge

inquisitor (n.) one who inquires, especially in a hostile manner

inscrutable (adj.) very hard to figure out, incomprehensible

insidious (adj.) appealing but imperceptibly harmful, seductive

insightful (adj.) the ability to perceive clearly or deeply; perceptive

insinuate (v.) to suggest indirectly or subtly; to introduce or insert (oneself) by subtle and artful means

insipid (adj.) without distinctive, interesting, or stimulating qualities; vapid

insomnia (n.) the inability to fall asleep

inspiration (n.) a force or influence that inspires someone

instill (v.) to introduce by gradual, persistent efforts; implant

instinct (n.) an inborn pattern of behavior; a powerful motivation or impulse

instinctively (adv.) arising from impulse; spontaneous and unthinking

insubordination (n.) not obeying authority : refusing to follow orders

insular (adj.) separated and narrow-minded; tight-knit, closed off

integrated (adj.) joined with something else; united; to open to people of all races or ethnic groups without restriction; desegregate

integrity (n.) adherence to moral and ethical principles; soundness of moral character; honesty

intellectuals (n.) those possessing or showing intellect or mental capacity; those who use intelligence and critical or analytical reasoning in either a professional or a personal capacity

intelligentsia (n.) intellectuals considered as a group or class, especially as a cultural, social, or political elite

intelligible (adj.) capable of being understood or comprehended

interject (v.) to insert between other things

interloper (n.) a person who interferes or meddles in the affairs of others

intermediate (adj.) coming between two things in time, place, order, character, etc.

internment (n.) the state of being interned; confinement

internal combustion engine (n.) an engine of one or more working cylinders in which the process of combustion takes place within the cylinders

interrogation (n.) an examination by questioning

interventionism (n.) the policy or doctrine of intervening, especially government interference in the affairs of another state or in domestic economic affairs

intimate (tr. v.) to communicate delicately and indirectly

intimately (adv.) privately, closely personal

intimidating (adj.) discouraging through fear

intolerance (n.) unwillingness to accept or respect the beliefs or practices of another

intonation (n.) accuracy of pitch in playing or singing; the rise and fall of the voice in speaking

intransigent (adj.) refusing to compromise, often on an extreme opinion

intricate (adj.) having many complexly interrelating parts or elements; complicated

intrigue (n.) the practice of engaging in secret schemes; the activity of making secret plans

intrinsic (adj.) belonging to the essential nature of a thing

intuition (n.) the faculty of knowing instinctively, without conscious reasoning

inundated (v.) covered with a flood; overwhelmed

invaluable (adj.) valuable beyond what can be reasonably estimated, priceless

inveterate (adj.) stubbornly established by habit

invigorating (adj.) giving strength and energy to

irascible (adj.) easily angered, prone to outbursts of temper

ire (n.) an expression of strong anger

iridescent (adj.) showing rainbow colors

ironically (adv.) contrary to what is expected or intended

irony (n.) a figure of speech in which the literal meaning of a locution is the opposite of that intended

irrational (adj.) lacking reason or sound judgment

irreparably (adv.) impossible to repair, rectify, or amend

irreplaceable (adj.) not able to be replaced

irreverent (adj.) lacking or exhibiting a lack of reverence; disrespectful

isolationist (adj.) one who favors a policy or doctrine of isolating one's country from the affairs of other nations by declining to enter into alliances, foreign economic commitments, international agreements, etc

itinerant (n.) one who travels from place to place

J

jejune (adj.) without interest or significance; dull; insipid; juvenile; immature; childish

jettison (v.) to cast overboard or off; to discard

jovial (adj.) endowed with or characterized by a hearty, joyous humor or a spirit of good-fellowship

jubilant (adj.) showing great joy, satisfaction, or triumph; rejoicing; exultant

juggernaut (n.) anything to which a person blindly devotes himself or is cruelly sacrificed

juncture (n.) a point of time; especially one made critical by a concurrence of circumstances

juxtaposition/juxtaposed (n./v.) the act of placing two things next to each other for implicit comparison

K

keen (adj.) intellectually sharp, characterized by strength and distinctiveness of perception, having great mental penetration

ken (n.) perception, understanding

kudos (n.) praise for an achievement

L

labyrinth (n.) a maze, an intricate combination of passages making it difficult to find the exit

laconic (adj.) using or involving the use of a minimum of words

lament (v.) a passionate expression of grief or sorrow

lamentation (n.) an expression of grief or sorrow

lampoon (v.) virulent satire in prose or verse that is a gratuitous and sometimes unjust and malicious attack on an individual

languorous (adj.) producing or tending to produce languor, weakness or weariness of body or mind; listless indolence or inertia

lapse (n.) a temporary failure of concentration, memory, or judgment

larceny (n.) obtaining another's property by theft or trickery

larder (n.) a place, such as a pantry or cellar, where food is stored

largesse (n.) the generous giving of lavish gifts

latitude (n.) freedom from normal restraints and limitations

laudable (adj.) deserving praise and commendation

laudatory (adj.) expressing or worthy of admiration or praise

lavish (adj.) given without limits; (v.) to give without limits

leeward (adj.) on or toward the side sheltered from the wind or toward which the wind is blowing; downwind.

leftist (n.) a member of the political Left or a person sympathetic to its views, embracing statist liberalism, Progressivism, fascism, and communism, and its variants who favor an expansive role for government

left-wing (adj.) members of a socialistic or fascistic political party or movement; embracing a variety of big government policies, ranging from welfare state socialism and paternalism to government ownership (communism) or control (fascism) of the means of production

legerdemain (n.) deception, slight-of-hand

lenient (adj.) demonstrating tolerance or gentleness

levity (n.) lightness in manner or speech, especially an attempt to inject humor in to an otherwise serious situation

liaison (n.) a usually secretive or illicit sexual relationship; a union; an intimacy; an interrelationship

liberal (n.) generous and plentiful (in a non-political sense); in politics, a liberal is one who is left of center and favors an activist and more expansive government

liberal education (n.) a system or course of education suitable for the cultivation of a free (Latin: *liber*) human being. It is based on the medieval concept of the liberal arts or, more commonly now, the liberalism of the Age of Enlightenment

licentious (adj.) displaying a lack of moral or legal restraints

lieu (n.) place, stead; idiom: in lieu of: in place of

lighthearted (adj.) carefree, cheerful, gay

lilting (adj.) a cheerful or lively manner of speaking or singing, in which the pitch of the voice varies pleasantly

lingerie (n.) women's intimate apparel; undergarments

lingonberries (n.) Swedish mountain cranberries, often made into preserves

lintel (n.) a horizontal supporting member above a window or a door

liquidate (v.) to destroy or kill; business: to sell (a business, property, etc.), especially to pay off debt

litany (n.) a lengthy recitation or enumeration

literary (adj.) pertaining to or of the nature of books and writings, especially those classed as literature

lithe (adj.) graceful, flexible, supple

loathe (v.) to feel disgust or intense aversion for; abhor

lockstep (n.) close adherence to and emulation of another's actions, as if marching together

logistically (adv.) organizationally; operationally

loquacious (adj.) talkative

lucid (adj.) clear, luminous, suffused with light

lucrative (adj.) producing money or wealth, profitable

lugubrious (adj.) mournful, dismal, or gloomy

lush (adj.) having a lot of full and healthy growth; covered with healthy green plants

luxurious (adj.) of a sumptuous, costly, or rich variety

lyrics (n.) a set of words that make up a song

M

macabre (adj.) involving death or violence in a way that is strange, frightening, or unpleasant

machinations (n.) crafty schemes; plots; intrigues

maelstrom (n.) a destructive whirlpool which rapidly sucks in objects

magnanimous (adj.) noble, generous

magnificent (adj.) extraordinarily fine; superb; making a splendid appearance or show

magnitude (n.) the great size or extent of something.

malaise (n.) a feeling of mental, moral, and spiritual unease

malefactors (n.) one that has committed a crime; a criminal; an evildoer.

malevolent (adj.) wanting harm to befall others

malicious (adj.) having or showing a desire to cause harm, with bad or evil intent

mandate (n.) an authoritative command

maneuvers (n.) planned and regulated movements of troops, war vessels, etc.

manifest (adj.) easily understandable, obvious; (v.) to show plainly; (n) a list of cargo or passengers on a ship, etc.

manifest (v.) to make clear or evident to the eye or the understanding; show plainly

manifestation (n.) outward or perceptible indication; materialization

manipulation (n.) skillful control by something or someone

marginalize (v.) to place in a position of marginal importance, influence, or power, to diminish in influence

maritime (adj.) connected with the sea or navigation

mastermind (n. or v.) a highly intelligent person, especially one who plans and directs a complex or difficult project

materialize (v.) to cause to become real or actual

matrimonial (adj.) of or relating to marriage

maudlin (adj.) weakly sentimental

meager (adj.) deficient in size or quality

mecca (n.) a place that attracts many people, from the Muslim holy shrine in Saudi Arabia

medley (n.) a mixture of differing things; or songs

megalomania (n.) A psychopathological condition characterized by delusional fantasies of power, relevance, omnipotence, and by inflated self-esteem

mellifluous (adj.) having a smooth, flowing sound; having a pleasing or rich sound

mementos (n.) an object or item that serves to remind one of a person, past event, etc.; keepsake; souvenir.

mendacious (adj.) having a lying, false character

mental capacity (n.) sufficient understanding and memory to comprehend in a general way the situation in which one finds oneself and the nature, purpose, and consequence of any act or transaction into which one proposes to enter

mentor (n.) a person who acts as a wise and trusted advisor

merciless/ly (adj./adv.) without mercy, cruel

mesmerized (v.) hypnotized; visually captivated

metamorphosis (n.) the change of form, shape, substance

metaphor (n.) a figure of speech in which a term or phrase is applied to something to which it is not literally applicable in order to suggest a resemblance

mete (v.) to distribute or apportion; allot; dole out

meteoric (adj.) characterized by a sudden or dramatic rise or fall; similar to a meteor in speed, brilliance or brevity

methodically (adv.) characterized by ordered and systematic habits or behavior

methodology (n.) a set or system of methods, principles, and rules for regulating a given discipline, as in the arts or sciences

meticulous (adj.) extremely careful with

metropolis (n.) a major city, especially the chief city of a country or region

metropolitan (adj.) of or relating to a large city, its surrounding suburbs, and other neighboring communities, especially in culture, sophistication, or in accepting and combining a wide variety of people, ideas, etc.

mezzanine (n.) a low story between two other stories of greater height in a building, especially when the low story and the one beneath it form part of one composition

microdot (n.) a photographic reproduction of printed matter reduced to the size of a dot for ease or security of transmittal

microfilm (n.) film on which very small photographs of the printed pages of a newspaper, magazine, etc., are stored

migraine (n.) a chronic neurological disorder characterized by recurrent moderate to severe headaches

milieu (n.) a person's social environment or social circle

militarize (v.) to equip with armed forces, military supplies, or the like; to transform something into a military use

millinery (n.) articles, especially women's hats, sold by a milliner

mindset (n.) a mental attitude or inclination; a fixed state of mind

minion (n.) a servile follower or subordinate of a person in power

mirror/s (v.) to reflect as if through a mirror

mischievous (adj.) playful in a naughty or teasing way; full of mischief

misconception (n.) a mistaken thought, idea, or notion; a misunderstanding

miscreant (n.) an evildoer; a villain

misgivings (n.) feelings of doubt about something

misnomer (n.) an incorrect or inappropriate name

mitigate (v.) to make less violent, alleviate

mobilization (n.) the act of putting armed services into readiness for active service; to organize or adapt industries

for service to the government in time of war

mock (v.) to make fun of someone with contempt, ridicule or derision

moderate (adj.) not extreme; (n.) one who expresses moderate opinions

modesty (n.) the quality of being modest; freedom from vanity or boastfulness; regard for decency of behavior, dress, etc.

modicum (n.) a small amount of something

modulate (v.) to pass from one state to another, especially in music

modus operandi (n.) a method of operating or functioning

mole (n.) a spy (as a double agent) who establishes a cover long before beginning espionage; one within an organization who passes on information

mollify (v.) to soften in temper

momentous (adj.). Of great significance, having great or lasting importance

momentum (n.) force or speed of movement; impetus, as of a physical object or course of events

monarchist (n.) one who supports the monarchy; the belief in monarchy

monarchy (n.) A state or nation in which the supreme power is actually or nominally held by a monarch; where supreme power or sovereignty held by a single person; e.g. a king or queen.

monologue (n.) a prolonged talk or discourse by a single speaker, especially one dominating or monopolizing a conversation; a form of dramatic entertainment, comedic solo, or the like by a single speaker

monopoly in restraint of trade (n.) a situation in which a single company or group owns all or nearly all of the market for a given type of product or service any tends to limit trade, sales and transportation in interstate commerce or has a substantial impact on interstate commerce. It is addressed by anti-trust laws.

monotony (n.) a lack of change that makes something boring

morose (adj.) gloomy or sullen

motif (n.) a recurring subject, theme, idea, etc., especially in a literary, artistic, or musical work

motivate (v.) to give (someone) a reason for doing something; incite; impel

mournful (adj.) feeling or expressing sorrow or grief; sorrowful

muckraker (n.) journalist during the Progressive era who searched for and exposed real or alleged corruption, scandal, or the like, especially in politics

mulling (v.) pondering, to think about carefully; consider

multicultural (adj.) of, pertaining to, or representing several different cultures or cultural elements

multiracial (adj.) of, pertaining to, or representing more than one race

multisyllabic (adj.) having more than two and usually more than three syllables

mundane (adj.) concerned with the world rather than with heaven, commonplace

municipality (n.) an administrative division composed of a defined territory and population; a local government entity serving a specific political unit such as a town or city

munificence (n.) generosity in giving

munitions (n.) military weapons, ammunition, gunpowder, equipment, and stores

musculoskeletal (adj.) concerning, involving, or made up of both the muscles and the bones

muse (v.) to think or meditate in silence, as on some subject

mutiny (n.) open rebellion against constituted authority, especially rebellion of sailors against superior officers

myopic (adj.) shortsighted; lacking foresight

myriad (adj.) consisting of a very great number

myth (n.) a traditional story, especially one concerning the early history of a people or explaining some natural or social phenomenon, and typically involving supernatural beings or events

N

nadir (n.) the lowest point of something

naifs (n.) naïve or ingenuous persons

naïve (adj.) having or showing a lack of experience or knowledge : innocent or simple

nary (adj.) not any, not one

nascent (adj.) in the process of being born or coming into existence

nationalism (n.) a devotion to the interests of one's own nation; desire for national advancement or independence

nationalize (v.) to transfer (a major branch of industry or commerce) from private to state ownership or control.

nationals (n.) citizens of a particular nation

naught (n.) nothing, zero, complete failure, ruin, destruction

nebulous (adj.) vaguely defined, cloudy

nefarious (adj.) heinously villainous

negligent (adj.) habitually careless, neglectful

negligible (adj.) so small, trifling, or unimportant that it may safely be neglected or disregarded

neophyte (n.) someone who is young or inexperienced

neutral (adj.) not taking part or giving assistance in a dispute or war between others

neutralize (v.) to counterbalance or counteract the effect of; render ineffective

niche (n.) a place or situation especially suited to a person or thing, a recess in a wall

nimble (adj.) quick, light, or agile in movement or action; deft

nirvana (n.) a state or place of great happiness and peace

nitroglycerin (n.) a colorless, thick, oily, flammable, highly explosive, slightly water-soluble liquid

noble (adj.) having, showing, or coming from personal qualities that people admire (such as honesty, generosity, courage, etc.)

nocturnal (adj.) relating to or occurring during the night

noisome (adj.) unpleasant, offensive, especially to the sense of smell

nomadic (adj.) wandering from place to place

nominal (adj.) trifling, insignificant, in name only

nomination (n.) an act or instance of nominating, especially to office

nonchalant (adj.) having a lack of concern, indifference

nondescript (adj.) lacking a distinctive character

nostalgia (n.) the state of being homesick; homesickness; a wistful or excessively sentimental yearning for some past period or irrecoverable condition

nostrum (n.) a scheme, theory, device, etc., especially one to remedy social or political ills; a panacea

notorious (adj.) widely and unfavorably known

novice (n.) a beginner, someone without training or experience

noxious (adj.) harmful, unwholesome

nuance (n.) a slight variation in meaning, tone, expression

nuclear fission (n.) a nuclear reaction in which a heavy nucleus (such as uranium) splits into two lighter nuclei (and possible some other radioactive particles as well)

nuclear power (n.) power derived from nuclear energy

numbers racket (n.) an illegal daily lottery in which money is wagered on the appearance of certain numbers in some statistical listing or tabulation published in a daily newspaper, racing form, etc.

nurture (v.) to assist the development of

O

obdurate (adj.) unyielding to persuasion or moral influences

obfuscate (v.) to render incomprehensible

objective (adj.) not influenced by personal feelings, interpretations, or prejudice; based on facts; unbiased

objet d'art (n.) an article of some artistic value

obliged (v.) to require or constrain, as by law, command, conscience, or force of necessity

oblique (adj.) diverging from a straight line or course, not straightforward

oblivion (n.) the condition or quality of being completely forgotten; total forgetfulness

oblivious (adj.) lacking consciousness or awareness of something

obnoxious (adj.) highly offensive, disgustingly objectionable

obsequious (adj.) excessively compliant or submissive

obsession (n.) someone or something that a person thinks about constantly or frequently

obsolete (adj.) no longer used, out of date

obstinate (adj.) not yielding easily, stubborn

obstreperous (adj.) marked by unruly or aggressive noisiness; stubbornly resistant to control

obtuse (adj.) lacking quickness of sensibility or intellect

octogenarian (n.) a person between 80 and 90 years old

odious (adj.) instilling hatred or intense displeasure

odd (adj.) singular or peculiar in a strange or eccentric way

odor (n.) a particular smell

odyssey (n.) an extended adventurous voyage or trip; an intellectual or spiritual quest

officious (adj.) marked by excessive eagerness in offering unwanted services or advice to others

ogre (n.) someone or something that is very frightening, cruel, or difficult to deal with; an ugly giant in children's books that eats people

oligarchy (n.) a form of government in which all power is vested in a few persons or in a dominant class or clique; government by the few

ominous (adj.) foreboding or foreshadowing evil

onerous (adj.) burdensome

opaque (adj.) not transparent or clear; thus, dense or difficult to understand or see through

operational security (n.) the process by which the government protects unclassified information that can be used against us

operative (n.) a worker, one engaged, or employed in some branch of work; a detective

operetta (n.) a genre of light opera, light in terms both of music and subject matter

opiate (n.) a drug containing opium or its derivatives, used in medicine for inducing sleep and relieving pain; causing dullness or inaction

opportune (adj.) suited or right for a particular purpose; occurring at a fitting or advantageous time

oppressive (adj.) very cruel or unfair; tyrannical

optics (n.) the branch of physical science that deals with the properties and phenomena of both visible and invisible light and with vision

optimum (adj.) the amount or degree of something that is most favorable to some end; most favorable or advantageous; best

optometrist (n.) a licensed professional who examines the eyes for prescribing corrective lenses or other treatment

opulent (adj.) characterized by rich abundance verging on ostentation

oration (n.) a speech delivered in a formal or ceremonious manner

ornate (adj.) highly elaborate, excessively decorated

orthodox (adj.) conventional, conforming to established protocol

ostentatious (adj.) characterized by or given to pretentious or conspicuous show in an attempt to impress others

ostracize (v.) to exile by ostracism; to exclude from a group by common consent

overbearing (adj.) domineering; having an arrogant superiority to an disdain for those whose views are inferior or unworthy

overwrought (adj.) excessively nervous or excited; agitated

p

paeans (n.) songs of praise or triumph

palatial (adj.) like a palace, opulent, large and impressive

pall (v.) to lose in interest or attraction

palpable (adj.) capable of being handled, touched, or felt; tangible

panacea (n.) a remedy for all ills or difficulties

pander (v.) to do or provide what someone wants or demands even though it is not proper, good, or reasonable

panoramic (adj.) any wide-angle view or representation of a physical space, whether in painting, drawing

paradox (n.) a self-contradictory and false proposition; a statement or proposition that seems self-contradictory or absurd but in reality expresses a possible truth

paranoia (n.) an unfounded or exaggerated distrust of others, sometimes reaching delusional proportions

paranoid (adj.) characterized by extreme and irrational fear or distrust of others

parched (adj.) dried out with heat; in need of water

pariah (n.) an outcast

parliamentary procedure (n.) the body of rules, ethics, and customs governing meetings and operations of clubs, organizations, legislative and other deliberative bodies

parochial (adj.) reflecting a narrow or limited point of view, provincial; of or relating to a church parish and the surrounding area

parquet (n.) flooring composed of wooden blocks arranged in a geometric pattern

parsimonious (adj.) frugal to the point of stinginess

partisan (n.) a follower, adherent

paternalistic (adj.) a policy or practice of treating or governing people in a fatherly manner, especially by providing for their needs without giving them rights or responsibilities

pathology (n.) a deviation from the normal

pathos (n.) a quality that evokes pity or sadness

patrician (n.) a member of an aristocracy or privileged class

paucity (adj.) smallness of quantity; scarcity; scantiness

pedantic (adj.) ostentatious in one's learning; overly concerned with minute details or formalisms, especially in teaching

pedestrian (adj.) commonplace, unimaginative; (n.) a person traveling on foot; a walker

penchant (n.) a tendency, partiality, preference

pending (adj.) while awaiting; until

penetrating (adj.) acute; discerning; piercing; sharp

peninsula (n.) a body of land surrounded by water on three sides; literally, almost an island

pensive (adj.) thoughtful; engaged in, involving, or reflecting deep or serious thought

perceptive (adj.) having or showing keenness of insight, understanding, or intuition

peremptory (adj.) an order or command that does not allow discussion or refusal; an arbitrary order

perennials (n.) lasting through many years, enduring

perfunctory (adj.) characterized by casual indifference, performed in a routine manner

periphery (n.) the outer boundary or fringe of something

peril (n.) danger, risk, exposure to injury, loss or destruction

permeate (v.) to spread throughout, saturate

pernicious (adj.) extremely destructive or harmful

perpetrator (n.) a person who perpetrates, or commits, an illegal, criminal, or evil act

perpetuate (v.) to continue indefinitely; make perpetual

perplex (v.) to confuse

persecution (n.) a program or campaign to exterminate, drive away, or subjugate people based on their membership in a religious, ethnic, social, or racial group

persevere (v.) to persist in anything undertaken; maintain a purpose in spite of difficulty, obstacles, or discouragement

persistently (adv.) persisting, especially in spite of opposition, obstacles, discouragement

persona non grata (adj.) personally unacceptable or unwelcome

personality cult (n.) that which arises when an individual uses mass media, propaganda, or other methods, to create an idealized, heroic, and at times, worshipful image, often through unquestioning flattery and praise

personification (n.) the practice of representing a thing or idea as a person in art, literature, etc.; an imaginary person that represents a thing or idea; see also **anthropomorphism**

perspicacious (adj.) having keen mental perception and understanding; discerning

pert (adj.) flippant, bold

peruse (v.) to read or look over in an attentive or leisurely manner

pervade (v.) to spread through all parts of something; to exist in every part of something

pervasive (adj.) having the tendency to spread throughout

perverted (adj.) A type of human behavior that deviates from that which is understood to be orthodox or normal.

petulance (n.) rudeness, irritability

phenomena (n.) facts, occurrences, or circumstances observed or observable; things that are remarkable or extraordinary

philanthropic (adj.) charitable, giving

philanthropist (n.) a person who gives money or gifts to charities, a wealthy person with a generous nature and concern for human welfare

philosophy (n.) a particular set of ideas about knowledge, truth, the nature and meaning of life, etc.

phlegmatic (adj.) not easily upset, excited, or angered, generally calm or unemotional

pianissimo (n.) very soft; a dynamic marking in music

picturesque (adj.) of a character as to suggest a picture, strikingly interesting or colorful

pillage (v.) to seize or plunder, especially in war

pinnacle (n.) the highest point

piqued (v.) to stimulate interest or curiosity

pivotal (adj.) vitally important, crucial

placate (v.) to soothe or mollify especially by concessions

platitude (n.) a trite, meaningless, or prosaic statement, generally directed at quelling social, emotional, or cognitive unease

plaudits (n.) an enthusiastic expression of approval

plausible (adj.) believable, reasonable

plenitude (n.) an abundance

plethora (n.) an abundance, excess

plight (n.) a condition, state, or situation, especially an unfavorable or unfortunate one

poignant (adj.) deeply affecting, moving

polemic (n.) an aggressive argument against a specific opinion

police state (n.) a country in which the activities of the people are strictly controlled by the government with the help of a police force

political puppet (n.) a politician or other political figure who is controlled by another (sometimes illegitimate or secret) person or party

polyglot (adj.) consisting of a mixture or confusion of languages

pompous (adj.) characterized by excessive self-esteem or exaggerated dignity; pretentious

ponder (v.) to consider deeply, meditate, to weigh carefully in the mind

populace (n.) the general public; the masses; a population

portend (v.) to serve as an omen or warning, to foreshadow danger

posthumously (adv.) arising, occurring, or continuing after one's death

postlude (n.) a voluntary at the end of a church service; a concluding piece or movement

precarious (adj.) not safe, strong, or steady; dependent on chance circumstances, unknown conditions, or uncertain developments

precipitate (v.) to hasten the occurrence of; bring about prematurely, hastily, or suddenly

precipitous (adj.) extremely or impassably steep

precision (n.) the quality or state of being precise, accurate

precluded (adj.) to make impossible, as by action taken in advance; prevent

precocious (adj.) advanced, developing ahead of time

precursor (n.) a person, animal, or thing that goes before and indicates the approach of someone or something else; harbinger

predicament (n.) a difficult, perplexing, or trying situation

predilection (n.) a partiality or disposition in favor of something; a preference

predominantly (adv.) in greater strength, influence or number; most frequent or common

pregnant (adj.) being with child; fraught, filled

prejudice (n.) an unfavorable opinion or feeling formed beforehand, often irrationally

prelude (n.) an introductory performance, event or action that serves as an introduction to a more important one

prematurely (adv.) occurring too soon, overhasty

premiere (adj.) first or paramount

premonition (n.) a feeling or belief that something is going to happen when there is no definite reason to believe it will

preoccupation (n.) the state of being preoccupied; absorption of the attention or intellect

preponderance (n.) superiority in weight, force, importance, or influence.

preposterous (adj.) contrary to nature, reason, or common sense; very foolish or silly

prescient (adj.) to have foreknowledge of events

presumably (adv.) by reasonable assumption

presumptuous (adj.) disrespectfully bold

pretense (n.) an appearance or action intended to deceive

pretext (n.) an ostensible or professed purpose; an excuse

prevail (v.) to be widespread or current; exist everywhere or generally; to be or prove superior in strength, power, or influence

prey (n.) one that is helpless or unable to resist attack; an animal taken by a predator as food

primitive (adj.) being in its earliest period; old-fashioned

prism (n.) a transparent glass or plastic object that usually has three sides and that separates the light that passes through it into different colors; a medium that distorts, slants, or colors whatever is viewed through it

pristine (adj.) unspoiled; remaining in its pure or natural state

private property (n.) land or belongings owned by a person or group and kept for their exclusive use

privation (n.) lacking basic necessities

privet hedge (n.) a fence formed by a row of closely planted shrubs or bushes

privy (adj.) participating in the knowledge of something private or secret, private; assigned to private uses

probation (n.) the release of an offender from detention, subject to a period of good behavior under supervision

proclivity (n.) a strong inclination toward something

procrastinate (v.) to postpone taking action until a later time

procure (v.) to obtain, acquire

prodigious (adj.) extraordinarily large in size, amount or extent

profane (adj.) lewd, indecent; (v.) to misuse (anything that should be held in reverence or respect

proficient (adj.) highly capable, expert, skilled

profligate (adj.) dissolute, extravagant

profound (adj.) reflecting great knowledge or insight, intense, extreme

profuse (adj.) plentiful, abundant

progenitors (n.) someone who first thinks of or does something; a person who begins something; something that is a model for something else

projected (v.) to throw, cast, or impel forward or onward

proletariat (n.) the working class, or wage earners in general

proliferated (v.) to grow rapidly in number, multiply quickly

prolific (adj.) producing in large quantities or with great frequency; highly productive

prolong (v.) to lengthen out in time; extend the duration of

promulgate (v.) to proclaim, make known

propaganda (n.) ideas, facts, or allegations spread deliberately to further one's cause or to damage an opposing cause

propagate (v.) to multiply, spread out

propel (v.) to drive, or cause to move, forward or onward

propensity (n.) an inclination, preference

propitious (adj.) favorable

proponent (n.) a person who fights for a cause, idea, or movement; a champion

proprietor (n.) the owner of a business establishment, hotel, etc.

propriety (n.) the quality or state of being proper, decent

prosaic (adj.) plain, lacking liveliness

proscribe (v.) to condemn, outlaw

protestations (n.) a strong or formal expression of dissent

protocol (n.) the original draft of a diplomatic document, especially of the terms of a treaty agreed to in conference and signed by the parties

prototype (n.) the original or model after which anything is formed

protracted (adj.) long; drawn out or lengthened in time,

provisional (adj.) serving for the time being, temporary

provenance (n.) place or source of origin

prowess (n.) extraordinary ability

proximity (n.) nearness in space, time, or relationship

prudence (n.) cautious, circumspect

pseudonym (n.) a fictitious name assumed to conceal identity

psyche (n.) the soul, mind, or personality of a person or group

psychiatrist (n.) a physician who specializes in the diagnosis and treatment of mental disorders

psychological (adj.) of, relating to, or arising from the mind or emotions

puerile (adj.) juvenile, immature

pugnacious (adj.) quarrelsome, combative

punctilious (adj.) very careful about behaving properly and doing things in a correct and accurate way

pundit (n.) a knowledgeable commentator who offers informed opinions on topics of interest

pungent (adj.) having a pointed, sharp quality—often used to describe smells

punitive (adj.) involving punishment

puppet government (n.) a government that is appointed by and whose affairs are directed by an outside authority that may impose hardships on those governed

purge (v.) remove (a group of people considered undesirable) from an organization or place in an abrupt or violent way

purloin (v.) to appropriate wrongfully and often by a breach of trust

purport (v.) to have or present the often false appearance of being or intending; profess

putative (adj.) commonly regarded as such, reputed, supposed

putrid (adj.) rotten, foul

Pythagorean theorem (n.) the theorem that the square of the hypotenuse of a right triangle is equal to the sum of the squares of the other two sides

Q

quagmire (n.) a difficult situation; a swamp

quaint (adj.) charmingly old-fashioned

qualify (v.) to limit, modify or restrict

quality control (n.) a system for verifying and maintaining a desired level of quality in an existing product or service by careful planning, use of proper equipment, continued inspection, and corrective action as required

quandary (n.) a perplexed, unresolvable state

quell (v.) to control or diffuse a potentially explosive situation

querulous (adj.) whiny, complaining

quest (n.) a search or pursuit made in order to find or obtain something

queue (n.) a line or sequence of people or vehicles awaiting their turn to be attended to or to proceed

quid pro quo (n.) one thing in return for another

quiescent (adj.) quiet, still, motionless

quintessential (adj.) the essence of a thing in its purest and most concentrated form; the most typical example or representative

quirk (n.) a peculiarity of behavior; an idiosyncrasy

quirky (adj.) characterized by eccentric habits and odd mannerisms; peculiar

quixotic (adj.) idealistic, impractical; from Cervantes hero Don Quixote

quota (n.) the share or proportional part of a total that is required from, or is due or belongs to, a particular district, state, person, group, etc.

quotidian (adj.) daily, usual or customary; routine

R

racism (n.) the belief that race accounts for differences in human character or ability and that a particular race is superior to others; discrimination or prejudice based on race

radicalism (n.) extreme, going to the root or origin, one who follows extreme principles

rail (v.) to scold, protest

rancid (adj.) having a terrible taste or smell

rancor (n.) deep, bitter resentment

rapport (n.) mutual understanding and harmony

rapprochement (n.) an establishment or resumption of harmonious relations, especially in international relations

rapt (adj.) completely fascinated by what one is seeing or hearing

rash (adj.) hasty, incautious

ration (n.) a particular amount of something (such as gasoline or food) that the government allows you to have when there is not enough of it

rationalize (v.) to think about or describe something (such as bad behavior) in a way that explains it and makes it seem proper, more attractive, etc.

ravage (v.) to bring heavy destruction on; devastate

reaffirmed (adj.) to state or assert positively; maintain as true

realm (n.) a field or domain of activity or interest; a kingdom

rebuffed (v.) a blunt or abrupt repulse or refusal, as to an offer

rebuke (v.) to criticize sharply, to reprimand

rebut (v.) to refute by evidence or argument, to oppose by contrary proof

recapitulation (n.) a brief review or summary, as of a speech

recede (v.) to move back or away; withdraw

recess(es) (n.) A remote, secret, or secluded place, often used in the plural; an indentation or small hollow

reciprocate (v.) to do (something) for or to someone who has done something similar for or to you

reconcile (v.) to return to harmony; (v.) to make consistent with existing ideas

reconnoiter (v.) to go to (a place or area) in order to find out information about a military enemy : to do a reconnaissance of (a place)

reconvene (v.) to come together again, especially after a pause in proceedings

recounted (v.) related in detail

rectitude (n.) uprightness, extreme morality

recuperating (v.) to recover from injury, illness or fatigue

recurrence (n.) to happen, come up, or show up again or repeatedly

redundant (adj.) characterized by verbosity or unnecessary repetition in expressing ideas; prolix

refinery (n.) an establishment for refining something, as metal, sugar, or petroleum to bring it to a fine or pure state, free from impurities

reflective (adj.) taking time to think carefully about things; thoughtful

refrain (v.) to stop yourself from doing something that you want to do

refuge (n.) a protection or shelter, as from danger or hardship

refugee (n.) someone who has been forced to leave a country because of war or for religious or political reasons

refurbish (v.) to restore

refute (v.) to prove to be false or erroneous, as an opinion or charge

regal (adj.) of or pertaining to a king; royal

regale (v.) to entertain lavishly or agreeably; delight

regime (n.) a form of government, a government in power

regimen (n.) a regulated course of diet, exercise or manner of living

regimentation (n.) the strict discipline and enforced uniformity characteristic of military groups or totalitarian systems

regurgitate (v.) to vomit; (v.) to throw back exactly

reign (n.) authority; the time during which one (as a sovereign) reigns

relent (v.) to become more lenient, compassionate, or forgiving; to give in

relief (n.) money, food, or other help given to those in poverty or need, particularly during the Great Depression

relinquish (v.) to give up or abandon; to retire from

relish (v.) to enjoy

reminiscent (adj.) tending to remind or remember

remnants (n.) the part of something that is left when the other parts are gone

remorseful (adj.) characterized by or due to remorse or regret for wrongdoing

remotes (n.) radio or television broadcasts originating from a point outside a studio

remuneration (n.) an amount of money paid to someone for the work that person has done; compensation

rendezvous (n.) an appointment or engagement between two or more persons to meet

renovate (v.) restore, return to original state; (v.) to enlarge and make prettier, especially a house

repatriation (n.) the process of returning a person to their place of origin or citizenship

repentant (adj.) penitent, sorry

repercussions (n.) something usually bad or unpleasant that happens as a result of an action, statement, etc., and that usually affects people for a long time

repetitive (adj.) characterized by or given to unnecessary repetition; boring

replete (adj.) full, abundant

repose (v.) to rest, lie down

reprehensible (adj.) deserving rebuke

repression (n.) the act of using force to control someone or something; the act of not allowing a memory, feeling, or desire to be expressed

reprieve (n.) a temporary delay of punishment

reprimand (v.) To reprove (someone) severely, especially in a formal or official way

reprise (n.) a repetition; a repeat

reprobate (n.) an evil or unprincipled person

reprove (v.) to scold, rebuke

republic (n.) a state in which the supreme power rests in the body of citizens entitled to vote and is exercised by representatives chosen directly or indirectly by them.

republican (n.) one who favors a republic as the best form of government, i.e. one who believes that the supreme power lies in the body of citizens entitled to vote for officers and representatives responsible to them or characteristic of such government

repudiate (v.) to reject, refuse to accept

repulse (v.) to disgust; (v.) to push back

reputable (adj.) of good reputation

reputation (n.) the common opinion that people have about someone or something

resentment (n.) indignation or ill will felt as a result of a real or imagined grievance

reservists (n.) those who serve in the reserve formations of a nation's armed forces

resigned/resignedly (adj./adv.) feeling or marked by resignation; acquiescent

resilient (adj.) able to recover from misfortune; able to withstand adversity

resolute (adj.) firm, determined

resolve (v.) to find a solution; (v.) to firmly decide

resonance (n.) intensification and prolongation of sound, especially of a musical tone, produced by sympathetic vibration

resonate (v.) to resound; to continue to produce a loud, clear, deep sound for a long time

respite (n.) a break, rest

resplendent (adj.) very bright and attractive, shining brilliantly

restitution (n.) reparation made by giving an equivalent or compensation for loss, damage, or injury caused

restive (adj.) resistant, stubborn, impatient

restrain (v.) to prevent (a person or animal) from moving by using physical force; to keep under control

restraint of trade (n.) any activity which tends to limit trade, sales and transportation in interstate commerce or has a substantial impact on interstate commerce. It is addressed by anti-trust laws.

restraints (n.) something that holds one back, bonds, self-control

resurgence (n.) a continuing after interruption; a renewal; a restoration to use, acceptance, activity, or vigor; a revival.

retaliate (v.) to do something bad to someone who has hurt you or treated you badly; to get revenge against someone

reticent (adj.) disposed to be silent, reserved

retiring (adj.) shy and reserve, modest

retorted (v.) to reply, especially to answer in a quick, caustic, or witty manner

retrospect (n.) the consideration or analysis of past events

revel (v.) to enjoy intensely

revelations (n.) something revealed or disclosed

reverberate (v.) to reecho or resound

revere (v.) to esteem, show deference, venerate

reverent (adj.) showing a lot of respect; deeply respectful

revoke (v.) to take back

revolutionary (adj.) one who supports abrupt, rapid, and drastic change; one who desires to subvert existing institutions, practices, etc.

revulsion (n.) a strong feeling of repugnance or disgust

rhetoric (n.) the skillful and persuasive use of language, overblown or intellectually empty language

rhythmic (adj.) of, relating to, or having rhythm; recurring with measured regularity

ridicule (v.) words or actions intended to evoke contemptuous laughter at or feelings toward a person or thing

right of passage (n.) any important act or event that serves to mark a passage from one stage of life to another

romantic (adj.) displaying or expressing love or strong affection; refers to music composed from the late 18th to the early 20th centuries in which the expression of emotion was predominant

roughshod (adj.) brutal or domineering

rucksack (n.) a type of knapsack carried by hikers, bicyclists, etc.

rule of law (n.) the principle that all people and institutions are subject to and accountable to law that is fairly applied and enforced; the principle of government by law

ruminate (v.) to contemplate, reflect

run-of-the-mill (adj.) merely average; commonplace; mediocre

ruse (n.) a trick

rustic (adj.) lacking refinement or elegance; coarse; made of unfinished or roughly finished wood

ruthless (adj.) showing no pity or compassion; cruel, merciless

S

sabotage (n.) malicious injury to work, tools, machinery, or any underhand interference with production by enemy agents during wartime

saccharine (adj.) sickeningly sweet

sacrifice (v.) to forfeit something highly valued for the sake of one considered to have a greater value or claim

sacrosanct (adj.) holy, something that should not be criticized

sagacious (adj.) of keen and farsighted penetration and judgment; discerning

sagacity (n.) the quality of being sagacious, shrewdness, soundness of perspective

sage (n.) a person renowned for his or her wisdom and sagacity; wise or astute

sainted (adj.) unusually good, kind, or patient

salami (n.) cured sausage, fermented and air-dried meat, originating from one

salient (adj.) significant, conspicuous

salutary (adj.) beneficial and thus tending to promote physical well-being

salutation (n.) a greeting or a variety of animals. Historically, salami was popular among Southern European peasants because it can be stored at room temperature for periods of up to 30–40 days once cut

samizdat (Russian) (n.) from the Russian for "by oneself," and "publishing house," it refers to privately printed dissident publications, such as those produced in German- and Soviet-occupied countries, and the Soviet Union, including Lithuania. Soviet dissident Vladimir Bukovsky summarized it as follows: "Samizdat: I write it myself, edit it myself, censor it myself, publish it myself, distribute it myself, and spend jail time for it myself."

sanctimonious (adj.) giving a hypocritical appearance of piety

sanction (v.) to give official permission or approval for

sanctuary (n.) a sacred place, a safe haven

sanguine (adj.) optimistic, cheery

sarcasm (n.) harsh or bitter derision or irony; a sharply ironical taunt; sneering or cutting remark

sartorial (adj.) of or pertaining to clothing or style or manner of dress

satiate (v.) to satisfy excessively

satirical (adj.) exhibiting the characteristics of satire, or a genre of literature (and sometimes graphic and performing arts), in which vices, follies, abuses, and shortcomings are held up to ridicule, ideally with the intent of shaming individuals, corporations, government or society itself, into improvement

saunter (v.) walk in a slow, relaxed manner, without hurry or effort

savoring (v.) taste (good food or drink) and enjoy it completely

savvy (adj.) well informed and perceptive; shrewd; (n.) practical understanding or knowledge of something

scapegoat (n.) one who is made to made to bear the blame for others or suffer in their place

scarfer (n.) a steelworker who burns impurities from the surface of steel slabs with a blowtorch before they are sent to the finishing mill

scathing (adj.) sharp, critical, hurtful

scenario (n.) an outline of the plot of a dramatic work

scholarly (adj.) concerned with academic learning and research, befitting a scholar

scintillating (adj.) sparkling

score (n.) twenty

scoundrel (n.) an unprincipled, dishonorable man, a villain

scourge (n.) a source of widespread dreadful affliction and devastation such as that caused by pestilence or war

scrounge (v.) to get or find something by looking in different places, asking different people, etc.

scruples (n.) a moral or ethical consideration or standard that acts as a restraining force or inhibits certain actions

scrutiny (n.) a searching study, inquiry, or inspection

secluded (adj.) isolated, hidden, removed

second-tier (adj.) used to describe a product, organization, etc. that is not among the biggest, most successful, or most important of its type

secular (adj.) worldly rather than spiritual

sedentary (adj.) sitting, settled

seedy (adj.) somewhat disreputable; squalid; shabby, unkempt

segregated (adj.) separated, isolated, such as in matters of race

segue (v.) follow in sequence

self-delusion (n.) the act or state of deceiving or deluding oneself

semantical (adj.) of or relating to meaning in language

semblance (n.) an outward or token appearance

seminal (adj.) original, important, creating a field

sentimentality (n.) the expression of tender feelings, sometimes to excess

sentiments (n.) feelings

sentries (n.) guards, especially a soldier posted at a given spot to prevent the passage of unauthorized persons

separation of powers (n.) an act of vesting the legislative, executive, and judicial powers of government in separate bodies

serenity (n.) a calm and untroubled state

serfdom (n.) the state of being a member of the lowest feudal class, attached to the land owned by a lord and required to perform labor in return for certain legal or customary rights

servile (adj.) subservient

sever (v.) to set or keep apart; divide or separate

shelve (v.) to put aside or postpone

shirk (v.) to avoid or neglect one's assigned duties or responsibilities

shrewd (adj.) having or showing an ability to understand things and to make good judgments; mentally sharp or clever

shrouded (adj.) shut off from sight or light, hidden, concealed

shun (v.) to keep away from deliberately, avoid consistently

siblings (n.) a brother or sister

siege (n.) a serious and lasting attack *of* something

simile (n.) a figure of speech in which two unlike things are explicitly compared, as in "she is like a rose."

simulate (v.) make in resemblance of or as a substitute for another

simultaneously (adv.) existing, occurring or operating at the same time

sinister (adj.) threatening or portending evil, ominous

siren call (n.) the enticing appeal of something alluring but potentially dangerous; from the Sirens in Greek mythology

skein (n.) a succession or series of similar or interrelated things; a length of yarn or thread

skeleton key (n.) a key that is made to open many different locks

skeptical (adj.) tending to question or doubt, disbelieving

slake (v.) to provide, do, or have what is required by (something)

sleuth (n.) a detective; someone who looks for information to solve crimes

slovenly (adj.)characterized by being untidy in dress or appearance, messy, sloppy

smart (adj.) elegant and stylish in manners or dress

smokescreen (n.) an action or statement used to conceal actual plans or intentions; a cloud of smoke created to conceal military operations

smug (adj.) Exhibiting or feeling great or offensive satisfaction with oneself or with one's situation; self-righteously complacent

snide (adj.) derogatory in a malicious, superior way

sobering (adj.) serious; tending to make sober or more serious; concerned with more important matters

sobriety (n.) the state of being sober; sedate, calm

social democratic (adj.) a political ideology that officially has as its goal the establishment of democratic socialism through reformist and gradualist methods.

socialism (n.) any of various theories or systems of social organization in which the means of producing and distributing goods is owned collectively or by a centralized government that often plans and controls the economy

socialist (n.) one who advocates government ownership and control of the means of production, capital, land, etc.; a statist

socio-economic status (n.) an economic and sociological combined total measure of a person's work experience and of an individual's or family's economic and social position in relation to others, based on income, education, and occupation

soft tyranny (n.) An idea first coined by Alexis de Tocqueville in his 1835 work *Democracy in America*, soft tyranny occurs whenever the social conditions of a particular community hinder any prospect of hope among its members. Whenever this all-encompassing hope is taken away from the people, liberal democracy fails and the door is opened for totalitarian movements, or political demagogues, to impose their will on the populace.

sojourn (n.) a temporary stay; a brief period of residence

solicitous (adj.) concerned, attentive

solidarity (n.) a unity of purpose or togetherness

solidify (v.) to make solid or hard; to become united

somber (adj.) serious, grave, dark, gloomy

somnolent (adj.) sleepy, drowsy

sophisticated/tion (adj./n.) cultured and refined, knowing and worldly-wise

sophistry (n.) the use of reasoning or arguments that sound correct but are actually false; subtly deceptive reasoning or argumentation

soporific (adj.) sleep-inducing; causing or tending to cause feelings of drowsiness

sovereign (adj.) having absolute authority in a certain realm

spare (adj.) lacking embellishment or ornamentation, plain

sparingly (adv.) given to or marked by prudence and restraint in the use of material resources

spate (n.) a sudden profusion, flood, rush, or outpouring

spawn (v.) to produce or generate

speculative (adj.) not based in fact

specimens (n.) something (such as an animal or plant) collected as an example of a particular kind of thing

spheres of influence (n.) a spatial region or concept division over which a state or organization has a level of cultural, economic, military, or political exclusivity, accommodating to the interests of powers outside the borders of the state that controls it

spire (n.) a tapering conical or pyramidal structure on the top of a building, particularly a church tower

spirit (v.) to carry off mysteriously or secretly

spiritual (adj.) of or relating to the spirit or soul, as distinguished from the physical nature

spontaneously (adv.) done or said in a natural and often sudden way and without a lot of thought or planning

spurious (adj.) false but designed to seem plausible

spycraft (n.) the skills and techniques employed by spies

squalid (adj.) marked by filthiness and degradation from neglect or poverty; very dirty and unpleasant

stalemate (n.) a contest, dispute, competition, etc., in which neither side can gain an advantage or win

stalwart (adj.) marked by outstanding strength and vigor of body, mind, or spirit; very loyal and dedicated

stamina (n.) strength of physical constitution; power to endure disease, fatigue, privation, etc.

statist (n.) one who advocates the concentration of extensive economic, political and related controls in the state at the expense of individual liberty. (adj.) a philosophy or policy which advocates the concentration extensive economic, political, and related controls in the state at the cost of individual liberty

statist liberalism (n.) a form of liberalism that advocates a greater role for government intervention to address societal inequalities, as opposed to classical liberalism which aims at greater individual liberty and autonomy; the former is essentially a contradiction in terms

stature (n.) the level of respect that people have for a successful person, organization, etc.

staunch (adj.) characterized by firmness, steadfastness, or loyalty

stealthily (adj.) quietly, unobtrusively

steely (adj.) coldly determined; hard

steeple clock (n.) an Early American pointed shelf clock with steeplelike finials bordering each side

stereotypical (adj.) something or someone that conforms to a fixed pattern

stevedore (n.) one who works at or is responsible for loading and unloading ships in port

stifle (v.) to keep in or hold back; repress

stigmatized (adj.) to characterize or brand as disgraceful or ignominious

stingy (adj.) not generous, not inclined to spend or give

stoic (adj.) unaffected by passion or feeling

stooge (n.) one who acts on behalf of another, esp. in a obsequious or secretive fashion

stoolies (n.) short for stool pigeon; an informer

strategic (adj.) of or relating to a general plan that is created to achieve a goal in war, politics, etc., usually over a long period of time

strategist (n.) one who has a plan of action designed to achieve a vision

strenuous (adj.) requiring tremendous energy or stamina

strictures (n.) laws or rules that limit or control something

strident (adj.) harsh, loud

strife (n.) vigorous or bitter conflict, discord, or antagonism

stringent (adj.) very strict; demanding close attention to details and procedures

stucco (n.) a durable finish for exterior walls, usually composed of cement, sand, and lime, and applied while wet

stunning (adj.) of a strikingly attractive appearance

stymie (v.) to hinder, block, or thwart

subdue (v.) to get control of (a violent or dangerous person or group) by using force, punishment, etc.

subjugate (v.) to bring under control, subdue

sublime (adj.) lofty, grand, exalted

submerged (adj.) covered with water

submissive (adj.) easily yielding to authority

subordinates (n.) occupying an inferior position, rank or class; secondary, minor

subside (v.) to become quiet or less active

substantial (adj.) true or real; not imaginary; solidly built; strong

subterranean (adj.) existing below the surface of the earth, underground

subtle (adj.) fine or delicate in meaning or intent; difficult to perceive or understand

subversive (adj.) intended or serving to subvert, especially intended to overthrow or undermine an established government

subvert (v.) to overturn or overthrow, destroy, ruin

succession (n.) the act or process of following in order or sequence; a group of people or things arranged or following in order

succinct (adj.) expressed in few words; concise; terse

succulent (adj.) tender, juicy, and tasty

succumb (v.) to submit to an overpowering force or yield to an overwhelming desire; give up or give in

sufficient (adj.) enough to meet the needs of a situation or a proposed end

suffused (adj.) spread over or filled

suicide (n.) the act of intentionally causing one's own death

sullen (adj.) bad-tempered and sulky; gloomy

sulphur (n.) an abundant, multivalent non-metal, sulphur is an element (symbol S) which is always found in steel in small quantities. Some sulphur is contained in the ore from which the iron is smelted; more sulphur is introduced by the coke and fuel used

summarily (adv.) in a prompt or direct manner; immediately; straightaway

summary execution (n.) a variety of execution in which a person is accused of a crime and then immediately killed without benefit of a full and fair trial.

sumptuous (adj.) luxuriously fine or large; lavish; splendid

superficial (adj.) concerned only with the surface, shallow

superfluous (adj.) being more than is sufficient or required; excessive. unnecessary or needless

superimposed (adj.) to lay or place (something) on or over something else

supersede (v.) to replace in power, authority, effectiveness, acceptance, use, etc., as by another person or thing.

superstructure (n.) the part of a structure (such as a ship or bridge) that is above the lowest part

suppress (v.) to hold back or stifle

surefire (adj.) bound to be successful or perform as expected

surmise (v.) to infer with little evidence

surreptitious (adj.) stealthy; secretive

surveillance (n.) the monitoring of the behavior, activities, or other changing information, usually of people and often in a surreptitious manner

susceptible (adj.) easily affected, influenced, or harmed by something

suspicious (adj.) inclined to suspect, especially inclined to suspect evil; distrustful; questionable

sustained (adj.) providing what is needed for (something or someone) to exist; continued

swarthy (adj.) of dark color or complexion

swath (n.) a long, wide strip of land

swaying (adj.) to swing back and forth or to and fro

swooning (n.) fainting; overwhelmed by ecstatic joy

sycophant (n.) one who flatters for self-gain

syllabus/pl: syllabi (n.) an outline or other brief statement of the main points of a discourse, the subjects of a course of lectures, the contents of a curriculum, etc.

sympathizers (n.) supporters; those who are in accord or commiserate

symptomatic (adj.) serving as a symptom or sign, especially of something undesirable

sync (n.) shortened form of synchronize; harmony or harmonious relationship; together

T

taboo (n.) a ban or an inhibition resulting from social custom or emotional aversion; a prohibition

taciturn (adj.) not inclined to talk

tackle (v.) to confront or take on a challenge

tactfully (adv.) possessing or exhibiting tact; considerate and discreet

tactless (adj.) displaying a lack of consideration; thoughtless

tainted (adj.) to affect with or as if with a disease; to corrupt morally; spoiled

tandem (adj.) in conjunction with, in association or partnership

tardiness (n.) lateness, the state of being delayed

tarnishing (v.) to dull the luster of; discolor, especially by exposure to air or dirt

taxidermist (n.) an individual who practices the art of preparing, stuffing , and mounting the skins of animals (especially vertebrates) for display

tedious (adj.) dull, boring

temerity (n.) audacity, recklessness

temper (v.) to moderate or soften; (n.) a habit of mind, especially with respect to irritability or patience, outbursts of anger

temperance (n.) moderation in action or thought; the act of refraining from the consumption of alcohol

tenacious (adj.) stubborn and unyielding, not easily letting go or giving up

tenets (n.) an opinion, doctrine, or principle held as being true by a person or especially by an organization

tentacles (n.) a flexible, mobile, elongated organ present in some species of animals, most of them invertebrates; power or influence that reaches into many areas

tentatively (adv.) uncertain, hesitant, provisional

tenuous (adj.) having little substance or strength

terminating (adj.) bringing to an end or halt

testament (n.) proof or evidence that something exists or is true

theatrical (adj.) of or pertaining to the theater or dramatic presentations

theology (n.) the study of the nature of God and religious truth; rational inquiry into religious questions

theoretical (adj.) pertaining or consisting only in theory, not practical, hypothetical

therapeutic (adj.) of or relating to the treatment of disease or disorders by remedial agents or methods

therapy (n.) the treatment of disease or disorders, as by some remedial, rehabilitating, or curative process

thermodynamics (n.) the science concerned with the relations between heat and mechanical energy or work, and the conversion of one into the other

thesis (n.) a proposition stated or put forward for consideration, especially one to be discussed and proved or to be maintained against objections; a subject for a composition or essay

threadbare (adj.) so frayed that the threads show, old and worn out

thwart (v.) to prevent the occurrence, realization, or attainment of

timorous (adj.) timid, fearful

tirade (n.) a long speech marked by harsh or biting language

tolerate (v.) to put up with; to endure

tome (n.) a large book

tomfoolery (n.) horseplay; foolish behavior, nonsense

tool and die (n.) the industrial art of manufacturing stamping dies, plastics molds, and jigs and fixtures to be used in the mass production of solid objects

toolmaking (n.) the process by which machinists in the manufacturing industries make jigs, fixtures, dies, molds, machine tools, cutting tools, gauges, and other tools used in manufacturing processes

tormentor (n.) one who causes mental or physical suffering

torrent (n.) a flood; a large outpouring

torrential (adj.) flowing or surging abundantly; wild

tortuous (adj.) winding

totalitarian (adj.) characterized by a government in which the political authority exercises absolute and centralized control and the people have virtually no authority

tract (n.) A leaflet or pamphlet containing a declaration or appeal, especially one put out by a religious or political group

tractable (adj.) easily controlled

tragic (adj.) dreadful, calamitous, disastrous, or fatal

tranquil (adj.) calm

transcript (n.) a written, typewritten, or printed copy; something transcribed or made by transcribing; an official report, such as a school record

transfixed (adj.) to make motionless with amazement, terror, etc.

transient (adj.) passing through briefly; passing into and out of existence

transitional (adj.) passage from one form, state, style, or place to another

trappings (n.) the accessories and adornments that characterize or symbolize a condition, office, etc.

traumatic (adj.) Serious injury or shock to the body, whether physical or psychological, from violence or accident

travelogue (n.) a lecture, slide show, or motion picture describing travels

treacherous (adj.) disloyal, betraying trust; unstable

treachery (n.) violation of faith; betrayal of trust; treason

trenchant (adj.) penetrating, keen, sharp, perceptive

trepidation (n.) fear, apprehension

trigonometry (n.) a branch of mathematics that studies relationships involving lengths and angles of triangles. The field emerged during the 3rd century BC from applications of geometry to astronomical studies.

trite (adj.) not original, overused

trivial (adj.) of little significance or value, ordinary, commonplace

truncate (v.) to shorten by cutting off

trussed (v.) tied, bound, secured

tsarist (adj.) of or relating to or characteristic of a tsar, the ruler of Russia

turf wars (n.) struggle for territory, power, control, or rights, particularly by criminal elements

turmoil (n.) a state of great commotion, confusion, or disturbance; tumult

turncoat (n.) a person who shifts allegiance from one loyalty or ideal to another, betraying or deserting an original cause by switching to the opposing side or party

U

ubiquitous (adj.) existing everywhere, widespread

ulterior (adj.) beyond what is seen or avowed; intentionally kept concealed

ultimate (adj.) happening or coming at the end of a process, series of events, etc.; greatest or most extreme

unabridged (adj.) complete, having nothing removed, or the most complete of its type

unaffected (adj.) not influenced or changed mentally, physically, or chemically

unambiguous (adj.) clear and precise, exhibiting no uncertainty

unanimous (adj.) having the agreement of all

uncanny (adj.) of supernatural character or origin

unceremonious/ly (adj./adv.) happening or done very suddenly and quickly with no effort to be careful or polite

uncharacteristically (adv.) unusual or atypical

unconstitutional (adj.) not constitutional; unauthorized by or inconsistent with the constitution, as of a country

unconventional (adj.) not adhering to convention; out of the ordinary

undaunted (adj.) courageously resolute especially in the face of danger or difficulty; not discouraged

undercurrents (n.) a hidden feeling or tendency that is usually different from the one that is easy to see or understand; a flow of water that moves below the surface of the ocean or a river

undermine (v.) to injure or destroy by insidious activity or imperceptible stages; to attack by indirect, secret, or underhand means; attempt to subvert by stealth

underpinnings (n.) something that serves as a foundation; undergarments

underscore (v.) to mark with a line or lines underneath, as for emphasis; to stress; emphasize

understatement (n.) a disclosure or statement that is less than complete; restraint or lack of emphasis in expression

undulate (v.) to move in waves

uneducable (adj.) incapable of being educated

unencumbered (adj.) not burdened, impeded, or hampered

unequivocal (adj.) admitting no doubt or misunderstanding; having only one meaning and interpretation

unfailing (adj.) never changing or becoming weaker even in difficult times

unflappable (adj.) persistently calm, whether when facing difficulties or experiencing success

uninitiated (adj.) not knowledgeable or skilled; inexperienced

unintelligible (adj.) not understandable; not intelligible

unnerved (adj.) to cause to become nervous

unobtrusive (adj.) not undesirably noticeable or blatant; inconspicuous

unorthodox (adj.) not customary, unusual

unprecedented (adj.) having no previous example

unpretentious (adj.) modest, free from ostentation, elegance, or affectation

unsavory (adj.) undesirable, objectionable morally offensive

unscathed (adj.) unharmed, uninjured, undamaged

unscrupulous (adj.) not scrupulous; unrestrained by scruples; conscienceless; unprincipled

unseasonably (adv.) not seasonable; being out of season

unsightly (adj.) unpleasant or offensive to look at; unattractive

unsophisticated (adj.) lacking refined worldly knowledge or tastes

untenable (adj.) incapable of being defended; indefensible

unwary (adj.) not cautious; not aware of possible dangers or problems

unwitting (adj.) not knowing, unaware. not intended

uproarious (adj.) making, or characterized by, an uproar; tumultuous; loud and boisterous

urbane (adj.) characterized by elegant manners, discriminating taste and broad education

usurp (v.) to seize by force, take possession of without right

utilitarian (adj.) relating to or aiming at usefulness, practical

utopia (n.) an imaginary and remote place of perfection; from Sir Thomas More's book *Utopia* (1516).

utterance (n.) the act of uttering; vocal expression; the power of speaking; speech

V

vacillate (v.) to fluctuate, hesitate

vacuum (n.) a space entirely devoid of matter; a space not filled or occupied; emptiness; void

vagrant (n.) one who has no established residence and wanders idly from place to place without lawful or visible means of support

vaguely (adv.) not clear in meaning; not completely formed or developed

vain (adj.) ineffectual or unsuccessful; futile

valedictorian (n.) the student who generally ranks highest in scholarship and delivers the farewell oration at a graduation ceremony

valiant (adj.) possessing valor, brave, courageous

vanguard (n.) the forefront in any movement, field, activity, or the like; the leaders of any intellectual or political movement

vanquished (adj.) defeated, subdued, conquered, overcome

vantage point (n.) a position which gives one an advantage or favorable place for action or defense

vapid (adj.) lacking flavor or liveliness, dull, bland

vaudeville (n.) theatrical entertainment consisting of a number of individual performances, acts, or mixed numbers, as by comedians, singers, dancers, acrobats, and magicians

vaulted (adj.) constituting an arched structure, usually made of stones, concrete, or bricks, forming a ceiling or roof over a hall, room, sewer, or other wholly or partially enclosed construction

vegetarianism (n.) the practice of subsisting on a diet composed primarily or wholly of vegetables, grains, fruits, nuts, and seeds, with or without eggs and dairy products

vehemently (adv.) marked by intense force or emotion

venal (adj.) willing to sell one's influence, especially in return for a bribe; open to bribery

veneer (n.) a way of behaving or appearing that gives other people a false idea of your true feelings or situation; an outer layer attached to the surface to make it look better

venerable (adj.) deserving of respect because of age or achievement

venerate (v.) to regard with respect or to honor

venturing (v.) to make or embark upon a venture; dare to go

venue (n.) the place where an event takes place

veracity (n.) truthfulness, accuracy

verbose (adj.) wordy, impaired by wordiness

verdant (adj.) green in tint or color

verify (v.) to prove the truth or accuracy of

verisimilitude (n.) something that has the appearance of being true or real

veritable (adj.) being in fact the thing named and not false, unreal, or imaginary

vernacular (n.) of, relating to, or using the language of ordinary speech rather than formal writing; relating to the common style of a particular time, place, or group

vestibule (n.) a lobby, entrance hall, or passage between the entrance and the interior of a building or railroad car

vestige (n.) a mark or trace of something lost or vanished

vex (v.) to confuse or annoy

vexing (adj.) confusing or annoying

viability (n.) the capacity to operate or be sustained

viable (adj.) practicable; workable

viaduct (n.) a bridge, esp. for carrying a road or across a valley, etc, consisting of a set of arches supported by a row of piers or towers

vicarious (adj.) experiencing through another

vicissitudes (n.) a change of circumstances or fortune, typically one that is unwelcome or unpleasant

vigilant (adj.) alert to signs of danger; alertly watchful

vignette (n.) a brief evocative description, account, or episode

vilification (n.) abusively disparaging speech or writing

to lower in importance, defame

vilify (v.) to make vicious and defamatory statements about

vindicate (v.) to avenge; to free from allegation; to set free

vindictive (adj.) disposed to seek revenge or hurt

vintage (n.) originally associated with wine production, it is a period in which something was made or was begun

vipers (n.) venomous snakes

virtuosity (n.) great technical skill, in musical performance, for example

virtuoso (n.) an individual who possesses outstanding technical ability in the fine arts, at singing or playing a musical instrument

virulent (adj.) marked by a rapid, severe, and destructive course

visage (n.) the face, countenance, or appearance of a person

visceral (adj.) characterized by or proceeding from instinct rather than intellect; earthy

visionary (adj.) of, relating to, or able to see visions in a dream or trance, or as a supernatural apparition; thinking about or planning for the future

vital (adj.) absolutely necessary; essential

vivacious (adj.) lively, sprightly

vividly (adv.) strikingly bright or intense, as color, light, etc.; full of life; lively; animated

vocation (n.) the work in which someone is employed, profession

vociferous (adj.) loud, boisterous

void (n.) an empty space; emptiness

volatile (adj.) unstable, explosive; subject to sudden and violent changes in temperament

voluntary/tarily (adj./adv.) done or undertaken of one's own free will

voluptuous (adj.) very attractive because of having large hips and breasts; giving pleasure to the senses

voracious (adj.) having or showing a tendency to eat very large amounts of food; a large appetite for something

vulgar (adj.) without refinement or taste, course, crude, gross

vulnerable (adj.) susceptible to being injured or wounded, open to attack, helpless

W

wafting (v.) born or carried through the air or water

wallow (v.) to roll oneself indolently; to become or remain helpless wafting

wane (v.) to decrease in size, dwindle

wanton (adj.) undisciplined, lewd, lustful

wary (adj.) watchful and cautious, leery, suspicious

watershed (n.) an event or period marking a turning point in a course of action or state of affairs

wealth redistribution (n.) the transfer of income, and wealth from some individuals to others by means of taxation, charity, welfare, public services, land reform, monetary policies, confiscation, etc. A central tenet of Marxist and leftist thought, wealth redistribution is also employed as a means of buying the votes of the recipient classes to secure and maintain power.

weathered (adj.) faded or altered by exposure to the weather

wending (v.) proceeding on or along

whim (n.) an odd or fanciful notion, fancy or desire

whimsical (adj.) unusual in a playful or amusing way

whisked (v.) take or move (someone or something) in a particular direction suddenly and quickly

wildcat strike (n.) a strike begun by workers spontaneously or without union approval

wiles (n.) devious or cunning stratagems employed in manipulating or persuading someone to do what one wants

willful (adj.) done by design; on purpose

wily (adj.) crafty, sly

winsome (adj.) charming, pleasing

wistful (adj.) full of yearning; musingly sad

witticism (n.) a witty remark or sentence

wizened (adj.) dry, shrunken, wrinkle

wont (adj.) accustomed; used to

workers' paradise (n.) the ultimate utopian state produced by the implementation of communist ideology; a Marxist illusion.

wrath (n.) vengeful anger, punishment

wreak (v.) to inflict or bring about

writhe (v.) to turn or twist, as in pain

wry (adj.) humorous in a clever and often ironic way;

Y

yield (v.) to give up, as to superior power or authority; to produce or provide, to generate

yoke (v.) to join, link

Z

zealot (n.) an excessively zealous person; fanatic

zealous (adj.) fervent, filled with eagerness in pursuit of something

zephyr (n.) a gentle breeze

Other Noteworthy References

Abbey, Edwin (1852-1911). An American artist, painter and illustrator who flourished in what is now called the "Golden Age" of illustration. He is best known for his paintings of Shakespearean and Victorian subjects and for the Holy Grail Series that hangs at the Boston Public Library.

Abraham Lincoln Brigade. American volunteers who fought on the "Republican" side during the Spanish Civil War (1936-39) against General Francisco Franco and the Loyalists, many of them communist in their sympathies. The volunteers were strongly susceptible to Bolshevik influence during the war.

Academy Award. Awards given annually by the Academy of Motion Picture Arts and Sciences to various categories of excellence in film.

Adler Planetarium. Founded and built in 1930 by Chicago philanthropist Max Adler, it was the first planetarium and astronomy museum built in the Western Hemisphere. It is the oldest in existence today.

Aetna. A small residential community of Gary, IN three miles east of downtown. Founded in 1881 as the site of the Aetna Powder Company, a munitions plant, it was annexed by Gary in 1924.

Aetna Powder Company (1881-1919). A munitions plant founded in 1881 in an area three miles east of what would become Gary, IN in 1906. The plant closed in 1919 after the end of WWI, later growing into a small residential subdivision of the city.

Afrika Korps. The German expeditionary force in Africa during the North African Campaign of World War II.

agent provocateur. An undercover agent who acts to entice others to commit an illegal or rash act or falsely implicate them in partaking in an illegal act

Amati. A family of violin makers who flourished in Cremona, Italy from 1538 to 1740. Their violins are considered equal to those of the Bergonzi, Guarneri and Stradivari families.

Ambassador Apartments. Fashionable apartment building located at 574 Monroe Street in Gary, IN.

America First Committee. Organized in 1940, it was the foremost non-interventionist pressure group against the American entry into World War II. Peaking at 800,000 paid members in 450 chapters, it was one of the largest anti-war organizations in American history. It shut down after the attack on Pearl Harbor.

American League for Peace and Democracy. Communist front group in the United States originally founded as the American League Against War and Fascism in 1933. It adopted the above name in 1937. Its membership, which included members of the Roosevelt administration, was based primarily in the working class and its leadership was largely socialist and communist. It was dissolved in 1939 after the Molotov-Ribbentrop Pact discouraged its non-communist members.

American Peace Mobilization. This group was created in 1940 from the remains of the American League for Peace and Democracy (previously known as the Comintern affiliate American League Against War and Fascism) and the Hollywood Anti-Nazi League, both of which were dissolved following the signing of the Molotov-Ribbentrop pact in 1939.

American Union of Swedish Singers. A Swedish-American male singing federation founded in 1892.

Amtorg Trading Corporation. An American company organized in 1924 by Armand Hammer on behalf of the Soviet Union to promote trade with the United States. It engaged in industrial espionage and also served as a front for Soviet political espionage.

Antisemitism. Prejudice against, hatred of, or discrimination against Jews as a national, ethnic, religious or racial group.

Archangel (Arkhangelsk). A city and the administrative center of Arkhangelsk Oblast, Russia. It lies on both banks of the Northern Dvina River near its exit into the White Sea, in the north of European Russia. During both world wars, Arkhangelsk was a major port of entry for Allied aid. During World War II, the city became known in the West as one of the two main destinations (along with Murmansk) of the Arctic Convoys bringing supplies to assist the Russians who were cut off from their normal supply lines.

Årjäng. Locality in the western Swedish province of Värmland about 20 kilometers from Norway.

Armistice. A temporary suspension of hostilities by agreement of the warring parties; truce. World War I ended with the Armistice of 1918.

Art Deco. An eclectic artistic and design style which had its origins in Paris in the first decades of the 20th century.

Axis Powers. The nations that fought in the World War II against the Allied forces. The Axis powers were united by their opposition to the West and the Soviet Union. They described their goals as breaking the hegemony of plutocratic-capitalist Western powers and defending civilization from communism.

Avietenaite, Madeleine (1893-1983). Born in Worcester, MA, she was head of the Lithuanian Red Cross, Lithuanian Information Service, and Commissioner-General of the Lithuanian Pavilion at the 1939 New York World's Fair. Published samizdat publications in Kaunas during the Nazi occupation of Lithuania along with Father Stasys Yla.

Axis. The alliance of Germany and Italy in 1936, later Japan and other nations, that opposed the Allies in World War II.

Balfe, Michael (1808-1870). An Irish composer, best-known for his opera *The Bohemian Girl*. After a short career as a violinist, Balfe pursued an operatic singing career, while he began to compose. In a career spanning more than 40 years, he composed 38 operas, almost 250 songs and other works.

Balkan Bakery. Bakery owned and operated by Alex Christoff and located at 1337 Adams Street in Gary's Central District.

Balkan Federation. The concept of a Balkan Federation emerged in the late 19th century from among left political forces in the region. The central aim was to establish a new political unity, a common federal republic unifying the Balkan Peninsula on the basis of internationalism, socialism, social solidarity, and economic equality.

Baltic countries. Lithuanian, Latvia and Estonia, all located on the Baltic Sea, and occupied by the Soviet Union in 1940 under the terms of the Molotov-Ribbentrop Pact. Their people suffered from mass deportations and genocide during the Stalin era, as well as occupation by the German army. They regained their independence in 1990.

Baltic Sea. A sea located between Central and Northern Europe and bordering the countries of Poland, Lithuania, Latvia, Estonia, Russia, Finland, Sweden, Germany, and Denmark, and draining into the Kattegat.

bandeau. A simple brassiere

Barrows, Alice (1878-1954). Active in education reform efforts in the first half of the 20th century, and later an official in the U.S. Office of Education, Alice Barrows was heavily involved in promoting William A. Wirt's Work-Study-Play System in the New York Public Schools in 1916-18. A member of the communist party since 1919, she was the Executive Secretary of the National Council of American-Soviet Friendship, a communist front group during WWII, and passed secrets to Soviet agents.

Bastiat, Claude Frederic (1801-1850). A French classical liberal theorist, political economist, and member of the French assembly notable for his pamphlet *The Law* (1850). His free market ideas have had a profound impact on libertarian thought and the Austrian school of economics.

Battle of Britain. Major aerial campaign fought during the summer and autumn of 1940 in which the German Luftwaffe tried to gain air superiority over the Royal Air Force as a prelude to launching Operation Sea Lion. The Germans lost 1,636 aircraft during the campaign compared to 1,087 British losses, forcing the Germans to postpone the invasion indefinitely.

Beaux-Arts Style. A very rich, lavish and heavily ornamented classical style taught at L'Ecole des Beaux Arts in Paris in the 19th century. It influenced the last phase of Neoclassicism in the United States, including Grand Central Station in New York.

Bellevue Hotel. Hotel in Washington, DC near the U.S. Capitol where Walter Krivitsky was assassinated in 1941.

Benchley, Robert (1889-1945). American humorist, writer, and film actor, known for his humorous articles and comedic movie shorts.

Bill of Rights. The first ten Amendments to the U.S. Constitution providing a formal statement of the fundamental rights of the people of the United States.

Björling, Jussi (1911-1960). Swedish tenor considered by many to have been the greatest singer of the 20th century. He sang at the Met from 1938 until his untimely death in 1960, with the exception of the war years. His operatic repertoire focused on the works of Puccini, Verdi, Gounod, Mascagni, and Leoncavallo. He was also a prolific recitalist, particularly in the United States.

Black Army. Armed groups of workers formed after the Russian Revolution and before the final Bolshevik suppression of other leftwing groups. They were the main strike force of the anarchists during the Russian Civil War.

Black Maria. A slang term for an enclosed police van used to transport prisoners, such as in the former Soviet Union.

Black market. The black, or underground, market is economic activity involving the buying and selling of merchandise or services illegally. The goods themselves may be illegal to sell (such as weapons or illegal drugs); the goods may be stolen; or the goods may be otherwise legal, but sold illicitly to avoid tax payments or licensing requirements.

Black Sea. A sea in Southeastern Europe bounded by Europe, Anatolia and the Caucasus, which drains through the Mediterranean into the Atlantic Ocean, via the Aegean Seas and various straits.

Blitz. Shortened from German 'Blitzkrieg', "lightning war"), it was the period of sustained strategic bombing of the United Kingdom by Nazi Germany during the World War II.

Bobbie-soxers. A 1940s sociological term applied to the often very zealous fans of Swing music, in particular its creators like singer Frank Sinatra, the first singing teen idol. Bobby soxers were usually teenage girls and young adult women from about 12 to 25.

Bohr, Niels (1885-1962). Danish physicist who made foundational contributions to understanding atomic structure and quantum theory, for which he received the Nobel Prize in Physics in 1922.

Bolshevik Old Guard. Those who were members of the Bolshevik party before the Russian Revolution of 1917, many of whom were either tried and executed by the NKVD during Stalin era purges, or died under suspicious circumstances.

Bolsheviks. The more radical majority of the Russian Social Democratic Party that advocated the abrupt and violent seizure of power by the proletariat (workers).

Bolshoi Opera Company. The Bolshoi Theatre was founded in Moscow in 1776 as a venue for ballet, opera and theatre. The opera company specializes in the classics of Russian opera, including Mussorgsky's *Boris Godunov*, Glinka's *A Life for the Tsar*, and Rimsky-Korsakov's *The Tsar's Bride*, Borodin's *Price Igor*, as well as the operas of Tchaikovsky.

Boris Goudunov. Major Russian opera composed by Modest Mussorgsky (1839-1881).

Brahms, Johannes (1833-1897). Leading German composer and pianist of the Romantic era.

Bridgeport Engineering Institute. A Connecticut technical college later acquired by Fairfield University in 1994.

Brighton. A town on the south coast of Great Britain famous as a health resort and for sea bathing.

British Military Intelligence (or Secret Intelligence Service). The agency which supplies the British Government with foreign intelligence.

Brotherhood of Sleeping Car Porters. Organized in 1925, this was first labor organization led by blacks to receive a charter from the American Federation of Labor (AFL).

Bulwinkle, Alfred (1883-1950). Democratic Congressman from North Carolina from 1933-1943.

Bulwinkle Committee. A committee of the U.S. House of Representatives headed by Democrat Congressman Alfred Bulwinkle (1883-1950) charged with investigating William A. Wirt's charges of communist infiltration into the Roosevelt administration for the purpose of collapsing the American economic system. The investigation was a result of charges Wirt made after attending a cocktail party in the home of Alice Barrows, a woman who was later found to be a member of the communist party.

Calumet Region Historical Guide. Between 1935 and 1942, the Federal Writer's Project of the Works Progress Administration (WPA) produced state guide books for 48 states, as well as for those for several territories and cities. The book for the Calumet Region was published in 1939.

Capra, Frank (1897-1991). Italian-born American film director responsible for many Academy Award-winning films, including *It Happened One Night, Lost Horizon, Mr. Smith Goes to Washington,* and *It's a Wonderful Life.* He also directed the World War II series *Why We Fight.*

Carmichael, Hoagy. A graduate of Indiana University, Hoagy Carmichael was an American composer, pianist, singer, actor, and bandleader. He is best known for composing the music for *Stardust, Georgia on My Mind, The Nearness of You,* and *Heart and Soul,* four of the most-recorded American songs of all time.

Catholic Youth Organization (CYO). An organization for young Catholics organized in 1930 by Bishop Bernard J. Sheil of Chicago.

Central District (Gary). A large residential and commercial district of Gary, Indiana located south of the Wabash Railroad tracks at 9th Avenue and extending to the Little Calumet River at about 28th Avenue. It was originally inhabited by the multi-ethnic and black population of Gary.

Century of Progress International Exposition. The name given to the World's Fair held in Chicago in 1933-34 celebrating the city's centennial. It was held on the Near South Side near Soldier Field and the Chicago Museum Complex. Unlike the classically inspired Columbian Exposition of 1893, the Century of Progress was modernist in outlook.

Chandler, Raymond (1888-1859). An American novelist and screenwriter, Chandler had an immense stylistic influence on American popular literature, and is considered by many to be one of the founders of the hard-boiled school of detective fiction.

chattering classes. a generally derogatory term often used by pundits and political commentators to refer to a politically active, socially concerned and highly educated section of the metropolitan middle class, especially those with political, media, and academic connections.

Chicago Loop. The central business district of Chicago, Illinois. The origin of the term *loop* is derived from the cable car, or elevated trains, turning loops in the downtown area.

Chicago, South Bend & South Shore Railroad. An interurban electric railroad line connecting Chicago with Hammond, East Chicago, Gary, Michigan City and South Bend.

Christie, Agatha (1890-1976). English author of 66 detective novels and 14 short story collections she wrote under her own name, most of which revolve around the investigations of such characters as Hercule Poirot, Miss Jane Marple, and Tommy and Tuppence. She also wrote the world's longest-running play, *The Mousetrap.*

Cleveland, Grover (1837-1908). The 22nd and 24th President of the United States; as such, he is the only president to serve non-consecutive terms. A classical liberal, he called out the troops to quell the Pullman strike in 1894.

Club SAR. Social, athletic and recreational organization founded in the 1930s to serve the people of Gary's Central District. Its organizers included future mayor, George Chacharis.

Cockcroft, Sir John (1897-1967). A British physicist who shared the Nobel Prize in Physics for splitting the atomic nucleus with Ernest Walton, and was instrumental in the development of nuclear power.

Columbian Exposition. Officially the World's Columbian Exposition (also called "White City"), it was the world's fair held in Chicago in 1893 to celebrate the 400th anniversary of Columbus' arrival in the New World in 1892. Classical in design, the fairgrounds occupied an area on the shore of Lake Michigan in Jackson Park. The Museum of Science and Industry, originally the Palace of Fine Arts, is the only surviving building from the fair.

Communist Party USA. Founded in 1919, this Marxist-Leninist political party is the largest communist party in the United States. Guided and financed by the Communist Party of the USSR from its inception, it has a long, complex history that is closely related to the histories of similar communist parties worldwide and the U.S. labor movement.

Corinthian. Of or relating to ancient Corinth or its people or culture; elaborate and ornate Greek columns

Coutan, Jules Felix (1848-1939). French sculptor and educator, best known in the United States for the sculptural group above the entrance to Grand Central Terminal in New York City.

Crimean Peninsula. Formerly a part of the Soviet Union, the Crimean Peninsula is located in the Ukraine on the northern coast of the Black Sea and on the western coast of the Sea of Azov. In 2014, the Russian Federation, under Vladimir Putin, ciaimed de facto sovereignty over the Crimean Peninsula.

Cromer, Melba (1903-1965). Born in Ashtabula, OH, Melba Cromer was a graduate of the Columbia School of Music. She taught music at Emerson School from 1929 until her death in 1965 (36 years). She was a member of the Auditorium Department and the school's primary accompanist. She lived in Hotel Gary and was admittedly fond of boogie woogie.

Currie, Lauchlin (1902-1993). A Canadian-born U.S. economist who served as White House economic adviser to President Franklin Roosevelt during World War II (1939 to 1945). He was identified as a communist and member of the Silvermaster spy ring by Whittaker Chambers and Elizabeth Bentley, a fact confirmed by the VENONA decrypts.

Dalsland. Western Swedish province located south of Värmland and west of Lake Vänern, the largest lake in Sweden.

David Copperfield. A novel published by English author Charles Dickens in 1850.

Democrat Party. Tracing its origins back to the Democratic-Republican Party, the modern Democratic Party was founded around 1828 and is one of the two major contemporary political parties in the United States, along with the younger Republican Party. Since the 1930s, the party has promoted a social-liberal platform, supporting social justice and a mixed economy.

Der Fueher's Face. A satirical musical number performed by Spike Jones and His City Slickers that mocked Adolf Hitler and the Nazis. Released in 1942, it was a parody of the Nazi anthem, the "Horst Wessel Song."

Dies, Martin (1900-1972). A Democratic member of the U.S. House of Representatives from 1931-1945, and 1953-1959, Dies was the first chairman of the Special Committee to Investigate Un-American Activities (HUAC).

Doc Savage. A fictional character originally published in American pulp magazines during the 1930s and 1940s. The heroic-adventure character would go on to appear in other media, including radio, film, comic books, and paperback books.

Dorsey, Tommy (1905-1956). An American jazz trombonist, trumpeter, composer, and bandleader of the Big Band era. He was known as "The Sentimental Gentleman of Swing", because of his smooth-toned trombone playing. He led a successful band from the 1930s into the 1950s. Frank Sinatra, Jo Stafford and the Pied Pipers were among his vocalists.

Do svidaniya (Russian). Translates as "till we meet again," or "goodbye."

Draugas (Friend). Lithuanian World-Wide Daily published in Chicago since 1909.

Dudley, Frank (1868-1957). An American landscape painter most noteworthy for his depictions of the Indiana Dunes. Also an important figure in Indiana dunes conservation, leading to the creation of the Indiana Dunes State Park in 1923 and Indiana Dunes National Seashore in 1974.

Duma. The Russian constituent assembly. First constituted by Czar Nicholas II in 1906, it was dissolved in 1917 by the Bolsheviks.

Duranty, Walter (1884-1957). Anglo-American journalist who served as the Moscow Bureau Chief of *The New York Times* (1922–36) and won a Pulitzer Prize in 1932 for a series of stories on the Soviet Union. As an apologist for the Stalin regime, Duranty denied the widespread famine and the Ukraine mass starvation (1932–33). Years later, there were calls to revoke his Pulitzer. Even *The New York Times* acknowledged his articles constituted "some of the worst reporting to appear in this newspaper."

Eastern Front. The theatre of war in Eastern Europe during World War II between the Soviet Union and Nazi Germany.

Edgar Bergen and Charlie McCarthy. Ventriloquist Edgar Bergen and his wisecracking dummy, Charlie McCarthy, made their radio debut on the Rudy Vallee program in 1936. They were given their own show in 1937, as part of the Chase and Sanborn Hour. Their program continued until 1956 under a variety of sponsors. It was one of the most popular radio programs on the air.

Edward VII, King (1841-1910). King of England from 1901-1910, following the death of his mother, Victoria. The "Edwardian Era" was named after him.

Egyptian. Of or relating to Egypt or its people or culture; a native or inhabitant of Egypt

Egyptologist. One who studies the culture and artifacts of the ancient Egyptian civilization.

Einstein, Albert (1879-1955). German theoretical physicist and philosopher of science who developed the general theory of relativity, one of the two pillars of modern physics (alongside quantum mechanics). His letter to President Roosevelt is what served as the catalyst for the Manhattan Project.

Eisenstein, Sergei (1898-1948). A pioneering Soviet Russian film director and film theorist, often considered to be the "Father of Montage." He is noted in particular for his silent films *Strike* (1924), *Battleship Potemkin* (1925) and *October* (1927), as well as the historical epics *Alexander Nevsky* (1938) and *Ivan the Terrible* (1944). His early focus on structural issues in film drew criticism from the Soviet film community, forcing him to issue public articles of self-criticism and commitments to reform his cinematic visions to conform to the increasingly specific doctrines of socialist realism.

Ekshärad. A locality in Hagfors Municipality of the province of Värmland, Sweden.

El Alamein. A town in Egypt located on the Mediterranean Sea, 66 miles west of Alexandria, that was the scene of two major battles during WWII.

Ellis Island. An island in upper New York harbor used as a U.S. immigrant examination station from 1892-1954.

Emerson Loyalty. School song composed in 1924 by instrumental music director, Hubert S. Warren.

Emerson School. The first unit school in Gary, Indiana, organized under William A. Wirt's Work-Study-Play system of education. Located at 716 E. 7th Avenue, the original school opened in September 1909 and closed in June 1981. It reopened in 1982 as the Emerson School for the Visual and Performing Arts which continued to use the building until 2008, when it moved to Miller. It is, arguably, the most famous public school building in America.

Ethiopia. A country located in the Horn of Africa that was invaded by the Italian army in 1935.

Eugene Onegin. A novel in verse by Alexander Pushkin published in 1833, and a classic of Russian literature.

Fabian Socialism. As it emerged in Great Britain in 1884, Fabian Socialism advocated socialism via gradualist and reformist, rather than revolutionary, means. The society laid many of the foundations of the British Labour Party. Fabians favored the same goals as many doctrinaire socialists and communists, including an animus towards private activity, property rights and entrepreneurship, while supporting high taxes, rationing, and control of individual choices.

Fadiman, Clifton (1904-1999). An American intellectual, author, editor, radio and television personality, he was the chief editor at Simon & Schuster. He also hosted the radio program *Information Please* from 1938 to 1948.

Fascism. A governmental system on the far-left of the political spectrum led by a dictator having complete power, forcibly suppressing opposition and criticism, regimenting all industry, commerce, etc., and exhibiting aggressive nationalistic and, often, racist characteristics.

Federal Bureau of Investigation (FBI). Operating under the jurisdiction of the U.S. Department of Justice, and founded in 1908, the FBI is the domestic intelligence and security service of the United States, which simultaneously serves as the nation's prime federal law enforcement agency.

Federal Theatre Project. A New Deal project to fund theatre and other live artistic performances in the United States during the Great Depression. It was one of five Federal One projects sponsored by the Works Progress Administration (WPA). The Mickey Mouse Theatre was one of these.

Fellow traveler. Person who sympathizes with the beliefs of an organization or cooperates in its activities without maintaining formal membership in that particular group.

Fermi, Enrico (1901-1954). Italian physicist, best known for his work on Chicago Pile-1 (the first nuclear reactor), and for his contributions to the development of quantum theory, nuclear and particle physics, and statistical mechanics. He is one of the men referred to as the "father of the atomic bomb."

Field Museum of Natural History. This Chicago museum originated at the Columbian Exposition of 1893 and moved from Jackson Park to its present location in 1921. It was named for its major benefactor, Marshall Field, in 1905.

fifth columnists. Persons residing in a country who are sympathetic to its enemies and serving their interests.

Five Year Plan. A list of economic goals formulated by General Secretary Joseph Stalin and based on his policy of Socialism in One Country. It was implemented in the Soviet Union between 1928 and 1932.

Flinn, Floyd (1907-1984). Born in Jasonville, Indiana, he graduated from Indiana State Teachers College (now Indiana State University) and taught general science and physics at Emerson High School from 1937 to 1959, after which he became administrative science supervisor for the Gary Public Schools from 1959 to 1972.

Founding Fathers. Political leaders and statesmen who participated in the American Revolution by signing the United States Declaration of Independence, taking part in the American Revolutionary War, and establishing the United States Constitution.

free market capitalism. A market-based economic system in which the forces of supply and demand are not controlled by a government or other authority. A free market contrasts with a controlled market or regulated market, in which government intervenes in supply and demand through non-market methods such as laws controlling who is allowed to enter the market, mandating what type of product or service is supplied, or directly setting prices.

French Revolution. A period of radical social and political upheaval in France from 1789 to 1799 that profoundly affected French and modern history, marking the decline of powerful monarchies and churches and the rise of democracy and nationalism.

Frigidaire. An American brand of consumer and commercial appliances. The brand was so well known in the refrigeration field in the early 20th century that many Americans called any refrigerator, whatever its brand, a "Frigidaire".

Froebel School. The second unit school built in Gary, Indiana under the superintendency of William A. Wirt (1874-1938). It opened in 1912 on a 15-acre tract of land at 15th and Madison St. in the multi-ethnic Central District.

Front organization. Any entity set up by and controlled by another organization , such as intelligence agencies, organized crime groups, banned organizations, such as the Communist Party USA.

Gardner, Earle Stanley (1889-1970). A lawyer and author of detective fiction who is probably best known for the Perry Mason mystery series.

Gary-Alerding Settlement House. This urban settlement house opened at 15th and Van Buren Streets in Gary's Central District in 1923 with donations of $100,000 from Judge Elbert H. Gary, and $30,000 from Bishop Herman J. Alerding of the Fort Wayne Diocese, of which Gary was then a part. The complex included St. Anthony's Chapel, designed to serve chiefly Mexican, Italian, and Spanish families of Gary. It closed in 1971.

Gary, Elbert H. (1846-1927). An American lawyer, county judge and corporate officer who was a key founder of U.S. Steel in 1901 and its chairman of the board for 25 years. When the world's largest steel mill was built on the southern shore of Lake Michigan in 1906, the board decided to name the city in his honor.

Gary College. Launched by William A. Wirt in 1932, Gary College was an attempt to provide area students with an opportunity to earn college credits locally and at low cost. Wirt's expanded educational vision for the city embraced an accredited junior college and, perhaps, a four-year program.

Gary, Indiana. A city in northwest Indiana on the shores of Lake Michigan. Founded in 1906 by the United States Corporation, which built the world's largest steel mill there, it was named after Elbert H. Gary, its chairman of the board.

Gary Plan. Another name for William A. Wirt's 'Work-Study-Play' system of education, particularly as it was promoted as a model in New York City and other urban centers.

Gary Post-Tribune. Newspaper published in Gary, Indiana from 1907 to 2000, when it moved its editorial offices to Merrillville. Following its acquisitions by the Sun-Times Media Group, its printing was consolidated with the Sun-Times in 2007. Founded as the *Gary Weekly*, it changed its name to the *Gary Tribune* in 1908, when it became a daily. It became the *Gary Post-Tribune* in 1923 after merging with the *Gary Evening Post*. It dropped the name Gary from its masthead in 1966 in an effort to broaden its regional appeal. From 1923 to 1986, it was a weekday evening paper and a morning weekend paper. It is now a morning paper.

George V (1865-1936). King of the United Kingdom and the British Dominions, and Emperor of India, from 6 May 1910 until his death in 1936. He was the grandson of Queen Victoria.

Gestapo. The German internal security police under the Nazi regime, known for its terrorist methods directed against those suspected of treason or questionable loyalty.

Glasgow. The largest city in Scotland, and the third largest in Great Britain. It is situated on the River Clyde in the country's West Central Lowlands. It was once famous for its shipbuilding industry.

Golden Gloves. The name given to annual competitions for amateur boxing in the United States.

Golden Tornado. The name for the football team at Emerson High School in Gary, IN.

Good Templars. A Sweden-based temperance society that encourages sobriety and abstinence from the use of alcohol.

Gordon, Henry "Hank" (1925-1996). A 1943 Emerson High School graduate and 1950 Purdue graduate in aeronautical engineering, he was an American astronaut and a colonel in the United States Air Force. He worked on the Boeing X-20 Dyna-Soar program. He flew combat missions in the Korean and Vietnam wars.

Gothenburg. The second largest city in Sweden and the fifth largest in the Nordic countries was the major point of embarkation for Swedish immigrants to the United States.

Gotland. Island in the Baltic Sea belonging to Sweden.

Grand Central Terminal. Built in 1913, a commuter (and former intercity) railroad terminal at 42nd Street and Park Avenue in Midtown Manhattan in New York City. One of the world's most famous and attractive train stations.

Great Lakes Naval Training Station. Completed in 1911, it is the home of the United States Navy's only boot camp, located near North Chicago, in Lake County, Illinois.

Great Purge. A campaign of political repression in the Soviet Union from 1934 to 1939, orchestrated by Joseph Stalin. It included a large-scale purge of the Communist Party and government officials, repression of peasants and the Red Army leadership, and widespread police surveillance, suspicion of "saboteurs", imprisonment, and arbitrary executions.

Great Soviet Experiment. A euphemism applied to the Bolshevik Revolution and the repressive and genocidal totalitarian state it created under Vladimir Lenin and, later, Joseph Stalin. Many naifs in the West, particularly in the intellectual and chattering classes, applied this term to what they viewed as the wave of the future.

Great War. Prior to WWII, WWI was called the "Great War." Fought between 1914 and 1918, it pitted the Triple Entente (England, France and Russia and, later, the U.S.) against the Central Powers of Germany and Austria-Hungary. More than 9 million combatants were killed in the war whose aftermath set the conditions for the rise of Hitler and Nazi Germany, and the success of the Russian Revolution.

Grieger, Hazel (1906-1993). Born in Wanatah, IN, she taught American history and English at Emerson from 1937-1971. She was a world traveler and recipient of the Freedom Foundation's Award for Classroom Teaching in 1962.

Gulag. The government agency that administered the main Soviet forced labor camp systems during the Stalin era, from the 1930s until the 1950s.

Gypsy. A member of a traditionally itinerant people who originated in northern India and now live chiefly in south and southwest Asia, Europe, and North America.

Hagfors. A city in the Swedish province of Värmland

Hälsa dem där hemma. Greet those at home, a Swedish folk song popular among Swedish immigrants.

Hammett, Dashiell (1894-1961). American author of hard-boiled detective novels, short stories, and screenplays. He created the characters of Sam Spade (*The Maltese Falcon*), and Nick and Nora Charles (The Thin Man series).

Harrison, Hazel (1899-1983). A graduate of Northwestern University, Hazel Harrison taught Auditorium at Emerson High School from 1929 to 1952 (26 years). As the head of the Auditorium Department, she wrote numerous plays performed by Emerson students, and elsewhere across the country.

Hellman, Lillian (1905-1984). An American author of plays, screenplays, and memoirs who supported a variety of left-wing political causes during her life, and was an uncritical apologist for Joseph Stalin.

Hepburn, Katherine (1907-2003). An American actress of film, stage, and television known for her headstrong independence and spirited personality. She was a leading lady in Hollywood for more than 60 years, and appeared in everything from screwball comedy to literary drama, receiving four Academy Awards for Best Actress. In 1999, she was named by the American Film Institute as the greatest female star in Hollywood history.

H. Gordon's & Sons. Better quality Gary, Indiana department store located at 801 Broadway. Opened in Tolleston in 1906, it moved to Broadway in 1923 and to this location in 1935. It closed in the 1970s.

Hilton, James (1900-1954). English novelist best remembered for several best-sellers, including Lost Horizon, Goodbye Mr. Chips, and Random Harvest, all of which were made into highly regarded films.

Himalayan Mountains. Home of the earth's highest peaks, including the highest, Mount Everest. The Himalayan range separates the Indian subcontinent from the Tibetan plateau.

His Master's Voice (HVM). A gramophone company founded in England that manufactured both record players and records. The trademark of the dog Nipper was used by the Victor Talking Machine Company, later RCA, in the United States.

Hiss, Alger (1904-1996). An American lawyer, government official, author, and lecturer. He was involved in the establishment of the United Nations both as a U.S. State Department and U.N. official, and served as a close advisor to President Roosevelt during the sensitive Dumbarton Oaks and Yalta conferences. Hiss was accused by Whittaker Chambers of being a Soviet spy in 1948 and convicted of perjury in connection with this charge in 1950. He did more damage to American and European security interests than any other communist spy in the U.S. government.

Hitler, Adolf (1889-1945). Austrian-born German politician and leader of the National Socialist German Workers Party (commonly known as the Nazi Party). He was Chancellor of Germany from 1933 to 1945, and served as head of state as Führer und Reichskanzler from 1934 to 1945.

Hitler-Stalin Pact (see also **Molotov-Ribbentrop Pact). A** non-aggression pact between Nazi Germany and the Soviet Union signed in Moscow in the late hours of August 23, 1939. The treaty also included a secret protocol that divided territories of Romania, Poland, Lithuania, Latvia, Estonia and Finland into Nazi and Soviet "spheres of influence," in anticipation of potential "territorial and political rearrangements" of these countries.

Honolulu. Capital of the State of Hawaii, on the island of Oahu.

Housatonic River. A river approximately 149 miles (240 km) long that begins in western Massachusetts and western Connecticut and flows south to southeast, and drains about 1,950 square miles (5,100 km2) of southwestern Connecticut into Long Island Sound.

House Committee on Un-American Activities. An investigative committee of the United States House of Representatives, it was created in 1938 to investigate alleged disloyalty and subversive activities on the part of private citizens, public employees, and those organizations suspected of having Communist or Fascist ties. President Roosevelt was quoted as saying that he didn't consider the communists as any present or future threat to the country, and suggested that Congressman Dies confine his investigations to the Fascists.

Hungarian Reformed Church. This Hungarian Protestant Church was located at 13th and Jackson Streets from 1920 to 1959, when it moved to Glen Park. It was dissolved in 2004.

Hyde Park. The neighborhood on the south side of Chicago in which the University of Chicago is located.

Illinois Central. A railroad in the central United States, with its primary routes connecting Chicago, Illinois, with New Orleans, Louisiana, and Mobile, Alabama.

Inner Sanctum Mysteries. A popular radio program that aired from January 7, 1941 to October 5, 1952, and was based on the generic title given to the mystery novels of Simon and Schuster. A total of 526 episodes were broadcast. The early 1940s programs opened with Raymond Edward Johnson introducing himself in a mockingly sardonic voice.

Innocents Clubs. Western liberals and left-wing radicals who believed they were advancing the cause of social humanism, but were in fact being manipulated by the Soviet Union to advance the latter's aims. The concept of 'Innocents Clubs' was invented by Willi Münzenburg to describe the those cynically duped by the Communists.

Istanbul (formerly Constantinople). Once the capital of the Byzantine Empire, and subsequently conquered by the Ottoman Turks, Istanbul is the largest city in Turkey, constituting the country's economic, cultural, and historical heart. It straddles the Bosphorus in northwestern Turkey, between the Sea of Marmara and the Black Sea.

Jeremiah. Old Testament prophet who warned of impending disaster

Jews. A nation and ethno-religious group originating in the Israelites or Hebrews of the Ancient Near East, the Hebrew or Jewish people; members of the tribe of Judah.

Kadets. The Party of People's Freedom was a liberal political party in the Russian Empire. They were allied with the White Russians against the Bolsheviks during the Russian Civil War. Party members were called Kadets.

Kaunas. Second largest city in Lithuania; the only provisional capital in Europe during the interwar period.

Kerensky, Alexander (1881-1970). A major political leader before and during the Russian Revolutions of 1917, Kerensky served as the second Prime Minister of the Russian Provisional Government until it was overthrown by the Bolsheviks under Vladimir Lenin in the October Revolution. He spent the rest of his life in exile, dying in New York City in 1970 at the age of 89.

Kipling, Rudyard (1865-1936). An English short-story writer, poet, and novelist. He is chiefly remembered for his tales and poems of British soldiers in India and his tales for children.

Klaipeda. Third largest city in Lithuania situated at the mouth of the Danė River where it flows into the Baltic Sea.

Klug, William (1912-1983). Emerson basketball coach and defensive specialist who led basketball team to NW Indiana crown in first season coaching at Emerson.

Kneeland, Hildegarde (1889-1994). A senior economist in the Agriculture Department during the New Deal who was also a secret member of the Communist Party USA and later identified as a an intelligence contact and informer in the KGB Archives. She maintained contact with the Perlo Group, a notorious underground party apparatus.

Koestler, Arthur (1905-1983). Hungarian-British writer and journalist whose political odyssey from communism to anti-communism informed his political novels, including *Darkness at Noon* (1940). He was a major 20th century voice against totalitarianism.

Kotora, Anne (later Anne K. Mistrovich/Masters) (1915-2002). Born in Gary, she graduated from Emerson High School in 1932 and Ball State Teachers' College in 1938. A violinist, she taught instrumental music at Emerson from 1938 to 1972 (34 years). She died in Cincinnati, OH.

Kramer, Charles (1906-?). Born Charles Krevisky, he was an American economist who worked for U.S. President Franklin D. Roosevelt as part of his brain trust. Evidence of Kramer's membership in the Communist Party USA (CPUSA) and his contacts with known Soviet agents comes from several sources, including the direct testimony of Whittaker Chambers, Elizabeth

Bentley, Lee Pressman, and Nathaniel Weyl; the Venona decrypts; and the Moscow archives of the Soviet Foreign Intelligence Service (SVR).

Kremlin. The seat of governmental power in the former Soviet Union, and presently the Russian government.

Krivitsky, Walter (1899-1941). The highest ranking Soviet intelligence officer to defect to the West in the years before WWII who revealed the plans of the Nazi-Soviet non-aggression pact weeks before the outbreak of war. He wrote an inside account of Stalin's underhanded methods titled *In Stalin's Secret Service* published in 1939, after appearing serially in the *Saturday Evening Post*.

Kulaks. The word kulak originally referred to independent farmers in the Russian Empire who emerged from the peasantry and became wealthy following the Stolypin reform, which began in 1906. The label of kulak was broadened in 1918 to include peasants who resisted handing over their grain to detachments from Moscow. During 1929-1933, Stalin's leadership of the total campaign to collectivize the peasantry meant that "peasants with a couple of cows or five or six acres more than their neighbors" were being labeled "kulaks." According to the political theory of Marxism–Leninism of the early 20th century, the kulaks were class enemies of the poorer peasants.

L. Short for elevated train, as in Chicago's Loop.

Larsson, Carl (1853-1919). One of the most popular Swedish artists of the late 19th and early 20th centuries. His illustrations of home and farm life have been wildly popular with Swedes and Swedish-Americans for more than a hundred years.

League of Nations. An intergovernmental organization founded as a result of the Paris Peace Conference that ended the First World War. It was the first international organization whose principal mission was to maintain world peace. Its primary goals included preventing wars through collective security and disarmament, and settling international disputes through negotiation and arbitration.

Lee, Adele Bohling (1898-1975). Auditorium and music teacher in the Gary Public Schools, including both Froebel and William A. Wirt. A composer of music and operettas, including *Hats Off*, *Words and Music*, and *Ask the Professor*.

Lend Lease. Formally titled *An Act to Further Promote the Defense of the United States*, and enacted March 11, 1941, it was a program under which the United States supplied Great Britain, Free France, the Republic of China and later the USSR and other Allied nations with materiel between 1941 and August 1945.

Lenin (Vladimir Ilyich Ulyanov) (1870-1924). Russian Marxist revolutionary and communist politician who led the October Revolution of 1917. His ruthless policies were responsible for death of thousands of his fellow countrymen.

Leningrad. Formerly Petrograd, or St. Petersburg, this second largest city of the former Soviet Union was renamed Leningrad in 1924, following the death of Vladimir Lenin. It suffered through a siege lasting from September 1941 to 1944 in which over 600,000 residents died.

Link, Maurine (1909-2015). A 1928 graduate of Emerson High School, Maureen Link subsequently worked in the office at Emerson from 1928 to 1974, many of these as secretary to Principal Everett A. Spaulding. Her tenure of 46 years was the longest of any Emerson staff member.

Lithuania. Largest of the three Baltic states, Lithuania gained its independence from Russia in 1918, but was later forcibly occupied by the Soviet Union in May 1940, and, then, by Nazi Germany from 1941-1944. It became part of the Soviet Union, again, from 1944 until 1990 when it regained its independence.

Lithuanian Pavilion. An exhibit at the 1939 New York World's Fair that showcased Lithuania's history and achievements during the brief period when the country enjoyed independence.

Loyalist. One who maintains loyalty to an established government, political party, or sovereign, especially during war or revolutionary change. In this instance, it refers to those allied with the Spanish Republic and opposed to the Nationalists under General Fernando Franco during the Spanish Civil War (1936-1939). Its loosely based coalition included centrists, communists, socialists and anarchists, including the Soviet Union. The Nationalists were supported by Nazi Germany. In many ways, it was a proxy war between the Soviet Union and Nazi Germany. American leftists fought in the war under the banner of the 'Abraham Lincoln Brigade.'

Lubyanka. Popular name for the headquarters of the KGB (formerly the NKVD) and affiliated prison on Lubyanka Square in Moscow, Russia.

Luftwaffe. Founded in 1935, the Luftwaffe was the aerial warfare branch of the German Wehrmacht (Defense Force) during World War II.

Lugan. Nickname, sometimes pejorative, for a Lithuanian that is said to have originated in Chicago where the largest Lithuanian population in the U.S. is located.

Lyons, Eugene (1898-1985). An American journalist and writer. A fellow traveler of Communism in his younger years, Lyons became highly critical of the Soviet Union and Communism after several years there as a correspondent of United Press International.

Macedonia. An ancient kingdom in the Balkan Peninsula, in Southern Europe: now constituting a region in Northern Greece, Southwest Bulgaria, and the Republic of Macedonia; formerly a constituent republic of Yugoslavia. The Republic of Macedonia declared its independence in 1991.

Manhattan Project. A research and development project that produced the first atomic bombs during World War II. The Manhattan Project operated under a blanket of tight security, but Soviet atomic spies still penetrated the program. On December 2, 1942, in a racquets court underneath the West Stands of Stagg Field at the University of Chicago, a team of scientists led by Enrico Fermi created man's first controlled, self-sustaining nuclear chain reaction.

Marian Order. The Marians of the Immaculate Conception are a Congregation of more than 500 priests and brothers in 19 countries around the world, including a number of Lithuanians. For many years, it published *Draugas,* the Lithuanian World-Wide Daily, which was founded in Chicago in 1909.

Markham, Beryl (1902-1986). A British-born Kenyan author, aviator, adventurer, and racehorse trainer. During the pioneer days of aviation, she became the first woman to fly solo across the Atlantic from east to west. She is now primarily remembered as the author of the memoir West with the Night.

Marshall Field's. Iconic department store which opened at State and Randolph Streets in Chicago in 1902. Acquired by Macy's in 2005.

Marxism-Leninism. A political ideology combining the scientific socialist concepts developed by Karl Marx and Friedrich Engels, collectively known as Marxism, with the theoretical expansions developed by Vladimir Lenin, collectively known as Leninism, which consist of anti-imperialism, democratic centralism, and party-building principles. Marxism-Leninism was the official ideology of the Communist Party of the Soviet Union and of the Communist International (1919-1943), making it the guiding ideology of the world communist movement. As such, it is the most prominent ideology associated with "Communism."

Master Race. The expression used by the Nazis in Germany for the race they wanted to create — a pure race of white people suited to rule the world.

Mauretania. The RMS Mauretania was an ocean liner built for the British Cunard Line, and launched on September 20, 1907. It was the world's largest and fastest ship until the launch of the RMS Olympic in 1911. Mauretania became a favorite among her passengers. After capturing the Blue Riband for the fastest transatlantic crossing during her 1909 inaugural season, Mauretania held the speed record for twenty years. Many immigrants made their crossing in the Mauretania, including those from Sweden.

Mein Kampf (My Struggle). An autobiographical manifesto published by Nazi leader Adolf Hitler in 1925-26, in which he outlines his political ideology and future plans for Germany.

Melgounov, Sergey (1879-1956). A Russian historian, publicist and politician best known for his opposition to the Soviet government and his numerous works on the Russian Revolution of 1917 and the Russian Civil War. His most famous book is *Red Terror in Russia*, published in 1924.

Mendelssohn, Felix (1809-1847). Leading symphonic composer of the Romantic era.

Mercader, Ramón (1913-1978). A Spanish communist who assassinated the Russian Marxist revolutionary Leon Trotsky in 1940, in Mexico. Declassified archives have shown that he was a Soviet agent.

Metro. Russian subway.

Middle East. A region that roughly encompasses a majority of Western Asia (excluding the Caucasus) and Egypt. The term is used as a synonym for Near East, in opposition to Far East. Arabs, Persians, and Turks constitute the largest ethnic groups in the region by population.

Midway, Battle of. A major sea battle marking the turning point of the war in the Pacific during World War II. On June 4, 1942, US aircraft flying from USS Enterprise, USS Hornet, and USS Yorktown attacked and sunk four Japanese carriers, forcing Admiral Yamamoto to withdraw.

Miller, Arthur (1915-2005). A prolific American playwright and essayist who wrote *Death of Salesman* and *The Crucible*, among other works. His political views and associations were decidedly left of center, and admitted helping many communist front groups in the 1940s.

Minimum wage. The lowest hourly, daily or monthly remuneration that employers may legally pay to workers. Equivalently, it is the lowest wage at which workers may sell their labor. It was introduced in the U.S. in 1938.

Molotov-Ribbentrop Pact (see also Hitler-Stalin Pact). A non-aggression pact signed in Moscow in the late hours of August 23, 1939 by the foreign ministers of Germany and the Soviet Union. The treaty also included a secret protocol that divided territories of Romania, Poland, Lithuania, Latvia, Estonia and Finland into Nazi and Soviet "spheres of influence," in anticipation of potential "territorial and political rearrangements" of these countries.

Monarchist. One who supports monarchy, e.g. the rule of the Tsar in Russia.

Moorish. Of or pertaining to a style of Spanish architecture from the time of the Moors.

Mrs. Miniver. Academy Award-winning film of a British family struggling to survive during the early months of WWII. Won awards for Best Picture, Best Actress (Greer Garson), Best Supporting Actress (Teresa Wright), and Best Director (William Wyler). Released June 4, 1942.

Museum of Science and Industry. This museum was opened in Chicago in 1933 in the former Palace of Fine Arts from the Columbian Exposition of 1893.

Mutual Broadcasting Network. An American radio network in operation from 1934 to 1999 during the golden age of U.S. radio drama. Mutual was best known as the original network home of *The Lone Ranger* and *The Adventures of Superman* and as the long-time radio residence of *The Shadow*.

Nancy Drew. A fictional girl detective in a mystery fiction series created by publisher Edward Stratemeyer and first appearing in 1930. The books have been ghostwritten by a number of authors under the collective pseudonym Carolyn Keene.

National Council of American Soviet Friendship. A communist front group which revolved around the *Friends of the Soviet Union*, founded in 1929. One of the major goals of the movement was to advance Soviet aims in the United States and lure unsuspecting liberals to serve Soviet purposes. Originally called the National Council on Soviet Relations, its name was changed to the NCASF in 1941. See **Alice Barrows**.

National Socialism. The name used for political ideologies which propose to merge nationalism and socialism, as was realized by the Nazi Party in Germany.

Negro (archaic). A member of a dark-skinned group of peoples originally native to Africa south of the Sahara. Since the 1960s, the term has fallen out of favor, being replaced by Black or African-American.

Neighborhood House. Urban settlement house run by the Presbyterian Church situated at 1700 Adams Street in Gary, IN. It provided a variety of social services to the immigrant and minority populations in the Central District.

Nelson, Ozzie (1906-1975). Popular American entertainer and band leader who originated and starred in The Adventures of Ozzie and Harriet on radio and television.

New Deal. The name given to the administration of Franklin Delano Roosevelt, 1933-1945 whose aim was to restore prosperity after the Great Depression. Despite considerable effort and expense, the economy did not recover fully until after WWII and may, in fact, have been lengthened by the big government policies instituted.

New Milford. A small town in southern Litchfield County, Connecticut, 14 miles north of Danbury. It is situated on the Housatonic River and the northeastern shore of Candlewood Lake.

New Sweden. A town in Aroostook County in northern Maine founded by Swedish immigrants in 1870.

Newton, Henrietta (1889-1954). Born in Calumet Township, Houghton County, Michigan in 1889, she graduated from Northwestern University in 1914 and taught at Froebel High School from 1915 to 1918. She taught United States history and civics at Emerson High School from 1918 to 1953. Emerson's annual social studies award is named in her honor.

New York Central Railroad. The New York Central Railroad was formed on March 17, 1853 by the consolidation of a number of smaller railroads between Albany and Buffalo. It eventually comprised a large network of lines in the NE United States before merging with the Pennsylvania Railroad in 1968 to form Penn Central, which went bankrupt in 1970.

New York World's Fair, 1939-40. The second largest American fair of all time covered the 1,216 acres of Flushing Meadows-Corona Park (also the location of the 1964–1965 New York World's Fair). It was exceeded in size only by St. Louis's Louisiana Purchase Exposition of 1904.

Nicholas II, Tsar (1868-1918). The last Emperor of Russia, Grand Duke of Finland, and titular King of Poland. He and his family were murdered by the Bolsheviks during the Russian Revolution.

NKVD. The People's Commissariat for Internal Affairs, abbreviated NKVD, was a law enforcement agency of the Soviet Union that directly executed the rule of power of the All Union Communist Party. It was closely associated with the Soviet secret police which at times was part of the agency and is known for its political repression and mass executions during the era of Joseph Stalin.

"No enemies to the left." A political slogan that originated during the French Revolution and reflected successive waves of avant-garde factions taking power. It was subsequently adopted by Alexander Kerensky during the provisional government in Russia in 1917, which isolated democratic conservatives and pro-monarchist forces and emboldened the Bolsheviks.

Non-Aggression Pact (see **Molotov-Ribbentrop Pact**).

North Star Singers. Swedish male chorus founded in Bridgeport, Connecticut in 1933. A member chorus of the American Union of Swedish Singers, founded in 1892.

Norton Park. A park in Gary's Central District named for Captain Horace Norton (1869-1947), General Agent of the Gary Land Company who also represented U.S. Steel's interests in Gary's political affairs. Formerly called Tyler Park.

Nuclear pile. A primitive type of nuclear reactor designed to create a sustained fission reaction; a device in which a nuclear reaction is maintained and controlled for the production of nuclear energy.

Oahu. The third largest and most populous of the Hawaiian Islands, and home of the state capitol, Honolulu.

Odessa. A Russian port on the Crimean Peninsula.

OGPU. The Soviet Union's secret-police organization (1923–1934); later known as the NKVD (1934-1946) and, later, the KGB (1954-1991).

Operation Barbarossa. The code name for Germany's invasion of the Soviet Union on June 22, 1941 during World War II. Over four million soldiers of the Axis powers invaded the USSR along a 2,900 km (1,800 mi) front, the largest invasion in the history of warfare. In addition to troops, Barbarossa used 600,000 motor vehicles and 750,000 horses.

Opiate of the masses. What Marx called religion.

Oppenheimer, Robert (1904-1967). An American theoretical physicist and professor of physics at the University of California, Berkeley who is among those called the "father of the atomic bomb" for his role in the Manhattan Project, the World War II project that developed the first nuclear weapons. Like a number of intellectuals of his era, however, he was drawn to communist ideas and lent his support to communist front groups, eventually losing his security clearance.

Oriental Institute. Founded by James Henry Breasted in 1919 with funds donated by John D. Rockefeller, Jr., the Oriental Institute is the University of Chicago's archeology museum and research center for ancient Near Eastern studies.

Palace Theater. Opened in 1925, this elaborate Gary, Indiana movie theater is located at 791 Broadway. It closed in 1972, a victim of Gary's downtown economic collapse.

Palmer, Gertrude (1904-1989). A native of Terre Haute, Indiana, she graduated from Northwestern University in 1927. After several years teaching at Jefferson and Franklin Schools in Gary, she taught dramatics, English, and Auditorium at Emerson High School from 1937 to 1967 (30 years). She produced dozens of plays, musicals and other stage productions at Emerson during her tenure.

Palmer, Stuart (1905-1968). American author of murder mysteries featuring Hildegarde Withers, a spinster schoolteacher.

Pepto-Bismol. Trade name for bismuth subsalicylate, an over-the-counter drug used to treat diarrhea, nausea, heartburn, indigestion, and upset stomach.

Perth Amboy, NJ. A city in Middlesex County, New Jersey, on Raritan Bay and adjacent to Staten Island, NY.

Petrograd. The former capital of the Russian Empire. The name was changed from the Germanic *St. Petersburg* to the Russian *Petrograd* at the start of WWI. In 1924, and the death of Lenin, the name of the city was changed to Leningrad, a symbol of its transition to a Socialist city. After the collapse of the Soviet Union in 1991, the name reverted to St. Petersburg.

Pierce, Gladys (1902-1987). Born in Hamilton County, IN, Gladys Pierce was a 1920 graduate of Emerson High School. She earned a degree in English from Indiana University in 1924 and returned to teach English at Emerson in 1926. She retired in 1969, after a tenure of 43 years, longest of any member of the teaching staff in the school's history.

Poles. A West Slavic ethnic group native to Poland, a nation located between Germany to the west and Lithuania, Belarus and Ukraine to the east.

Politics makes strange bedfellows. An aphorism that conveys the idea that political interests can bring together people who otherwise have little in common. This saying is adapted from a line in the Shakespeare's play *The Tempest*: "Misery acquaints a man with strange bedfellows." It is spoken by a man who has been shipwrecked and finds himself seeking shelter beside a sleeping monster.

Popular Front. A political coalition of leftist parties against fascism, such as that formed among European countries during the 1930s. A movement cynically sponsored by communists as a means of gaining power and as a tool to recruit liberals and other like-minded leftists to their cause.

Prohibition. Prohibition in the United States was a nationwide ban on the sale, production, importation, and transportation of alcoholic beverages that remained in place from 1920 to 1933. It was mandated by the 18th Amendment (Volstead Act) and repealed by the 21st Amendment.

Progressive. One favoring or promoting political or social reform through government action, or even revolution; a political movement in the United States from the 1890-1930 advocating such reforms. American Progressives were heavily influenced by the social welfare agenda of Benito Mussolini.

Public school (England). What would be called a private school in the United States.

Pullman, George (1831-1897). An American engineer and industrialist who designed and manufactured the Pullman sleeping car and founded the company town of Pullman, Illinois, which housed the workers who manufactured them. His Pullman Company also hired African-American men to staff the Pullman cars, who became known and widely respected as Pullman porters, providing elite service.

Pulp fiction. Popular fiction dealing with lurid or sensational subjects, often printed on rough, low-quality paper manufactured from wood pulp.

Purdue University. This land grant university located in West Lafayette, Indiana was founded in 1869. It is part of the Big Ten Conference. It is widely known for its science, engineering, agriculture and technology programs.

Purge (see Great Purge).

Pushkin, Alexander (1799-1837). Russian author of the Romantic era who is considered by many to be the greatest Russian poet and the founder of modern Russian literature. Author of *Eugene Onegin*, among other works.

Pythagoras (ca 570 – 490 BC). Greek mathematician and philosopher and founder of the Pythagorean School.

Pythagorean theorem. A relation in Euclidean geometry among the three sides of a right triangle. It states that the square of the hypotenuse (the side opposite the right angle) is equal to the sum of the squares of the other two sides.

Queen Anne (1665-1714). Queen of England from 1702-1714; also a style of decorative arts and furniture that reached its height during her reign and persisted after George I ascended the throne (1714-1727). Also, an architectural style in the United States and Great Britain in the 1870s.

Red Army. The military forces of the Soviet Union.

Red baiters. Those who denounced or deprecated others as political radicals, especially those who were communists. Naturally, communists used it as a term of opprobrium to cover their own subversive or traitorous activities.

Republican Party. Founded by anti-slavery activists in 1854, it is one of the two major contemporary political parties in the United States. Its conservative platform traces its roots to classical liberalism with an emphasis on its economically liberal policies in supporting free markets, limited government, and laissez-faire economics, while supporting socially conservative policies.

Republicans (Russian). One of several factions united in the White Russian movement during the Russian Civil War.

Resur, Kenneth W. (1904-1993). Born in Portland, IN, Kenneth Ward Resur graduated from Ball State Teacher's College and also attended the Chicago Musical College. He taught instrumental music at Froebel School from 1929 to 1949, and Horace Mann School from 1949 until his retirement in 1964. He also directed the U.S. Steel Carillco Band. His high school bands won 351 first place awards at Midwest marching band competitions over the course of his career, an achievement that earned him the title of "Gary's Music Man."

Revolutionary era. The period of the American Revolution, 1775-1783.

Reynolds, Gertrude (1897-1980). Born in Iowa, she was a 1919 graduate of the University of South Dakota with a B.A. in Physical Education. She taught Physical Education at Emerson from 1928 to 1954 (26 years). She married Ralph P. Deputy in 1952. She died in Merrillville, IN in 1980.

River Styx. A river in Greek mythology that formed the boundary between Earth and the Underworld.

Robert's Rules of Order. The short title of a book, written by Brig. Gen. Henry Martyn Robert, containing rules of order intended to be adopted as a parliamentary authority for use by a deliberative assembly.

Robespierre, Maximilien de (1758-1794). French lawyer and politician, and one of the best-known and most influential figures of the French Revolution, often accused of being instrumental in the Reign of Terror, for which he was arrested and executed.

Roerich, Nicholas (1874-1947). Russian-born artist, mystic, theosophist, archaeologist, philosopher and public figure noted for his prolific depictions of the Himalayan landscape, which were suffused with esoteric symbolism. Settling in New York City in 1920, he inspired a coterie of followers who built the Master Apartments in 1928-29 as a combined cultural center and residential apartment building. He moved to India in the 1930s and died there.

Rolfe, Arthur John (1896-1976). Born in Red Wing, MN, he graduated from Ada, MN High School in 1914 and Carlton College in 1918, where was All-State in football and basketball. After coaching in Anaconda, Montana, he began teaching at Emerson High School in 1928. He led many championship football teams during his 34-year tenure as head football coach. He retired in 1962.

Rommel, Erwin (1891-1944). Popularly known as the "Desert Fox," Rommel was a German Field Marshall in World War II, notable chiefly as a tank commander of the Afrika Korps in North Africa and in the invasion of France. He was forced to commit suicide by Adolf Hitler, after having been linked to the assassination attempt on Hitler's life in 1944.

Roosevelt, Franklin D. (1882-1945). The 33rd President of the United States who led the country through the Great Depression and World War II. His administration, which greatly expanded the powers of the federal government, was called the New Deal.

Russian Civil War. A multi-party war in the former Russian Empire fought between the Bolshevik Red Army and the White Army, the loosely allied anti-Bolshevik forces. Many foreign armies warred against the Red Army, notably the Allied Forces and the pro-German armies. The Red Army defeated the White Armed Forces of South Russia in the Ukraine and the army led by Aleksandr Kolchak in Siberia in 1919.

Russian Empire. A state that existed from 1721 until overthrown by the short-lived liberal February Revolution in 1917, and, soon after, by the Bolshevik Revolution. One of the largest empires in world history, it stretched over three continents, and was surpassed in landmass only by the British and Mongol empires.

Russian Orthodox Church. The Russian Church, also known as the Orthodox Christian Church of Russia or The Moscow Patriarchate, constitutes an autocephalous (having its own head or chief bishop) Eastern Orthodox Church under the jurisdiction of the Patriarch of Moscow, which is in communion with the other Eastern Orthodox Churches. Following the capture of the city of Constantinople in 1453 A.D., the Russian Orthodox Church saw itself as the "Third Rome," the legitimate successor to the Church of Constantinople.

Russian Revolution. The collective term for a series of revolutions in Russia in 1917, which dismantled the Tsarist aristocracy and led to the creation of the Russian SFSR, or USSR, under the control of the Bolshevik Party and Vladimir Lenin.

St. Casimir Lithuanian Church. A Lithuanian Catholic Church located at 1359 Lincoln Street in Gary, IN. It also operated a elementary school at 1380 W. 15th Avenue. The church was organized in 1916. The final Mass was performed in 1998.

St. Mary's Russian Orthodox Church. Built in 1912, St. Mary's was located at 1575 Fillmore Street in Gary's Central District. In 1959, it relocated to 45th and Maryland in Glen Park, and in 1999 to Grand Boulevard in Merrillville.

St. Petersburg. Former capital of the Russian Empire. The name was changed from the Germanic *St. Petersburg* to the Russian *Petrograd* at the start of WWI. In 1924, and the death of Lenin, the name of the city was changed to Leningrad, a symbol of its transition to a Socialist city. After the collapse of the Soviet Union in 1991, the name reverted to St. Petersburg.

Saints Helen and Constantine Greek Orthodox Church. Dedicated on Easter Sunday, in 1919, this elaborate Byzantine style church was located at 510 West 13th Avenue in Gary's Central District. It was used until 1971 when the congregation moved to Merrillville. The building is now owned by the Koinonia Missionary Baptist Church.

Saint-Saens, Camille (1835-1921). A French composer, organist, conductor, and pianist of the Romantic era. He is known especially for *his Carnival of the Animals, Danse Macabre, Samson and Delilah* (opera), *Piano Concerto No. 2, Cello Concerto No. 1, Havanaise, Introduction and Rondo Capriccioso,* and *Symphony No. 3* (Organ Symphony).

Sayers, Grace (1900-1981). A native of Jefferson, Iowa, she graduated from Northwestern University in 1924. She taught vocal music at Emerson High School from 1925 to 1964 (39 years), where she founded the A Cappella Choir. She earned her M.A. in Music in 1940, also from Northwestern. She died in Colorado Springs in 1981.

Seabees. Members of the United States Navy Construction Battalion (CB). The Seabees built bases, roadways and airstrips in a wide variety of military theaters in World War II, often in the face of hostile enemy fire.

Sekulovich, Mladen (aka Karl Malden) (1912-2009). A 1931 graduate of Emerson High School, Karl Malden was a Serbian-American actor whose career spanned seven decades. He won the 1951 Academy Award for Best Supporting Actor for *A Streetcar Named Desire* and was nominated in 1954 for his supporting role in *On the Waterfront*. He appeared in more than 60 films and several television series, most notably *The Streets of San Francisco*.

Sevastopol. Founded in 1783, this major port city is situated on the Crimean Peninsula of the Ukraine (formerly part of the Soviet Union), now under the control of the Russian Federation. Chiefly famous for the Siege of Sevastopol (1854–1855) carried out by the British, French, Sardinian, and Turkish troops during the Crimean War, of which the Charge of the Light Brigade was the most notable engagement.

Shadow, The. A collection of serialized dramas, originally appearing in 1930s pulp novels, and then in a wide variety of media, primarily radio. Details of the title character have varied across various media, but he is generally depicted as a crime-fighting vigilante with psychic powers posing as a "wealthy young man about town." The radio drama asked: "Who knows what evil lurks in the hearts of men? The shadow knows!"

Shedd Aquarium. Named for John G. Shedd, a protégé of Marshall Field, this indoor public aquarium opened in Chicago on May 30, 1930.

Sheet & Tin Mill. A division of U.S. Steel in Gary, IN that produced tin and rolled steel products.

Show trial. (Law). A trial conducted primarily to make a particular impression on the public or on other nations, esp one that demonstrates the power of the state over the individual; the public trial of a political offender conducted chiefly for propaganda purposes.

Siberia. Part of Russia since the 17th century, Siberia is an extensive geographical region, consisting of almost all of North Asia from the Ural Mountains to the watershed between the Pacific and Arctic drainage basins. Siberia was also the location of scores of slave labor or repatriation camps to which the Soviet Union transferred millions of persons, many of whom died there or in the process of relocation.

Silvermaster, Nathan (1898-1964). An economist with the United States War Production Board (WPB) during World War II, Silvermaster was the head of a large ring of Communist spies in the U.S. government. It is from him that the FBI Silvermaster File documenting the Bureau's investigation into Communist penetration of the Federal government during the 1930s and 1940s, takes its name. He was identified by Elizabeth Bentley and by the VENONA decrypts.

Sinatra, Frank (1915-1998). An American singer and film actor who began his musical career in the swing era as a boy singer with Harry James and Tommy Dorsey. His stalled career was reborn in 1953 after he won the Academy Award for Best Supporting Actor in *From Here to Eternity*. He starred in both dramatic roles and musicals, including *The Man with the Golden Arm, The Manchurian Candidate, High Society, Pal Joey, Guys and Dolls* and *On the Town*.

Slavic. One of a race of peoples widely scattered over eastern, southeastern and central Europe and/or their language, culture, etc.

Social justice. Marxist code words for government-engineered income redistribution in the pursuit of a egalitarian socialist utopia by authoritarian means. By concentrating power in the hands of the State, it stands in opposition to free market capitalism, and the the notion that man has an inviolable right to his own life, liberty and property.

Socialist realism. As conceived by Stalin, Zhdanov, and Gorky, socialist realism prescribed a generally optimistic picture of socialist reality and of the development of the Communist revolution. Its purpose was indoctrination in the spirit of socialism.

Socialist welfare state. A social system whereby the state assumes primary responsibility for the welfare of its citizens, as in matters of health care, education, employment, and social security.

Soldier Field. Opened in 1924, Soldier Field is an American football stadium on the Near South Side of Chicago. It is now the oldest NFL stadium and, since 1971, home of the Chicago Bears.

Southampton. Major port city on the southern shore of England and the home port for the transatlantic passenger services operated by Cunard.

South Shore Railroad. First organized in 1901, it runs passenger service between Chicago's Randolph Street Station and South Bend. It was renamed the Chicago, South Shore & South Bend Railroad in 1925. Its Gary station is located at 3rd and Broadway.

Southwark. Inner borough of London opposite the central City of London and south of the Thames.

Sovietology. Study of the Soviet Union, especially of its government.

Spanish Civil War. A war fought from July 17, 1936 to April 1, 1939 between the Republicans, who were loyal to the established Spanish Republic, and the Nationalists, a rebel group led by General Francisco Franco. The Nationalists prevailed, and Franco ruled Spain for the next 36 years, from 1939 until his death in 1975. As a prelude to WWII, the Nationalist forces received munitions and soldiers from Nazi Germany and Fascist Italy, while the Soviet Union and Mexico intervened in support of the "Loyalist", or "Republican", side. American communists in the Abraham Lincoln Brigade fought on the "Republican" side.

Spaulding, Everett A. (1885-1971). Born in Wells County, IN, he attended Indiana State Teachers' College in Terre Haute from 1903 to 1905, and graduated with a degree in biology from Franklin College in 1909. He taught zoology at Emerson from 1910 to 1912. In 1912, he was appointed principal, a post he would hold for 40 years. He is responsible for the Emerson zoo and art collection. When he retired in 1952, he was the dean of Indiana school principals. His portrait was dedicated to the school in 1949. He died in 1971 in Decatur, Adams County, and is buried in Prairie Vine Cemetery, Morocco, Newton County, Indiana.

Stagg Field. Amos Alonzo Stagg Field is the name of two different football fields for the University of Chicago. The earliest Stagg Field is probably best remembered for its role as the site of the first nuclear reaction by Enrico Fermi and other scientists during the Manhattan Project on December 2, 1942. The site was designated a National Historic Landmark on February 18, 1965.

Stalin, Joseph (1878-1953). Born in the Russian province of Georgia as Iosif Vissarionovich Dzhugashvili, he adopted the name Stalin (Steel) between 1910 and 1912. He was one of the leaders of the Russian Revolution who served as General Secretary of the Central Committee of the Communist Party of the Soviet Union from the late 1920s until his death. As the ruthless dictator of the Soviet Union, he was responsible for the death of millions of his own countrymen in the course of modernizing the country and defeating Nazi Germany.

Stalingrad. A city in southwestern Russia on the Volga River. During the Russian Civil War (1918–20), Joseph Stalin organized the city's defense against the White Russian armies, and it was later renamed in his honor. During WWII, the Battle of Stalingrad, among the bloodiest battles in the history of warfare, reduced the city to rubble. It is considered by many as the turning point of the war.

Statist liberalism. In contrast to classical liberalism, statist liberalism employs big government as a tool to promote social justice and economic redistribution. It is based on the belief that the state should control either economic or social policy, or both, to some degree.

Steffens, Lincoln (1866-1936). Leading muckraking journalist of the Progressive era who was an apologist of the Soviet regime.

step-ins. Panties with wide legs; also a combination undergarment combing a camisole and panties; a term used from the late 1920s to the 1940s.

Stockholm. Capital and largest city of Sweden.

Stool pigeon. A stool pigeon; someone acting as an informer or decoy for the police; slang: "stoolie."

Southampton. Major port city on the south coast of England, located 75 miles south-west of London

Stockyard Inn. Famous Chicago steakhouse located near the Union Stock Yards. It closed in 1976.

Stratford. Town in Fairfield County, Connecticut on Long Island Sound, and adjacent to Bridgeport.

Stratford-upon-Avon. Village in England where William Shakespeare was born (1564) and buried.

Suwalki. A district in southwestern Lithuania, near the Polish border that was a subject of dispute between Poland and Lithuania.

Svanskog. Small town near the southern border of the Swedish province of Värmland.

Szilard, Leo (1898-1964). Hungarian-American physicist and inventor who conceived the nuclear chain reaction in 1933, patented the idea of a nuclear reactor with Enrico Fermi, and in late 1939 wrote the letter for Albert Einstein's signature that resulted in the Manhattan Project that built the atomic bomb.

Talbot, Minnie (1882-1964). Born in Berlin, Wisconsin in 1882, she earned her B.A. in Mathematics from the University of Wisconsin in 1905. She taught algebra, geometry and trigonometry at Emerson High School from 1918 to 1951. She retired to her hometown of Berlin, Wisconsin and died there in 1964.

TASS. The Telegraph Agency of the Soviet Union. The central agency for the collection and distribution of domestic and international news for all Soviet newspapers, radio and television stations. Established in 1925, it had a monopoly on official state information which was delivered in the form of the *TASS Report.*

Third Reich. Nazi Germany, or the Third Reich, is the common name for the country of Germany while governed by Adolf Hitler and his National Socialist German Workers' Party (NSDAP) from 1933 to 1945.

Tiffany glass. Refers to the many and varied types of glass developed and produced from 1878 to 1933 at the Tiffany Studios, by Louis Comfort Tiffany and a team of other designers, including Clara Driscoll.

Tinsman, Esther (1899-1985). Much beloved biology teacher at Emerson High School. A native of Dundee, Michigan, she graduated with a two-year degree from Michigan State Normal School (now Eastern Michigan University) in 1919. She came to Gary to teach, first at Beveridge School in Tolleston. She earned her A.B. in biology at the University of Michigan in 1928, and taught biology at Emerson High School from 1929 to 1964 (35 years). She retired to Colorado Springs and died there in 1985 at the age of 86.

Todd, Laurence (1882-1957). An American journalist who worked as a news agency correspondent in Washington, DC. A committed radical, Todd worked as personal secretary to Socialist Congressman Meyer London from 1915 to 1916. He is best remembered as a correspondent for the Soviet news agency TASS for nearly three decades.

Toscanini, Arturo (1867-1957). Italian conductor who was one of the most acclaimed musicians of the late 19th and 20th centuries. He was music director of La Scala Milan, the Metropolitan Opera, and the New York Philharmonic Orchestra. As the first music director of the NBC Symphony Orchestra (1937-1954), and through its radio and television broadcasts, and many recordings, he became a household name in the United States, and elsewhere.

Trianon Ballroom. The name given to ballrooms in a number American cities during the big-band era. The first and most prominent Trianon opened in 1922 in the Woodlawn neighborhood of Chicago, Illinois. Designed by renowned theater architects Rapp & Rapp, it was owned and operated by William and Andrew Karzas.

Trotsky, Leon (1879-1940). A Russian Marxist revolutionary and theorist, Soviet politician, and the founder and first leader of the Red Army. A contender for leadership of the Soviet Union, he was removed from power and deported in 1929. He was later assassinated in Mexico on orders from Stalin.

Trotskyism. The theory of Marxism advocated by Leon Trotsky. Trotsky identified as an orthodox Marxist and Bolshevik-Leninist, and supported founding a vanguard party of the working-class. His politics differed sharply from those of Stalinism, as he opposed the idea of Socialism in One Country, championing proletarian internationalism, and a dictatorship of the proletariat based on working-class self-emancipation and mass democracy. He opposed the unaccountable bureaucracy developed under Stalin after Lenin's death.

Troyanovky, Alexander. Served as the first ambassador to the United States from the Soviet Union following the latter's diplomatic recognition in Nov. 1933, and until 1938.

Tsar Nicholas II (1868-1918). The last Emperor of Russia, Grand Duke of Finland, and titular King of Poland, he and his family were murdered by the Bolsheviks on July 17, 1918.

Tukhachevsky, Mikhail Nikolayevich (1893-1937). A Marshal of the Soviet Union, commander in chief of the Red Army (1925–1928), and one of the most prominent victims of Joseph Stalin's Great Purge.

Turf wars. A colloquial term for a bitter struggle for territory, power, control, or rights, such as that between rival street gangs, or organized crime elements.

Twentieth Century Limited. An exclusive express passenger train operated by the New York Central Railroad from 1902 to 1967, during which time it would become known as "The Most Famous Train in the World." It traveled between New York's Grand Central Station and Chicago's LaSalle Street Station in 16 hours, making only four intermediate stops.

U-boat. A military submarine; the anglicized version of the German word U-Boot.

United Press International (UPI). United Press International is an international news agency, whose newswires, photo, news film and audio services provided news material to thousands of newspapers, magazines and radio and television stations for most of the 20th century.

United States Constitution. The supreme law of the United States that established the nature and structure of the U.S. government, and the fundamental rights of its citizens.

United States Steel Carillco Band. Reputed to be the finest non-professional band in the world, the Carillco Band was led by Kenneth Ward Resur from 1937 to 1964.

University of Chicago. Founded in 1890 by philanthropist John D. Rockefeller on land donated by Marshall Field, the University of Chicago is a private research university located in the Hyde Park neighborhood of Chicago, west of the site of the Columbian Exposition of 1893. The first sustaining nuclear chain reaction took place beneath its Stagg Field.

Urals. A mountain range that runs approximately from north to south through western Russia, from the coast of the Arctic Ocean to the Ural River and northwestern Kazakhstan. It forms part of the conventional boundary between the continents of Europe and Asia.

Useful idiots. A term attributed to Vladimir Lenin to describe liberals, Progressives and socialists and others perceived as propagandists for a cause whose goals they are not fully aware of, and who are used cynically by the leaders of the cause. The Soviet Union, through the Communist Party USA, cynically manipulated many useful idiots during the 1920s, 30s , 40s, and beyond to support their agenda.

USO. United Service Organization. A nonprofit organization that provides programs, services and live entertainment to United States troops and their families

Värmland. Western Swedish province bordering Norway famous for its wood and pulp paper industries, and as the home of authors Selma Lagerlöf and Gustaf Fröding, among others.

Vasa Order of America. A Swedish-American fraternal organization founded in New Haven, CT in 1896 during the height of Swedish immigration to the United States. It has chapters throughout the United States.

Vaudeville. A theatrical genre of variety entertainment that was especially popular in the United States and Canada from the early 1880s until the 1930s. A typical vaudeville performance was made up of a series of separate, unrelated acts grouped together on a common bill

Veidt, Conrad (1893-1943). German-born actor who appeared in more than 100 silent and talking pictures. He was typically cast in villainous roles, including spies and Nazis, the most famous of which were in *The Thief of Bagdad, Casablanca, Nazi Agent,* and *All Through the Night.*

Vilnius. Lithuanian capital and largest city. First mentioned in the 1323, it became a center of culture, and of Jewish life. Occupied by the Poles from 1920-1939, it was seized by the Soviets in 1939, occupied by the German army from 1941-1944, and, again, absorbed by the Soviets from 1944-1990. With the initial Soviet occupation in 1940, between 20,000 and 30,000 of the city's inhabitants were arrested by the NKVD and sent to gulags in the far eastern areas of the Soviet Union. During the Holocaust, German army units murdered about 95% of the 265,000-strong Jewish population of Lithuania, many of whom lived in Vilnius and its environs. It is now the capital of an independent Lithuania and a center of Lithuanian commerce, art and culture.

Volga. The longest river in Europe, the Volga flows through central Russia and is widely viewed as the national river of Russia.

Volstead Act. Named for Congressman Andrew Volstead, the National Prohibition Act, known informally as the Volstead Act, was enacted to carry out the intent of the Eighteenth Amendment, which established prohibition in the United States. It was repealed in 1933.

Von Mises, Ludwig (1881- 1973). A philosopher, Austrian School economist, sociologist, and classical liberal, Mises became a prominent figure in the Austrian School of economic thought and is best known for his work on praxeology, *Human Action*. Fearing a Nazi takeover of Switzerland, where he was living at the time, Mises emigrated to the United States in 1940. Mises had a significant influence on the libertarian movement in the United States in the mid-20th century. Mises predicted in 1920 that socialism would never work.

walleyed pike. A freshwater perciform fish native to most of Canada and to the Northern United States.

Walton, Ernest (1903-1995). An Irish physicist and Nobel laureate noted for his work with John Cockcroft in "atom-smashing" experiments conducted at Cambridge University in the early 1930s. He became the first person in history to artificially split the atom, thus ushering in the nuclear age and the development of nuclear power.

War Production Board. Established by President Franklin D. Roosevelt on January 16, 1942, the War Production Board was an agency of the United States government that supervised war production during World War II.

Warnke, Harry. American fighter pilot killed when his F6F Bobcat crashed into the mountains of the Koolau Range on the Island of Oahu. A 1939 graduate of Emerson High School in Gary, IN, his remains were recovered 63 years later and interred in Westville, IN.

Warren, Charles Dudley (1829-1900). An American essayist, novelist, and friend of Mark Twain, with whom he co-authored the novel The Gilded Age: A Tale of Today. He is famous for the aphorism "Politics makes strange bedfellows."

Warren, Hubert S. (1889-1969). A Native of Herman, MN, Hubert Warren graduated from the North Dakota State College of Science and earned his Master's degree from the VanderCook College of Music. He taught instrumental music at Emerson High School from 1920 to 1956 (36 years). He composed *Emerson Loyalty* in 1924 as well as other music for band.

Waterbury, CT. A city in CT located 33 miles southwest of Hartford and 77 miles northeast of New York City. Founded in 1674, Waterbury was formerly a center of the brass and castings industry.

WAVES. An acronym for Women Accepted for Volunteer Emergency Service, the WAVES was established on July 30, 1942 as a division of the United States Navy.

Wehrmacht. The unified armed forces of Germany from 1935 to 1945, consisting of the Heer (army), the Kriegsmarine (navy) and the Luftwaffe (air force).

Weimar Republic. A democratic federal republican government established in Germany in 1919. It lasted until the rise of Adolph Hitler in 1933.

Westendorf, Frederick. Roman Catholic priest and director of the Gary-Alerding Settlement House from 1935-1943. He officiated at the author's parents' wedding in 1934.

White Army. Those who fought against the Bolsheviks in the Russian Civil War (1917-1922).

White City. An alternate name for the Columbian Exposition of 1893 because of its white stucco buildings, it was also the name given to an amusement park that operated on the same site from 1905 to 1946. Other amusement parks across the country, and the world, were called "White City," reflecting the subsequent amusement park boom.

White, Harry Dexter (1892-1948). An American economist, senior U.S. Treasury department official, and an active agent of Soviet espionage. Newly opened Soviet records and the Venona decrypts show that he passed secret state information to the Soviets during World War II. One of many Soviet agents and sympathizers who insinuated themselves into the Roosevelt administration.

White Russian/White Army. A Russian who fought against the Bolsheviks in the Russian Revolution and Civil War.

William Tell Overture. Overture composed by Gioachino Rossini for his opera *William Tell* in 1829. It was noteworthy as the opening theme music of *The Long Ranger* radio and television programs, beginning in 1933.

Williams, Esther (1921-2013). An American competitive swimmer and actress best known for a number of Hollywood "aquamusicals."

Wirt, Mildred Harter (1895-1969). Third wife of superintendent William A. Wirt of the Gary Public Schools. She came to Gary in 1918 and taught Auditorium at Froebel School from 1919 to 1926. She married Wirt in 1927 and became head of Speech and Drama for the Gary Schools in 1929. During her career, she developed a philosophy of the role of auditorium training in the school curriculum, and wrote several articles on auditorium theory, and taught summer courses in auditorium subjects at Northwestern University and the University of Chicago. In 1948, she earned a Ph.D. in education from Jefferson College in Jefferson, Texas, with a thesis entitled, "Educational Philosophy of the Gary Public Schools."

Wirt, William A. (1874-1938). Superintendent of schools in Gary, Indiana from 1907-1938 who pioneered the Work-Study-Play, or Platoon System, of education. In 1934, Wirt went public with charges that communists in the Roosevelt administration were attempting to collapse the American economic system.

Wolfpacks. Mass-attack tactics against convoys used by German U-boats against Allied vessels during World War II.

Work-Study-Play System. Name given to Progressive educational reform movement introduced in 1909 by William A. Wirt (1874-1938) in the Gary, Indiana Public Schools which promoted a balanced curriculum of academic study, hand-on learning, and physical education. Aspects of the system were adopted in hundreds of school systems across the country.

WPA (Works Progress Administration). New Deal program embracing a variety of activities designed to revive the American economy during the Great Depression.

Yamamoto, Admiral Isoroku (1884-1943). A Japanese Marshal Admiral and the commander-in-chief of the Combined Fleet during World War II. A graduate of the Imperial Japanese Naval Academy, he died when American code breakers identified his flight plans and his plane was shot down. His death was a major blow to Japanese military morale during World War II.

Yla, Stasys (1908-1983). Lithuanian priest, educator and prolific author. With Madeleine Avietenaite, he produced samizdat newspapers in Kaunas during Nazi occupation. He spent 1943-1945 in Stutthof concentration camp, emigrated to U.S. in 1950 where he served as chaplain to Sisters of Immaculate Conception in Putnam, CT, from 1955-1983. He died in Chicago while on a speaking engagement.

Zhukov, Marshal (1896-1974). Georgy Konstantinovich Zhukov was a Soviet career officer in the Red Army who, in the course of World War II, played a pivotal role in liberating the Soviet Union and other nations from occupation by the Axis Powers, including the defense of Stalingrad, and, ultimately, in the occupation of Berlin. He is the most decorated general officer in the history of the Soviet Union and Russia.

Bibliography

Applebaum, Anne. *Iron Curtain: The Crushing of Eastern Europe, 1944-1956*. New York: Anchor Books, 2012.

Atbashian, Oleg. *Shakedown Socialism*. Lebanon, TN: Greenleaf Press, 2010.

Austin, Paul Britten. *On Being Swedish*. Coral Gables, FL: University of Miami Press, 1968.

Bastiat, Frederic. *The Law*. Irvington-on-Hudson, NY: Foundation for Economic Education, 1998. Online at: http://fee.org/files/doclib/20121116_thelaw.pdf

Bentley, Elizabeth. *Out of Bondage: The Story of Elizabeth Bentley*. New York: Devin-Adair, 1951.

Besancon, Alain. *A Century of Horrors: Communism, Nazism, and the Uniqueness of the Shoah*. Wilmington, DE: ISI Books, 2007.

Bourne, Randolph S. *The Gary Schools*. Boston, MA: Houghton Mifflin, 1916.

The Calumet Region Historical Guide. Compiled by the Workers of the Writers' Program of the Work Projects Administration. East Chicago, IN: Garman Printing Co., 1939.

Chambers, Whittaker. *Witness*. Washington, DC: Gateway Editions, 1952.

Cohen, Ronald. *Children of the Mill: Schooling and Society in Gary, Indiana, 1906-1960*. Bloomington: Indiana University Press, 1990.

Conquest, Robert. *Reflections on a Ravaged Century*. New York: W.W. Norton & Co., 2000.

Courtois, Stephane, et al. *The Black Book of Communism: Crimes, Terror, Repression*. Cambridge, MA: Harvard University Press, 1999.

Deriabin, Peter and Frank Gibney. *The Secret World*. Garden City, NY: Doubleday & Company, 1959.

Dies, Martin. *Martin Dies' Story*. New York: Bookmailer, 1963.

Dunning, John. *On the Air: The Encyclopedia of Old-Time Radio*. New York: Oxford University Press, 1998.

Emersonian [Emerson High School yearbook]. Gary, IN: 1939-1945.

Evans, M. Stanton. *Blacklisted By History: The Untold Story of Senator Joe McCarthy and His Fight Against America's Enemies.* New York; Crown Forum, 2009.

Evans, M. Stanton and Herbert Romerstein. *Stalin's Secret Agents: The Subversion of Roosevelt's Government*. Threshold Editions, 2013.

Groom, Winston. *1942: The Year That Tried Men's Souls*. New York: Grove Press, 2005.

Hastings, Max. *Inferno: The World at War, 1939-1945*. New York: Alfred A. Knopf, 2011.

Haynes, John Earl and Harvey Klehr. *In Denial: Historians, Communism and Espionage*. San Francisco: Encounter Books, 2003.

Haynes, John Earl and Harvey Klehr. *The Secret World of American Communism.* New Haven, CT: Yale University Press, 1995.

Higgins, Tom. *The Fabric of Froebel.* [Merrillville, IN, c. 2010]

Hirsch, E.D. *Cultural Literacy: What Every American Ought to Know.* New York: Vintage, 1988.

Hirsch, E.D. *The Knowledge Deficit: Closing the Shocking Education Gap for American Children.* New York: Mariner Books, 2007.

Hirsch, E. D., Joseph F. Kett and James Trefil. *The New Dictionary of Cultural Literacy: What Every American Needs to Know.* Houghton Mifflin Harcourt, 2002.

Hirsch, E.D. *The Schools We Need: And Why We Don't Have Them.* New York: Anchor Books, 1999.

Hollander, Paul, ed. *From the Gulag to the Killing Fields: Personal Accounts of Political Violence and Repression in Communist States.* Wilmington, DE: ISI Books, 2006.

Jordan, George Racey. *From Major Jordan's Diaries.* New York: Harcourt Brace & Co., 1952.

Available at: http://arcticbeacon.com/books/Maj_Geo_Racey_Jordan-FROM_MAJOR_JORDANS_DIARIES.pdf

Kern, Gary. *A Death in Washington: Walter Krivitsky and the Stalin Terror.* New York: Enigma Books, 2003.

Koestler, Arthur. *Darkness at Noon.* New York: Macmillan, 1941.

Koestler, Arthur and Ignazio Silone. *The God That Failed.* New York: Harper & Brothers, 1949.

Krivitsky, Walter. *In Stalin's Secret Service: Memoirs of the First Soviet Master Spy To Defect.* New York: Enigma Books, 2000.

Lane, James B. *"City of the Century": A History of Gary, Indiana.* Bloomington: Indiana University Press, 1978.

Lorenzen, Lilly. *Of Swedish Ways.* New York: Barnes and Noble Books, 1964.

Lyons, Eugene. *The Red Decade.* New York: Bobbs-Merrill Co., 1941.

Lyons, Eugene. *Assignment in Utopia.* New York; Harcourt, Brace & Co., 1937.

Malden, Karl. *When Do I Start? A Memoir.* New York: Simon & Schuster, 1997.

Maximoff, Gregor. *The Guillotine at Work: Twenty Years of Terror in Soviet Russia.* Chicago: The Chicago section of the Alexander Berkman Fund, 1940.

Melgounov, Sergey. *The Red Terror in Russia.* London: J.M. Dent, 1925.

Milosz, Czeslaw. *The Captive Mind.* New York: Vintage International, 1951, 1990.

Moore, Powell. *The Calumet Region: Indiana's Last Frontier.* Indianapolis: Indiana Historical Bureau, 1959, 1977.

Muggeridge, Malcolm. *Winter in Moscow.* North Yorkshire, UK: House of Stratus, 2003.

Ostrowski, James. *Progressivism: A Primer on the Idea Destroying America.* Buffalo, NY: Cazenovia Books, 2014.

Radosh, Ronald and Alan Radosh. *Red Star Over Hollywood: The Film Colony's Long Romance with the Left.* San Francisco: Encounter Books, 2006.

Reisman, George. *Why Nazism Was Socialism and Why Socialism Is Totalitarian.* Kindle edition. [n.p.] TJS Books 2014.

Romerstein, Herbert and Eric Breindel. *The Venona Secrets: Exposing Soviet Espionage and America's Traitors.* Washington, DC: Regnery Publishing, 2000.

Schweikart, Larry and Michael Allen. *A Patriot's History of the United States: From Columbus's Great Discovery to the War on Terror.* New York, Sentinel, 2004.

Sepetys, Ruta. *Between shades of gray.* New York: SPEAK, an imprint of Penguin Random House, 2011.

Snyder, Timothy. *Bloodlands: Europe Between Hitler and Stalin.* New York; Basic Books, 2010.

Solzhenitsyn, Aleksandr. *The Gulag Archipelago, 1918-1956: An Experiment in Literary Investigation, Parts I-II.* New York: Harper & Row, 1974.

Solzhenitsyn, Aleksandr. *The Gulag Archipelago, 1918-1956: An Experiment in Literary Investigation, Parts III-IV.* New York: Harper & Row, 1975.

Svengalis, Kendall F. *Gary, Indiana: A Centennial Celebration.* North Stonington, CT: Duneland Press, 2006.

Taylor, Robert N., Jr. and Connie A. McBirney, eds. *Peopling Indiana: The Ethnic Experience.* Indianapolis: Indiana Historical Society, 1996.

Tzouliadis, Tim. *The Forsaken: An American Tragedy in Stalin's Russia.* New York: The Penguin Press, 2008.

Ulam, Adam B. *The Bolsheviks: The Intellectual, Personal and Political History of the Triumph of Communism in Russia.* New York: Collier Books, 1965.

Valtin, Jan. *Out of the Night: Memoir of Richard Julius Herman Krebs.* Edinburgh, Scotland: Nabat / AK Press, 1941, 2004.

Von Mises, Ludwig. *Socialism.* Auburn, AL: Ludwig Von Mises Institute, 1922, 2015.

West, Diana. *American Betrayal: The Secret Assault on Our Nation's Character.* New York: St. Martin's Press, 2013.

Yla, Stasys. *A Priest in Stutthof: Human Experiences in the World of Subhuman.* New York: Mayland Books, 1971.

Biographies

A native of Gary, Indiana, and graduate of Emerson High School, Kendall Svengalis received his B.A. in English literature (1970) and M.A. in American history (1973) from Purdue University in West Lafayette. His M.A. thesis was entitled *Progressive Education in Indiana: William A. Wirt and the Gary Schools, 1906-1920.* In 1975, he received his M.L.S. from the University of Rhode Island's Graduate School of Library and Information Studies. He has also done graduate work in American history at Brown University. In 1976, Ken joined the staff of the Rhode Island State Law Library, and was appointed State Law Librarian in 1982, a position he held until his retirement in 2002. From 1985-2002, he also served as an Adjunct Professor of Library and Information Studies at the University of Rhode Island. A nationally renowned expert in cost-effective law library acquisitions, he has published the *Legal Information Buyer's Guide & Reference Manual* annually since 1996 and for which he received the prestigious Joseph L. Andrews Bibliographical Award from the American Association of Law Libraries. He is currently President of New England LawPress/Duneland Press.

In 2006, Ken published *Gary, Indiana: A Centennial Celebration* to honor the city of his birth. He is currently working on a history of Emerson High School, which was the flagship school of Superintendent William A. Wirt's world famous 'Work-Study-Play' system of education. Ken is also President of the Rhode Island Swedish Heritage Association, and Vice-President of the Jussi Björling Society - USA, which honors the career and legacy of the 20th century's greatest operatic tenor. *Conspiracy on the Housatonic,* his first work of historical fiction, and the first installment in the Ellen Anderson mystery series, was published in 2014.

Ellen Haffling Svengalis is a native of Stratford, Connecticut, and the inspiration for the novel's heroine. A graduate of Bunnell High School in Stratford and Norwalk State Technical College, she has been employed as computer programmer and analyst for a number of business concerns, including the NASDAQ. She is currently editor of *Musiktidning,* the national newspaper of the American Union of Swedish Singers (AUSS); as well as the organization's webmaster. She performs multiple roles for New England LawPress/Duneland Press, including those of editor, graphic designer, and webmaster.

Ken and Ellen reside in the rolling hills of central Connecticut and spend their leisure time as a vocal and instrumental duo performing Swedish folk music at Swedish and Scandinavian folk festivals in the Northeast. In 2004, they were featured soloists on the AUSS Grand Concert program in Dearborn, Michigan, and, in 2005, on a 17-day American Union of Swedish Singers' chorus tour of Sweden. Ken's ancestry is Swedish and Lithuanian, while Ellen's is 100% Swedish.

The Ellen Anderson Mystery Series

The Inaugural Entry:

Strange lights emanating from an abandoned Victorian mansion on the Housatonic River in the historic town of Stratford, Connecticut arouse the suspicion of Ellen Anderson, a precocious seventeen-year-old Swedish-American girl detective. When her preliminary investigation reveals that the mansion's previous owners are deceased, and the house is tied up in a prolonged probate court battle, Ellen suspects that something far more sinister is afoot, ultimately with profound implications for national security. Join Ellen and her boyfriend and bibliophile, Ken Swenson, in this intriguing World War II tale of mystery, suspense and budding romance set in 1942, shortly after the attack on Pearl Harbor.

The Sequel:

In August, 1942, two months after the conclusion of Conspiracy on the Housatonic, Ellen and her father board the 20th Century Limited on their way to the steel city of Gary, Indiana, where he has war-related business with a local defense contractor. In the train's observation car, Ellen meets Natalia Boroskova, a refugee from Stalin's genocidal police state whose parents were liquidated in the Great Purge of 1937, and who is now being trailed by Soviet agents. Ellen discovers that Natalia is also headed to Gary to live with her uncle, a former member of the White Russian Army. Shortly after enrolling at Emerson High School, Ellen learns that the school's precious art collection has been stolen in the middle of the night. As she investigates the crime, she uncovers a conspiracy far more ominous to the United States and free people everywhere.

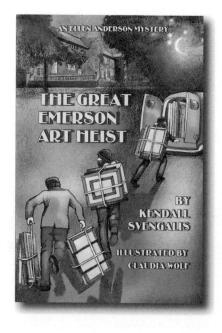